A.N. ZAIDEL' and E.Ya. SHREIDER

# VACUUM ULTRAVIOLET
# SPECTROSCOPY

Translated by Z. LERMAN

ISRAEL PROGRAM FOR SCIENTIFIC TRANSLATIONS

ANN ARBOR–HUMPHREY SCIENCE PUBLISHERS

ANN ARBOR • LONDON • 1970

ANN ARBOR–HUMPHREY SCIENCE PUBLISHERS, INC.
Drawer No. 1425, 600 S. Wagner Road, Ann Arbor, Michigan 48106

ANN ARBOR–HUMPHREY SCIENCE PUBLISHERS, LTD.
5 Great Russell Street   London W.C. 1

Library of Congress Catalog Card Number 71–204378
SBN 250 39973 3
UDC 543.42

This book is a translation of
SPEKTROSKOPIYA VAKUUMNOGO UL'TRAFIOLETA
Izdatel'stvo "Nauka"
Moskva 1967

## PREFACE

The last decade witnessed an overall upsurge in ultraviolet spectroscopy, mainly following the expansion of rocket and satellite measurements in outer space and the work done on thermonuclear fusion. Despite the technical difficulties encountered in the vacuum UV, the number of reports published on the subject is over 2000 and continues increasing rapidly.

In our opinion, the absence of a comprehensive reference book summarizing the fundamental experimental methods in vacuum UV spectroscopy, describing the main equipment, radiation sources and detectors, and presenting in a systematic fashion the principal findings of recent years has so far slowed down further development in this field. The two monographs published on the subject — one by T. Lyman, *The Spectroscopy of the Extreme Ultraviolet* (second edition published in New York in 1928) and the other by H. Bomke, *Vakuumspectroskopie* (Leipzig, 1937) — are now of no more than historical significance.

Detailed description of original equipment and work on the light elements was published by B. Edlen in 1934 (*Nova Acta Reg. Soc. Sci. Upsal.*, ser IV, **9**, No. 6. 1934). We would like to take this opportunity to thank Prof. Edlen for kindly providing us with the original publication and other reports from his laboratory. No other books were published on the subject to the best of our knowledge, except the comprehensive *Bibliography of Vacuum Ultraviolet Spectroscopy*, U.S. Department of Commerce (LD 401498). This *Bibliography* proved extremely helpful in our work, and we are grateful to Dr. McNelly of the Argonne National Laboratory (U.S.A.) for making a copy of this valuable publication available to us.

In our selection of the material for the present book, we were guided by one principle: to survey the most significant contributions to the methods of measurement and the experimental results in atomic spectroscopy, without touching on the various developments in photochemistry, spectroscopy of condensed phases, and molecular spectroscopy. As a rule, we covered the literature published up to early 1966. Later publications were included only in exceptional cases.

References in the text are sometimes given according to the authors' names and sometimes according to the numbers in the bibliographical listings at the end of each chapter. We wish to emphasize that this "discrimination" was entirely unintentional and unpremeditated and in no way reflects our attitude toward the various contributions. We were guided solely by stylistic and technical considerations, which prescribed omission of authors' names in certain cases.

In the preparation of the book for print, we were greatly assisted by Yu.I. Ostrovskii, who read through the entire manuscript and offered some valuable remarks. Also we would like to acknowledge the help of V.I. Gladushchak and E.P. Andreev, who reviewed portions of the book.

Readers' critical comments will be greatly appreciated by the authors who all too well realize that the book is far from perfect. It is our humble hope, however, that the book will nevertheless prove useful, primarily to those who take their first steps in this exceedingly difficult and yet intriguing branch of spectroscopy.

*A.N. Zaidel'*
*E.Ya. Shreider*

# TABLE OF CONTENTS

# INTRODUCTION

The vacuum or the far ultraviolet designates the spectral region which extends roughly from 10 to 2000 Å.

The long-wave limit of this region is fairly definite, as it is near 2000 Å that the region of continuous absorption of oxygen begins, extending far into the short-wave spectrum. Because of this, the spectra at wavelengths shorter than 1800–1900 Å can never be observed using conventional spectroscopic equipment: the entire short-wave radiation (except a small "window" near 1200 Å, where oxygen is transparent) is absorbed on its way from the source to the slit and inside the instrument. It is for this reason that observations of short-wave spectra are carried out with vacuum spectroscopes, i.e., with instruments pumped down to sufficiently low pressures.

The short-wave limit of the vacuum ultraviolet, on the other hand, is much less definite. Here the vacuum ultraviolet overlaps with the soft X-ray spectrum, and no distinct features are available for clearly differentiating between the two spectral regions. However, the methods for the excitation and measurement of X-ray spectra are different from the usual methods of UV spectroscopy, and we will therefore concentrate only on the optical techniques.

The use of vacuum equipment is not the only difficulty encountered in the far ultraviolet. Two additional difficulties include the great shortage of transparent materials for vacuum UV optics and inadequacy of the conventional radiation detectors, in particular, standard photographic emulsions, whose short-wave response limit falls near 2300 Å, mainly due to the absorption of the short-wave radiation in the gelatin used as the emulsion base.

The shortest wavelengths that can be recorded with conventional spectroscopic equipment used in the near ultraviolet correspond to the Hg I line at 1849 Å.

Schumann was the first to transgress this boundary by 30 Å, using a specially built quartz spectrograph with a very short focus. In the course of his work, it became clear to Schumann that further advance in the short-wave region was ruled out by the absorption of light in the air, in the optics, and in the gelatin. He managed to find a material which remained transparent down to about 1250 Å — fluorite, $CaF_2$ — and developed a gelatin-free photographic plate. These Schumann plates are successfully used to this very day, some 70 years after their invention. Equipped with these two new powerful tools, the spectroscopists advanced down to the short-wave transmission limit of fluorite. The newly discovered spectral region from 1850 to 1250 Å was appropriately named the Schumann spectrum. Schumann also observed the brightest of the lines at shorter wavelengths, e.g., the $L_\alpha$ hydrogen line at 1216 Å, although the absorption of fluorite at these wavelengths is substantial.

Schumann's wavelength measurements were highly unreliable: as he was using a $CaF_2$ prism, he was obliged to extrapolate the experimental dispersion curve of fluorite, originally obtained from measurements in the near ultraviolet, far into the short-wave region. As a result, the wavelength of $L_\alpha$ was determined with an error exceeding 200 Å.

The next breakthrough in short-wave spectroscopy was accomplished by Lyman, who was the first to apply to concave-grating spectrograph in the vacuum UV. He thus avoided the difficulties associated with the absorption of the short-wave radiation in the spectrograph optics and advanced down to 500 Å in the far ultraviolet.

On the other hand, the use of diffraction gratings led to fairly accurate wavelength measurements in the new spectral region. To this end, Lyman developed the method of overlapping of successive orders in spectra. Further advance into the vacuum UV, however, was limited by the rapid fall of the reflection coefficient of diffraction gratings under normal incidence and by the exceptionally low grating efficiency below 500 Å.

This difficulty was overcome by Millikan, Bowen, and Sawyer, who manufactured a fine-grooved grating using a diamond cutting edge under extremely delicate pressure. These gratings proved to be more efficient and consequently advanced the spectroscopists down to 200 Å, although for very bright sources only.

Shorter wavelengths were first recorded using the considerable increase in the reflection coefficients of glass and metals at incidence angle close to 90° (grazing incidence). Grazing-incidence spectrographs would measure spectra to 5–6 Å.

The development of vacuum techniques in the last decade led to the design of high-dispersion spectrographs, whereas the improved photocells and photomultipliers permitted switching over to the more accurate photoelectric recording techniques. Sources of short-wave radiation also moved to a new level of sophistication. However, despite all these advances, the work in the vacuum ultraviolet unquestionably presents many more difficulties than the near ultraviolet. On the other hand, the need to master the far ultraviolet is now felt much more acutely than ten years ago.

Indeed, the specostroscopists who originally discovered this part of the spectrum could apparently foresee only one line of research, namely the study of emission and absorption spectra of atoms and ions. The conditions under which these spectra were produced and observed had no relation whatsoever to the normal natural conditions in the Earth's atmosphere, so that there was hardly any hope of finding any practical applications of the far ultraviolet.

This situation persisted up to the 1950s, and the relatively few spectroscopists working in the vacuum UV mainly concentrated on wavelength measurements and the classification of atomic and molecular spectra. Intensity measurements occupied only a minor fraction of their time.

During the last 15 years, however, at least two new directions of research led to a radical revision of our outlook on the role of the far ultraviolet. One of these new developments entailed direct observations of celestial objects outside the Earth's atmosphere. The short-wave radiation of the Sun is absorbed in the upper atmosphere and is thus directly responsible for the ionization processes, molecular dissociation, and photochemical reactions which take place at high altitudes. This was a well-known fact. However, direct observations of the ultraviolet radiation of the Sun had been unfeasible before the first rockets and artificial satellites were launched. The original estimates of the effects of the ultraviolet radiation on the Earth's atmosphere were therefore very crude attempts, based on highly approximate models of the Sun and extrapolations of the energy distribution to the short-wave part of the solar spectrum from observations in the visible and the near ultraviolet.

The first rockets launched some 20 years ago carried diffraction-grating spectrographs and provided fragmentary information on the solar spectrum at wavelengths shorter than 3000 Å. Rocket and satellite measurements have steadily developed since then, and this appears to be one of the most promising lines of research in vacuum UV spectroscopy. These measurements naturally not only cover the solar spectrum, but also the spectra of planets, stars, and nebulae, where our knowledge is again highly deficient. Detailed studies of the spectra of these objects, however, will become possible only after the launching of an orbiting observatory or establishment of an astrophysical observatory on the Moon.

Another no less important application of vacuum UV spectroscopy is concerned with the study of processes in hot plasma and in thermonuclear fusion research. Although now it seems that we are even farther away from the ultimate goal of fusion than we believed ten years ago, fusion research has gone into high gear all over the world and the contribution of plasma spectroscopy is by no means negligible. A substantial, if not the dominant, part of the hot plasma emission falls in the vacuum ultraviolet. Measurements of this emission provide one of the principal techniques of hot plasma diagnostics.

Alongside with these fundamental lines of research, vacuum ultraviolet spectroscopy covers a number of ancillary topics. These are primarily related to the high actinic power of the short-wave radiation, which triggers a large number of chemical reactions and transformations that are very difficult to catalyze by other agents. Photochemical work using short-wave radiation constitutes a separate subject, which is associated mainly with chemical, and not spectroscopic, problems, and as such it falls outside the scope of our book.

Another valuable application of the vacuum UV spectrum is also connected with chemical problems. This is the emission spectral analysis. Until recently, chemists only worked in the visible, the near ultraviolet, and partly in the infrared spectrum. And yet, the most sensitive lines of numerous elements have wavelengths below 2000 Å, and by using analytical lines at longer wavelengths we seriously impair the sensitivity of the determination. The considerable advances in vacuum spectroscopy techniques have made it available for routine analytical applications. Vacuum UV spectroscopy is now mainly used for the determination of carbon, sulfur, and phosphorus in metals.

Excitation and ionization processes of atoms and ions can also be successfully studied in the vacuum ultraviolet.

The original problem of identification and classification of spectra in the vacuum ultraviolet still attracts considerable attention. Much is still to be done in this direction, especially with regard to intensity measurements and line profiles. The situation regarding wavelength determination and line identification is also far from satisfactory. The results available so far have been obtained with much lower accuracy and on a much smaller scale than in other, more accessible spectral regions. The resolving power attainable in the vacuum ultraviolet is still much lower than the resolving power in the visible. As a result, we have virtually no information on the hyperfine structure of spectral lines in the vacuum ultraviolet, no exact interferometric measurements of wavelengths. Radiant energy sources emitting a sufficiently strong continuous spectrum of known energy distribution (like the blackbody spectrum) are not available for the vacuum ultraviolet, either.

Rapid progress in the field of vacuum UV spectroscopy requires immediate development of adequate spectral instruments, radiation detectors, and energy sources.

We would like to stress that the concerted efforts devoted to the "conquest" of the infrared spectrum, which only some 15 or 20 years ago was even a greater unknown than the vacuum ultraviolet, have so far led to the development of equipment which makes measurements and observations in the near infrared no more difficult than routine measurements in the visible. The infrared spectrum has thus become widely accessible to research and to practical applications. The vacuum ultraviolet is, unfortunately, in a less favorable position in this respect, and one of the immediate problems is the development of high-power equipment.

# CHAPTER I

# Radiant Energy Sources

## 1. PROPERTIES OF SOURCES

Various radiation sources commonly used in the visible spectrum prove to be inapplicable to the vacuum ultraviolet. This is apparently so because the photon energy in the visible and the near ultraviolet is a few electron volts, whereas in the vacuum UV the photon energies reach several hundreds of electron volts. The plasma of the radiant energy sources used in the vacuum ultraviolet should therefore contain a sufficient concentration of electrons with energies of hundreds of eV, or, in other words, "hot" sources should be used.

This automatically disqualifies various incandescent objects and filaments for use as sources of continuous radiation, since at the maximum attainable temperatures of solids ($\approx 4000\,°\mathrm{C}$) the spectral luminance $b_\lambda$ of a blackbody near 1000 Å is about $10^{-9}$ of the luminance near 6000 Å, whereas near 500 Å the luminance drops further by a factor of $10^{14}$.

The conventional sources of line spectra, in which the atomic lines are excited, are inadequate for the vacuum UV region, since the energies of the highest terms of the great majority of atoms and molecules, with the exception of atomic helium, neon, argon, and fluorine, do not exceed 15 eV, and for most elements these energies are below 10 eV. Thus only the lines of the atoms of some inert gases and fluorine may have wavelengths shorter than 800 Å, whereas most atomic and molecular spectra are characterized by wavelengths greater than 1200 Å.

Line spectra in the short-wave region can be obtained only by using special sources

1

where the high specific discharge power is sufficient to produce strong ionization and to excite the lines of multiply charged ions. Continuous spectra in the Schumann region are emitted by molecular hydrogen, and at shorter wavelengths by inert gases beyond the limits of the respective series and by high-power capillary discharges. All these sources are described in detail in what follows.

The radiation sources are divided into different groups according to their specific uses.

1. *Sources for excitation and investigation of photochemical reactions.* These sources are expected to produce a high luminous flux in the relevant spectral region. Detailed knowledge of the actual energy distribution in the emitted range of wavelengths is generally of secondary importance.

2. *Sources for absorption spectroscopy.* Continuous spectrum sources are needed which produce a sufficiently strong continuum in the relevant wavelength range, although in some cases absorption can be studied with the aid of line spectra also.

3. *Sources for atomic and ionic emission spectroscopy and for wavelength measurement.* A high-voltage (or a low-voltage) condensed discharge in vacuum or in an inert gas is generally used for this purpose.

The high-voltage vacuum sparks which excite the lines of multiply charged ions are associated with relatively strong electric fields. The resulting Stark effect both broadens and shifts the spectral lines. The Stark shift apparently amounts to tenths and hundredths of an angstrom, and it must be taken into consideration in high-precision wavelength measurements.

4. *Sources for determining the spectral energy distribution and energy calibration of instruments.* Sources with an accurately known spectral distribution of luminance can be used as standard reference sources. The preparation of standard sources for the vacuum ultraviolet is not a simple undertaking; synchrotron radiation and the emission of a hydrogen discharge were tentatively applied for this purpose.

## 2. THE CONTINUUM AND THE LINE SPECTRUM
## OF MOLECULAR HYDROGEN

### Emission of molecular hydrogen

The continuous spectrum of molecular hydrogen extends from about 5000 Å to 1650 Å. It is associated with the transition of the hydrogen molecule from the upper stable electron state $1s\sigma2s\sigma^3\Sigma_g^+$ to the lower unstable electron state $1s\sigma2p\sigma^3\Sigma_u^+$.

Various authors suggested using a hydrogen discharge as a standard light source in the ultraviolet, and the effect of various discharge parameters on the intensity distribution in the emission of molecular hydrogen was therefore studied [1–10]. The peak of the $b_\lambda = f(\lambda)$ curves lies near 2000 Å. The existence of this peak was predicted by the theory [11–13].

The energy distribution in the hydrogen continuum can be approximately calculated for various vibrational levels using the Franck–Condon principle. However, it is only seldom known which of the vibrational levels are actually excited under the particular experimental conditions. Thus, in the presence of inert gases, the peak of the $b_\lambda = f(\lambda)$ curve is shifted toward longer wavelengths [4, 14, 15], and it therefore follows that the hydrogen in the discharge tube should be absolutely free from chance impurities if we are to obtain a constant energy distribution in the spectrum.

Hydrogen should also be substantially dry, since water vapor enhances the atomic hydrogen spectrum in comparison with the molecular spectrum. This is apparently due to the adverse effect of adsorbed water on the recombination of hydrogen atoms at the tube walls [16].

Various studies have shown that the intensity of deuterium-filled discharge tubes in the near ultraviolet is higher than the intensity of hydrogen tubes [9, 17, 18]. In the vacuum ultraviolet, however, this enhancement is virtually unnoticed, and deuterium cannot be recommended as a working gas.

The energy distribution in the hydrogen continuum (i.e., the relative number of photons) for the vacuum ultraviolet has been determined in [6, 6a, 8]* (Figure 1).

Hydrogen discharge tubes will function in a wide range of currents and pressures. For pressures between 0.3 and 1.5 T, the energy distribution appears to be independent of pressure [8]. For discharge tube capillaries with 4–5 mm bore, the variation of current from 100 to 400 mA in high-voltage hydrogen lamps and from

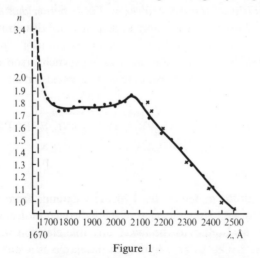

Figure 1

Energy distribution in the spectrum of a hydrogen lamp:

× data of Gonsalves [10], • data of Gladushchak and Shreider [8].

* The dependence of the spectrograph transmission on wavelength was ignored in [6].

2.5 to 5 A in low-voltage lamps does not change the energy distribution in the molecular hydrogen continuum [8, 19].

The hydrogen line spectrum between 1670 and 900 Å can also be used as a standard source (with a known intensity distribution). This spectrum is associated with transitions in the system of singlet terms $1s\sigma 2p\sigma\ ^1\Sigma_u^+ - (1s\sigma)^2\ ^1\Sigma_g^+$ and $1s\sigma 2p\pi\ ^1\pi_u - (1s\sigma)^2\ ^1\Sigma_g^+$.

Molecular hydrogen does not show the characteristic molecular band spectrum, because the distance between the vibrational levels of a hydrogen molecule is comparable with the distance between its rotational levels.

Optimal excitation of singlet and triplet terms is apparently achieved under entirely different conditions, and the variation of pressure and current in the discharge tube therefore does not affect the energy distribution in the continuous and the line spectra [8], although it may substantially alter the energy distribution between these two spectra. Therefore, these spectra should be used as standard sources only separately, the continuum between 2500 and 1700 Å, and the line spectrum between 1670 and 1100 Å.*

The energy distribution in the hydrogen line spectrum, ignoring the monochromator transmission, was measured by a number of authors [6a, 21–23]; Gladushchak and Shreider [8] made measurements with allowance for the monochromator transmission and showed that for a 4–5 mm bore discharge tube, the spectral energy distribution remained constant despite pressure variation from 0.2 to 0.5 T and current variation from 100 to 400 mA. The cathode material (aluminum or nickel) does not affect the energy distribution. The line spectrum between 1670 and 1110 Å is shown in Figure 2. The spectra were traced with entrance and exit slit widths of 2 Å.

The energy distribution in the line spectrum depends on the actual resolving power of the instrument. If a hydrogen discharge is used as a standard source (with the energy distribution listed in Table 1), the tracing should be made with the same resolving power. This can be accomplished by varying the slit width until the resolution of the fine details in the spectrum matches the tracing shown in Figure 2.

## Tube design

Open hydrogen tubes are generally used in the vacuum ultraviolet. LiF windows are not very suitable, since their transmission is lowered by the discharge; the windows can be protected from discharge damage if they are placed at a distance of a few centimeters from the discharge gap, so that the stream of charged particles does not hit the window [24]. Hydrogen lamps of this design are manufactured by the Moscow Lamp Factory (model FLV-25) [24a].

---

* Below 1100 Å, the energy distribution is distorted by the absorption in molecular hydrogen.

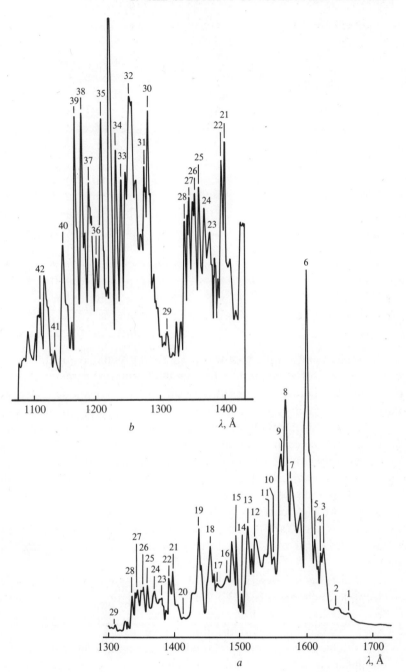

Figure 2

A tracing of the hydrogen discharge spectrum at $\lambda = 1300$—$1700$ Å $(a)$ and at $\lambda = 1100$—$1400$ Å $(b)$.

Table 1

| Point | λ, Å | Relative number of photons | Point | λ, Å | Relative number of photons | Point | λ, Å | Relative number of photons |
|---|---|---|---|---|---|---|---|---|
| 1 | 1670 | 0.39 | 15 | 1496 | 1.7 | 29 | 1315 | 0.31 |
| 2 | 1647 | 0.49 | 16 | 1481 | 0.90 | 30 | 1275 | 1.4 |
| 3 | 1636 | 1.7 | 17 | 1475 | 0.90 | 31 | 1270 | 1.2 |
| 4 | 1630 | 1.6 | 18 | 1460 | 1.6 | 32 | 1257 | 1.6 |
| 5 | 1619 | 1.9 | 19 | 1437 | 1.8 | 33 | 1234 | 1.1 |
| 6 | 1607 | 6.7 | 20 | 1422 | 0.34 | 34 | 1225 | 1.4 |
| 7 | 1590 | 2.9 | 21 | 1401 | 1.4 | 35 | 1209 | 1.6 |
| 8 | 1576 | 4.1 | 22 | 1394 | 1.3 | 36 | 1204 | 0.84 |
| 9 | 1560 | 3.2 | 23 | 1379 | 0.62 | 37 | 1185 | 1.2 |
| 10 | 1553 | 1.5 | 24 | 1374 | 0.74 | 38 | 1174 | 1.7 |
| 11 | 1546 | 2.2 | 25 | 1366 | 0.87 | 39 | 1162 | 1.9 |
| 12 | 1533 | 1.6 | 26 | 1349 | 0.97 | 40 | 1150 | 1.06 |
| 13 | 1515 | 2.0 | 27 | 1344 | 1.0 | 41 | 1131 | 0.41 |
| 14 | 1505 | 0.80 | 28 | 1333 | 1.1 | 42 | 1107 | 0.78 |

A very convenient and simple tube was proposed by Watanabe and Tousey [25] (Figure 3). A cylindrical aluminum cathode is used, 4 cm in diameter, 25 cm long. The housing of the monochromator entrance slit serves as the anode. The discharge is passed through a capillary 4 mm in diameter and 10 cm long. The inner capillary wall is platinized; this promotes hydrogen recombination, thus increasing the contribution of the molecular spectrum to the total emission of the tube. An aluminum diaphragm protects the entrance slit from discharge damage. The capillary, the cathode, and the monochromator entrance slit are water-cooled. The hydrogen pressure is ≈1T, the monochromator pressure for a slit width of 100 $\mu$ is $10^{-3}$ T, current 400 mA. At high currents, noticeable cathode sputtering is observed. A stabilized rectifier ($U \approx 2000$ V) ensures constant emission intensity to within about 1%. A similar discharge tube of slightly different dimensions was described by Vilesov [26].

More powerful tubes are described in [23, 27–31]. As an example, consider the kW two-electrode discharge tube [23]. We see from Figure 4 that the water tubes ensure effective cooling of the discharge capillary; the electrodes are also water-cooled. Quartz beakers welded to the quartz tube separate between the rubber seals and the discharge zone. Strong cathode sputtering at high currents leads to unstable burning in the tube, and the stability is improved by using a hollow cathode. The ignition potential is 2–2.5 kV. The electrode voltage drop in a burning tube is 500–700 V. The ignition potential can be lowered by using high-frequency ignition.

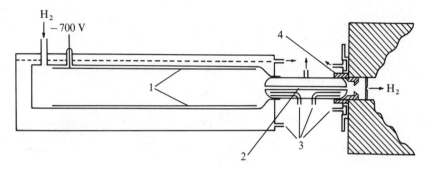

Figure 3

A simple hydrogen lamp:

1) aluminum cathode,   2) capillary,   3) water cooling,   4) coupling to monochromator.

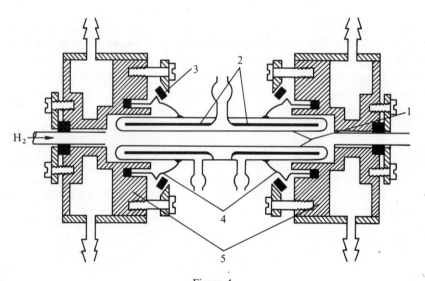

Figure 4

A high-power hydrogen lamp:

1) discharge capillary,   2) water tubes,   3) rubber seal,   4) quartz beakers,   5) electrodes.

In this case, the ignition potential is lowered virtually to the lamp burning potential.*
This tube should not be supplied by alternating current, since the resulting elec-
trode sputtering leads to considerable contamination of the monochromator slit.
D.C. operation reduces the contamination, since the cathode is far from the slit.
Hydrogen lamps with their nonmonotonic spectral intensity curve (Figure 5) are

* Special stabilization circuits will give constant intensity to within 1% [32].

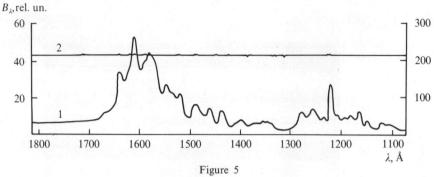

Figure 5

The spectrum of a hydrogen lamp.

Curve 1, without feedback (scale on the right);   curve 2, with feedback (scale on the left).

highly inconvenient for absorption measurements between 1700 and 900 Å [23]. This shortcoming can be eliminated by using a feedback arrangement, whereby part of the beam leaving the monochromator is channelled off to control the lamp current, so that the luminous flux from the monochromator is maintained constant (a simple servo system).

A hydrogen lamp for photochemical work is described by Warneck [21]. It is driven by a microwave generator and gives a power output of the order of $3 \cdot 10^{15}$ quanta/sec at wavelengths between 1400 and 1650 Å; the same power is radiated in $L_\alpha$. This source is particularly valuable for photochemical work, because no other high-intensity sources are available at wavelengths between 1470 Å (the Xe resonance line) and 1849 Å (the Hg resonance line).

## 3. THE LYMAN CONTINUUM

In 1824 Lyman, discharging a capacitor through a narrow capillary filled with a few torr of helium, discovered an emission continuum extending from the visible to the X-ray spectrum [33]. Later the Lyman continuum was observed with discharges in various gases. It could be produced by charging a capacitor of a few microfarads to a voltage ranging from a few thousand to tens of thousands of volts. A spark gap is generally connected with the capillary, and the width of the gap determines the breakdown voltage.

At low current densities a line spectrum is observed, and it is only at high current densities (up to 30,000 A/cm$^2$) that the line spectrum develops into a continuum. The brightest lines, however, do not disappear: they remain superimposed on the continuum. Studies in the visible and the near ultraviolet show that the appearance

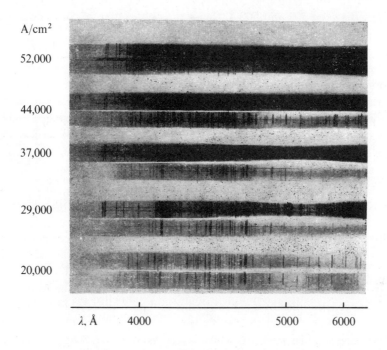

Figure 6

Continuum intensity as a function of current density and capillary material. Top curves, for a glass capillary; bottom curves, for an $Al_2O_3$ capillary.

of the spectrum is independent of pressure and the gas: it is completely determined by the current density and the wall material [34, 37]. We see from Figure 6 that as the current density increases, the relative intensity of the continuum becomes higher. The wall material determines the exact density at which the transition from line spectrum to continuum is observed. Thus, for instance, current densities of 29,000 A/cm² in a glass capillary produce a strong continuum, whereas in an $Al_2O_3$ capillary the line spectrum changes to a continuum only at 52,000 A/cm². The Lyman continuum is thus produced by the passage of the discharge through the vaporized wall material [38, 39].

The appearance of the continuous spectrum is associated with free-free and free-bound transitions [40]. Kramers [41] developed a theory for calculating the emission intensity in the simplest cases. It has been shown theoretically [42, 43] and confirmed experimentally [35, 44, 45] that in the visible and the near ultraviolet the emission intensity is independent of frequency. The principal advantages of this radiation source are the following:

1. The spectrum covers a wide range of wavelengths, from the visible region to

soft X rays. Between 300 and 600 Å, this is the only source of continuous radiation (except the synchrotron).

2. The pressure in the source is low.

3. The electric circuitry and the system are very simple.

The principal shortcomings of this source are the following:

1. Emission and absorption lines of the vaporized wall material are superimposed on the continuous spectrum (e.g., the atomic and ionic lines of oxygen and silicon).

2. The capillary is inevitably damaged; this severely limits the service life of the discharge tube and may also damage the slit of the spectroscopic instrument.

3. The source is relatively unstable and is unsuitable for photoelectric recording of spectra.

These shortcomings were partly eliminated by Garton [46, 47, 48], who proposed several designs of Lyman discharge tubes.

The first design [46] (Figure 7) constitutes a certain improvement of the tube originally suggested in [49]. The capillaries are easily replaced, and the cathode geometry protects the slit from all possible damage. The tube 1 is made of Pyrex glass. A Kovar coupling 2 with a brass flange 4 is attached to the front end of the tube. The flange is coupled by a rubber gasket to the instrument slit or to the absorbing volume. The tube has an earthed flange 3, which is joined to a brass cylinder 5 by a rubber gasket and a washer 6, which is screwed onto the cylinder. The cathode 7 is held by three steel wires 8, which are soldered to the cylinder 5. The quartz capillary 9 and its wider part 10 are supported by glass wool 11 in the Pyrex tube 12, which is held in the flange 13, fastened by two rings between the cylinders 5 and 14. Steel wires 15 connect the aluminum anode 16 to the second cylinder. The tube is closed by a glass window 17, which is pressed to the rubber gasket by a slip-on nut 18.

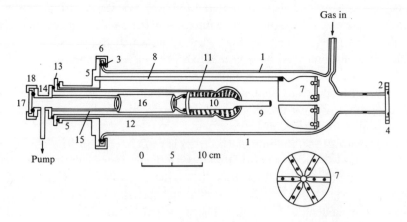

Figure 7

A discharge tube for the Lyman continuum.

A new discharge tube with an improved supply circuit was suggested by Garton in 1959 [47]. This tube with slight modifications has become quite popular since [48, 50, 51].

Garton's fundamental idea was to increase the capillary bore so as to avoid deterioration of the discharge tube. To achieve adequate continuum intensity, the discharge power had to be increased accordingly. The self-inductance and the ohmic resistance of the circuit therefore had to be reduced: Garton used low-inductance capacitors, short-wire connections, and eliminated the spark gap. The electric circuit parameters were as follows: breakdown voltage $U \approx 10 \, kV$, capacitance $C = 10 \, \mu F$, self-inductance $L \approx 2 \cdot 10^{-5} \, mH$, resistance $R \approx 0.1$ ohm, time constant $\tau \approx 2 \, \mu sec$.

A cross section through Garton's improved tube is shown in Figure 8. This source gives repeated flashes of fairly constant integrated brightness, and the photoelectric recording of the spectrum is greatly simplified.*

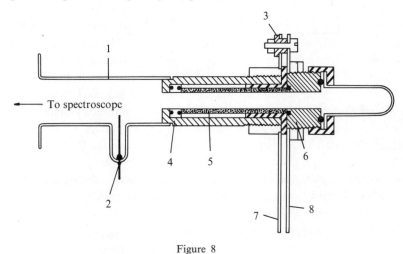

Figure 8

An improved discharge tube for the Lyman continuum:

1) glass tube,   2) tungsten lead supplying ignition voltage,   3) insulator,   4, 6) electrodes,
5) corundum tube, 5 cm long, 1 cm bore.   7, 8) buses.

Reeves et al. [44, 45] measured the absolute brightness of Garton's lamp with a capillary [46] (bore 4 mm, length 50 mm, discharge energy 450 J) and with a wide-bore tube [47] (bore 10 mm, discharge energy 240 J, short powerful flashes), and of Norrish and Oldershaw's lamp [54] (capillary bore 2.5 mm, length 3 cm, discharge energy 100 J). Figure 9 plots the maximum brightness temperature of these tubes vs. the wavelength. For Garton's lamp with a wide-bore tube, the brightness temperatures are substantially higher than for the other lamps, reaching 30,000 °K.

* Photoelectric recording systems for the Lyman continuum are described in [52, 53].

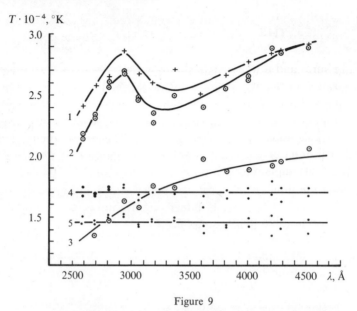

Figure 9

Maximum brightness temperature vs. wavelength:

1, 2) curves for Garton tubes, discharge energy 240 J [47] (curve 1, $U = 5$ kV, $C = 18\,\mu$F;
curve 2, $U = 7$ kV, $C = 10\,\mu$F);    3) curve for tube with capillary and 100 J discharge energy [54];
4, 5) first and second brightness maxima in a tube with 450 J discharge energy [46].

Thus, between 2500 and 4500 Å, Garton's wide-bore tube with short powerful flashes gives a higher instantaneous brightness for lower discharge energy compared to the capillary tube. This suggests that tubes of this kind should preferably be used for the study of absorption spectra of impulsive discharges. The presence of the igniter electrode in these tubes makes them readily synchronizable with the discharge being studied [55].

Tubes with capillaries are still being used, alongside with wide-bore tubes. A new type of a Lyman tube with a capillary was described by Morlais and Robain [56]. In this source, a discharge originating on the inner surface of the tube (a creeping spark) ignited the discharge in a 3–8 mm bore capillary at a pressure below $10^{-5}$ T. Circuit parameters: $C = 0.5\,\mu$F, $L = 2 \cdot 10^{-5}$ mH, $U = 30$ kV. Under these conditions, a high-intensity continuum is emitted between 6000 and 900 Å, virtually without any absorption and emission lines. Between 900 and 450 Å, numerous lines are superimposed on the spectrum.

An original electrical circuit for the excitation of the Lyman continuum is considered by Kulikov et al. [56a].

## 4. THE INERT GAS CONTINUA

At higher gas pressures and lower current densities than those in Lyman discharge tubes, the vaporization of the wall material is insignificant, and the main contribution is from the gas in the capillary. Under these conditions, a discharge in an inert gas excites a continuous spectrum in the vacuum ultraviolet. These continua are associated with the excitation of little studied molecules and molecular ions of the inert gases, and their exact origin has not been determined with any certainty so far. There were only few attempts to interpret the actual mechanism responsible for the appearance of these continua.

Some success has been achieved in the interpretation of the helium continuum [57–58a]. This continuum lies between 580 Å and 1100 Å; it is associated with the transitions of excited $He_2$ molecules back to the ground state. The continuum has two peaks, one near 800 Å and the other near 670 Å. The first peak is apparently linked with transitions from lower excited states, and the second with transitions from high-lying states.

The helium continuum was first observed by Hopfield [59] between 600 and 1050 Å. Subsequently it was investigated by Tanaka and co-workers [57, 58, 60–64].

Instability of the electric circuit and low flash frequencies interfered with routine application of this continuum in photoelectric measurements. Gradual improvement of the electrical circuitry and the discharge tube design largely eliminated the main difficulties for photoelectric recording [62, 65]. We will therefore completely ignore the old ineffective methods of excitation of the helium continuum, concentrating on the recent results of Tanaka and co-workers [57, 58, 62].

A highly convenient and fairly simple tube was described in [62] (Figure 10). The entire tube is made of quartz, with aluminum electrodes and 8 mm bore discharge capillary. The service life of the lamp is over 500 hrs, but after 125 hrs of burning the tube must be washed with alkali to dissolve the sputtered aluminum. A scavenging system with differential pumpout is used (see §21): the helium is cleaned in a liquid-nitrogen carbon trap and is delivered to a forevacuum chamber, passing through tube 6, capillary 5, and slit 9; finally, it is pumped out through the monochromator entrance slit. At nearly atmospheric source pressure and $20\,\mu$ slit, the pressure in the monochromator is $10^{-3}$ T.

Figure 11 shows the electric circuit: capacitance $C \approx 0.002\,\mu\text{F}^*$, $U \approx 10\,\text{kV}$, $R \approx 50\,\text{kohm}$, short connecting wires. The pulse repetition rate depends on the circuit parameters and the width of the spark gap; it ranges from 300 to 5000 $\text{sec}^{-1}$. The average current is 90–120 mA. The spark gap in series with the capillary is 2 mm wide for electrodes 6 mm in diameter. The spark is stabilized by a strong jet of air.

---

* The capacitance used in [65] was as high as 0.1 $\mu$F.

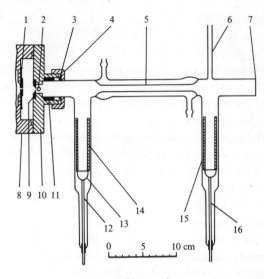

Figure 10

A discharge tube for the excitation of the helium continuum:

1) monochromator entrance slit, 2) opening for manometer, 3) metallic ring, 4) turnbuckle, 5) water-cooled capillary, 6) gas inlet tube, 7) quartz window, 8) monochromator, 9) pre-slit, 10) source holding plate, 11) rubber gasket, 13) tungsten support, 14) earthed aluminum anode, 15) aluminum cathode, 12 and 16) quartz-tungsten leads.

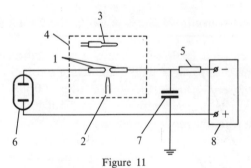

Figure 11

Electric supply circuit of the helium continuum tube:

1) tungsten electrodes, 2) compressed air jet, 3) quartz-mercury lamp, 4) body, 5) resistor, 6) discharge tube, 7) capacitor, 8) rectifier.

The breakdown potential is lowered by illuminating the interelectrode gap with a mercury-quartz lamp: its radiation produces air ionization and electrode photo-effect, thus enhancing the dielectric breakdown.

The electrodes burn out rapidly and often have to be replaced. The emission is recorded with a photomultiplier. The pressure and the current density are selected empirically; they depend on the tube dimensions.

Figure 12 plots the photocurrent $I_{ph}$ measured near the emission maximum of the discharge vs. the pressure $p$ and the current $I$ in the source. Clearly, the optimal pressure is about 38 T and the optimal current is above 125 mA; however, to suppress electrode sputtering, currents of 90 mA should not be exceeded. Figure 13 shows the energy distribution in the helium continuum as recorded at the output of the spectro-scopic instrument. The spectrum tracing was made under the following conditions: helium pressure 36 T, $U \approx 9.5$ kV, $I = 90$ mA, $C = 0.002\ \mu F$, $R = 50$ kohm, inter-electrode gap 2 mm, pulse repetition frequency 4500–5000 sec$^{-1}$, monochromator band width 0.5 Å.

In the short-wave region, a number of helium bands are observed at 662, 648, and 601 Å, as well as the resonance He line. The spectrum shows some impurity lines: the resonance neon lines, the hydrogen Lyman series, atomic and ionic lines of oxygen and carbon. These lines can be successfully used as reference markers in wavelength measurements.

Tanaka et al. have shown that the helium continuum is suitable for absorption measurements between 600 and 1100 Å (see §33, §39).

The spark gap in later work was replaced with a thyratron, which greatly improved the source stability [58a, 63].

The continuum intensity depends on the pulse repetition rate. The optimal fre-quency is around 5000 sec$^{-1}$. The intensity fluctuations in the thyratron circuit are

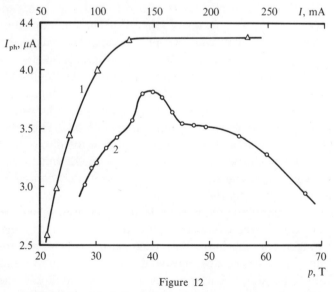

Figure 12

The intensity of the helium continuum vs. current (1) and pressure (2).

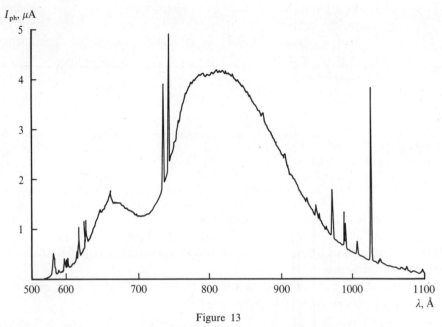

Figure 13

Energy distribution (in terms of photocurrent) in the helium continuum (600–1100 Å).

at most 1–2%, whereas in the circuit with a spark gap the intensity is variable to within 3–4% (the recorder time constant is about 0.1 sec). Energy measurements have shown that the substitution of thyratron for the spark gap increases the continuum intensity ($\lambda = 810$ Å) by a factor of four [63]. The luminous flux through the monochromator exit slit may reach $10^8$ photons/sec. The energy distribution in this continuum was measured in [63, 66], but the measurements ignored the variation of the monochromator transmission with wavelength. If this effect is allowed for, the helium continuum can be used as a standard source.

Besides the 600–1100 Å continuum, a new helium continuum between 4000 and 1100 Å has been recently discovered [67] and studied [57, 58]. This continuum is possibly associated with the appearance of helium ions in the discharge. Enhancement of this continuum was observed simultaneously with the enhancement of the ionic helium lines, whereas the continua of other inert gases are enhanced in synchronism with the atomic lines of the gas.

The 1100–4000 Å continuum is observed at helium pressures of 100–800 T if the spark gap is removed from the circuit of Figure 11. The higher the pressure, the stronger the continuum. The capacitance in various experiments ranges from 0.01 to 0.4 $\mu$F. High helium pressure is needed to avoid development of glow discharge. We see from the circuit in Figure 11 that, in the absence of the spark gap, the ignition potential is determined by the gas pressure in the discharge tube.

Figure 14 shows a photoelectric tracing of the spectrum of 600 T helium. In the helium continuum, the intensity rapidly increases with the wavelength from 1300 to 1500 Å. After that, it remains virtually independent of wavelength. The intensity of this continuum is comparable with that of the hydrogen continuum. The new helium continuum, as far as we know, has not been used in absorption measurements. The spectrum between 1100 and 1700 Å may possibly prove more suitable for this purpose than the hydrogen line spectrum.

Continua of other inert gases were also obtained [61, 64, 68–71, 72].

The xenon continuum extends from 1500 to 2200 Å [68–70, 72]. It was produced in an electrodeless discharge tube of 4–12 mm bore and 30 cm length; the pressure in various tests ranged from 50–350 T. The discharge was excited by a 125 watt

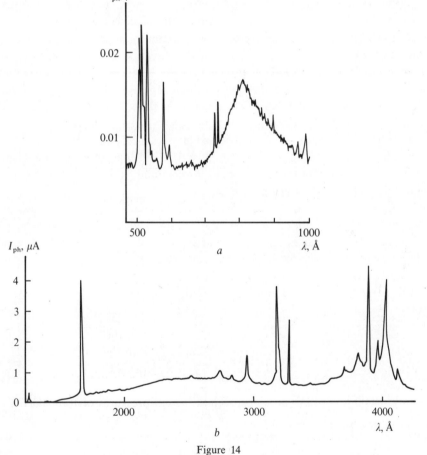

Figure 14

Photoelectric tracing of the helium continuum between 500 and 1000 Å (*a*) and between 1500 and 4000 Å (*b*).

magnetron microwave oscillator (frequency 2450 MHz). Absorption bands of $Xe_2$ molecules are superimposed on the continuous spectrum (between 1483 and 1488 Å), as well as some lines of incidental impurities: C I (1657 Å) and Hg lines (1808 Å and 1849 Å). The xenon continuum is successfully excited in a tube with internal electrodes, supplied by a low-frequency alternating current [70]. Transformer power about 1 kW, voltage 15 kV, pressure range 30–200 T. The continuous spectrum breaks up into two continua: one with a maximum near the xenon resonance line (1470 Å), and the other near 1700 Å.

The continuous spectra of other inert gases lie at different wavelengths: the krypton continuum extends from 1240 to 1800 Å, the argon continuum from 1070 to 1600 Å, the neon continuum from 740 to 1000 Å.* The xenon continuum is the brightest, and the neon continuum is the weakest of the inert gas continua. The strong xenon and krypton continua can even be produced in tubes not connected to a vacuum system, provided the gas is cleaned by a barium getter placed inside the tube.

We see from Figure 15 that the continuous spectrum of neon shows two regions: one begins at 744 Å and falls off rapidly in the direction of longer wavelengths; the other is peaked around 820 Å. At pressures below 100 T, only the first continuum develops, and the second is observed only at high pressures. The argon continuum is excited at pressures around 200 T. The intensity of this continuum is substantially higher than the intensity of the helium continuum in the same region [64]. The maxima of the argon continuum are observed at 1075, 1265, and 1500 Å.

Figure 16 shows the intensity distribution in the continua of all the inert gases. Somewhat more exact data for Ar, Kr, and Xe were obtained in [72]. They are given in Figure 17, reproduced from this source.

We see from Figures 16 and 17 that each continuum covers a fairly narrow range of wavelengths. To obtain a continuous spectrum in a wider range of wavelengths, the continua of several gases can be excited simultaneously in one discharge tube [73]. In a mixture of two gases, however, the emission intensity of one component is always substantially higher than that of the other component. Thus, for instance, argon will never emit bright radiation in the presence of xenon.

Another possible approach to the problem of continua superposition is to excite the different gases in separate discharge tubes, which are mounted in tandem with a LiF window between them. Of the three possible combinations for the heavy inert gases, Ar + Xe, Kr + Xe, and Ar + Kr, only the last two proved successful. Ar and Kr emit a continuous spectrum from 1070 to 1700 Å, with a virtually constant brightness distribution between 1200 and 1500 Å. Kr and Xe emit a continuous spectrum from 1240 to 1900 Å, and the continuum intensity is fairly constant between 1350 and 1650 Å [73].

---

* The long-wave limit of the continuum is not fixed, varying with the excitation circuit. Microwave excitation produces a narrower continuum.

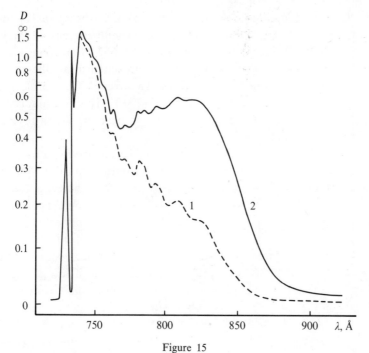

Figure 15

Photographic density $D$ vs. wavelength in the neon continuum:

1) non-condensed discharge,   2) condensed discharge.

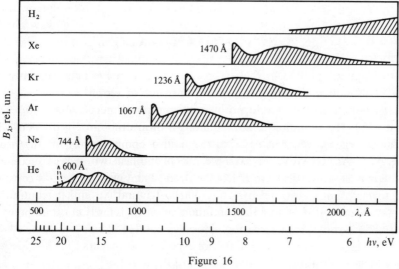

Figure 16

Inert gas continua.

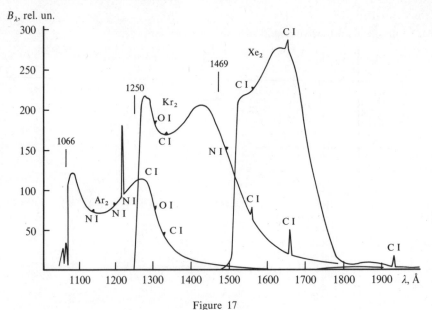

Figure 17

The continua of the heavy inert gases.

A pulsed circuit without a spark gap, similar to that used for the excitation of the helium continuum (see Figure 11), led to the discovery of new argon continua between 1600 and 2100 Å and between 1067 and 850 Å and new xenon continua above 2000 Å and below 1470 Å. For neon and krypton, no new continua were discovered [58].

## 5. SYNCHROTRON RADIATION

The electromagnetic radiation of electrons accelerated in a synchrotron produces an intense continuous spectrum in a wide range of wavelengths. Theories of this synchrotron radiation were developed by Ivanenko and Pomeranchuk [74] and by Schwinger [75]. The radiation is emitted along a tangent to the electron orbit with an angular divergence which is equal to the ratio of the electron rest energy to its total energy $E$. At 100 MeV, for example, the light beam width is about 2°. The radiation power is proportional to $E^4$. As the electron energy increases, the maximum is shifted toward shorter wavelengths. The synchrotron radiation is partly polarized (degree of polarization close to 85%), and the electric vector lies in the orbital plane of the electron. Synchrotron radiation can be calculated in relative or in absolute units. It was studied in detail in a number of experimental papers [76–79]. Measurements in the vacuum ultraviolet were made in [76] and [79].

Tomboulian and Hartman [76] carried out a detailed experimental check of

Schwinger's theory [75]. They measured $P(\lambda, t)$, the instantaneous power (in all directions) per unit wavelength interval around $\lambda$.

Figure 18 plots the experimental distribution of radiation power at various electron energies. At high energies, the peak shifts toward shorter wavelengths, in accordance with the theory. The half-width of the distribution curve increases with the decrease in energy, and the radiated power is nearly constant at all wavelengths. Similar curves were also obtained in [79].

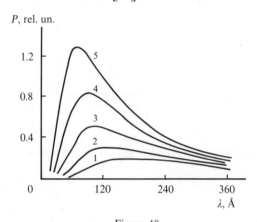

Figure 18

Radiation power distribution for various electron energies:

1) 240 MeV,   2) 260 MeV,   3) 280 MeV,   4) 300 MeV,   5) 320 MeV.

Expressions for the energy distribution at a certain angle between the orbital plane and the spectrograph axis were also derived. Figure 19 shows how the energy varies with this angle.

An experimental verification of the theory was obtained between 2800 and 4800 Å (Figure 20), between 80 and 200 Å (Figure 21), and also between 60 and 350 Å (Figure 22). The power per unit wavelength interval at various wavelengths was measured. The experimental curves closely follow the theoretical predictions. Between 170 and 250 Å, the energies were measured in 1 Å intervals at various wavelengths for 321 and 233 MeV electrons. The experimental energy ratios were compared with the results of theoretical calculations, and a close fit was established. Special experiments were staged in order to determine the degree of polarization of the synchrotron radiation for various electron energies (Figure 23). Again a good fit between theory and experiment was observed.

A comprehensive experimental check of the theory shows that the synchrotron radiation can be used as a standard continuous spectrum source. However, synchrotrons and other accelerators are not popular tools in vacuum UV spectroscopy, as they are prohibitively expensive and too unwieldy. An interesting idea is to use the

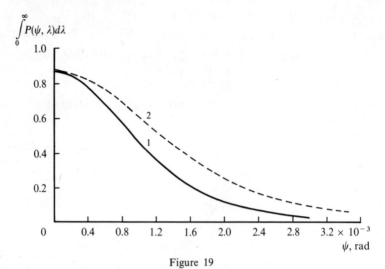

Figure 19

Angular distribution of the total electron radiation energy:

1) 321 MeV,   2) 233 MeV ($\psi$ is the azimuthal angle of observation, reckoned from the orbital plane of the electrons).

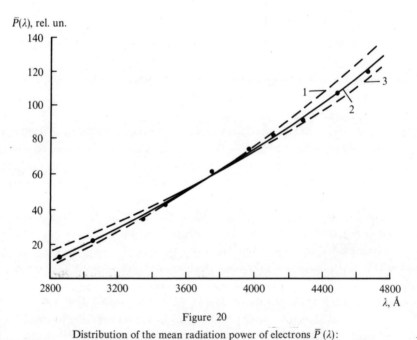

Figure 20

Distribution of the mean radiation power of electrons $\bar{P}(\lambda)$:

1) 60 MeV (theoretical curve),   2) experimental curve,   3) 65 MeV (theoretical curve).

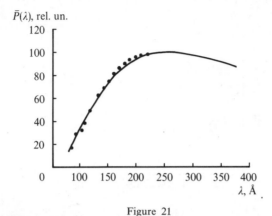

Figure 21

Distribution of the mean radiation power $\bar{P}(\lambda)$ of 233 MeV electrons
(solid curve—theoretical, dots—experimental data).

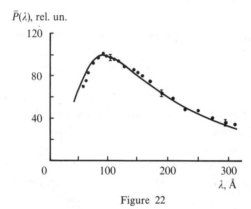

Figure 22

Distribution of the mean radiation power $\bar{P}(\lambda)$ of 321 MeV electrons
(solid curve—theoretical, dots—experimental data).

synchrotron only as a primary standard for the calibration of other sources and radiation detectors.

The exceptional stability and high intensity of the synchrotron radiation and the complete absence of lines in its spectrum, make it an invaluable source for absorption spectroscopy (see §38). In particular, it was the application of a synchrotron that first led to the discovery of a number of autoionization lines in the spectrum of inert gases (see §38). Synchrotrons may also be applied to the measurement of optical constants of solids, since this is the only known source of polarized light in the vacuum ultraviolet at this stage.

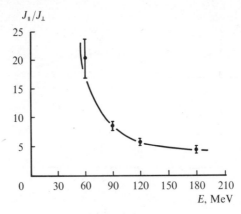

Figure 23
The degree of polarization of synchrotron radiation ($J_{||}/J_{\perp}$ vs. the electron energy.
$J_{||}$ and $J_{\perp}$ are integrated over the entire azimuthal angle $\psi$
(solid curve—theoretical, dots—experimental data).

## 6. CONTINUOUS-OPERATION SOURCES OF LINE SPECTRA

### The positive column of a glow discharge

Low current densities excite only atomic lines in the positive column. Tubes filled with a few tor of inert gases (even narrow capillaries) show only the atomic resonance lines in the vacuum ultraviolet. The overall number of these lines is small, and the positive column emission can hardly be used in absorption spectroscopy or for reflectance measurements. Sources of this kind, however, are very popular in photochemistry, as the resonance emission of the inert gases triggers numerous chemical reactions.

Discharge conditions not unlike those in the positive column are observed in the electrodeless discharge. In the USA electrodeless discharges are commonly excited by standard 125-watt microwave oscillators of 2450 MHz frequency. The great advantage of the electrodeless sources lies in the simple conditioning requirements of the tubes and the low gas absorption in the tube walls [80].

Various resonance lamps for photochemical reactions have been described [81–84]. Figure 24 shows a tube used by Okabe [81]. The 18 mm bore tube with a LiF window is mounted in the slit of a microwave cavity resonator. (In some tubes, the window is water-cooled.) Water vapor and other impurities lower the line intensities, and the inert gas in the tube is therefore cleaned with a getter, e.g., Ba–Al–Ni. The service life of these tubes is about 10 hrs, since the window becomes covered with an unhealthy deposit and its transmittance decreases.

Krypton-filled resonance lamps emit only two lines below 2000 Å, 1165 Å and

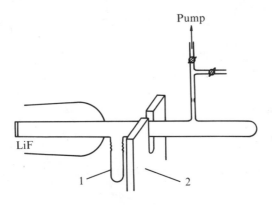

Figure 24

A microwave discharge tube:

1) quartz tube with getter,    2) microwave cavity.

1236 Å. The 1236 Å line is substantially stronger than the 1165 Å line. At a certain optimal pressure (about 1 torr), the krypton resonance lines reach their maximum intensity.

Xenon lines also emit only two resonance lines in the vacuum ultraviolet, 1295 Å and 1470 Å, and the latter is substantially stronger.

The xenon and krypton line intensities increase when the gases are mixed with helium or neon [81, 83, 85]. The optimal concentration of the heavy gas in the light gas is a few hundredths of a percent. Other mixtures have also been studied. In particular, a 1 T mixture of argon with 10% of hydrogen gives an exceptionally strong $L_\alpha$ line. The mixture containing 20% $N_2$ and 80% Ar produces very strong nitrogen multiplets $\lambda = 1493$ Å and $\lambda = 1743$ Å and a weak triplet $\lambda = 1200$ Å (probably due to the reabsorption of the resonance triplet). Mixtures of argon with oxygen or nitrogen oxide also favorably bring out the oxygen resonance line at 1303 Å.

Lamps with internal electrodes, as well as electrodeless lamps, are used as sources of line spectra [85–89]. The best results, i.e., maximum intensity, are again attained using krypton and xenon in mixture with neon, argon, and especially helium. For a total pressure of about 1 T, some 0.01 T of krypton or xenon are added. The currents vary between wide limits: in the early lamps [87] currents of up to 50 A were used, and in later designs the current was generally increased to 200–300 mA [85, 86].

Figure 25 plots the variation of the xenon line intensity against the discharge current. We see from the figure that as the current is increased, the Xe resonance line $\lambda = 1470$ Å becomes weaker. The curves were obtained for a lamp filled with a xenon–helium mixture to a total pressure of about 6 T and xenon partial pressure of about 0.3 T.

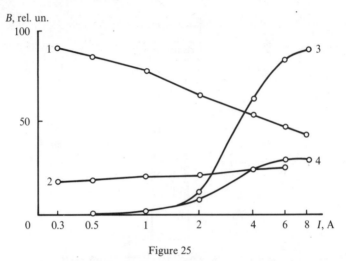

Figure 25

Intensity of some lines in the xenon lamp spectrum vs. the current:

1) Xe I (1470 Å),   2) Xe I (1295 Å, scale 4:1),   3) Xe II (2476 Å, scale 1:4),   4) Xe II (1245 Å).

A useful hot-cathode lamp emitting xenon resonance lines is shown in Figure 26.* The fluorite window is bonded with epoxy glue grade OK–50 (see §21). The discharge capillary is a dense molybdenum-wire spiral. The inner diameter of the spiral is 4 mm, and its length is 12 mm. Longer capillaries do not give stronger light. The supply circuit is shown in Figure 27. The heating current before discharge ignition is 3.5 A, dropping to 2.5 A after ignition; the lamp current is 200 mA, service life about 100 hrs.

A mercury lamp producing a strong 1849 Å line is described in [90]. A high-intensity arc burning in a low-pressure mixture of inert gases is proposed in [91]. An original low-voltage arc producing a high-intensity helium resonance line is described in [92].

**Hollow cathode**

Hollow-cathode tubes have been used for more than 50 years in a wide range of spectroscopic studies: for the classification of spectra, for the study of hyperfine structure of lines, in spectroscopic analysis [93–95]. In vacuum UV spectroscopy, the hollow cathode was first applied by Paschen in his study of the Hg II spectrum [96].

A useful hollow-cathode discharge tube for the vacuum ultraviolet was proposed by Hinteregger et al. [65] (Figure 28). A graphite hollow cathode 2 is supported by a steel ring 4 to which steel rods 3 screwed into an aluminum flange 12 are attached.

* This lamp is manufactured by the Moscow Lamp Factory under the trade name of KsR-1.

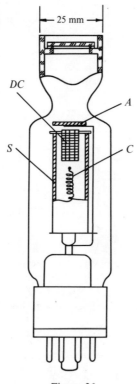

Figure 26

A lamp giving off high-intensity xenon line radiation. A is the anode, DC is the discharge capillary, C is the cathode, and S is the screening cylinder.

Insulating sleeves 5 protect the rods against ion bombardment. A double-walled anode 9 is made of high-grade aluminum. The anode is water-cooled (13). The anode is attached to a Pyrex tube 1 with aluminum flanges 7, Teflon gaskets 6, and asbestos sleeves 8. One end of the glass tube 1 is connected by a Teflon gasket to the entrance flange 10 of the monochromator; the other end of the tube is attached to the aluminum flange 12. The aluminum flange is provided with a vacuum seal into which a tube 14 leading to the vacuum system is fitted with a mushroom nipple 11. For discharge currents of 300 mA and pressures of $0.1 - 1$ T, He I, He II, Ne I, Ne II, Ar I, and Ar II lines are observed.

The main shortcoming of this source is that the discharge is liable to spread into the space between the cathode and the gas inlet. This shortcoming is particularly noticeable in work with helium. It has been eliminated in a modified design of the tube [97] (Figure 29). We see from the figure that the tantalum cathode (12 mm diameter, 200 mm long) is connected to the gas inlet. The cathode is inserted into an aluminum holder and is enclosed in a tube which protects it against ion bombardment.

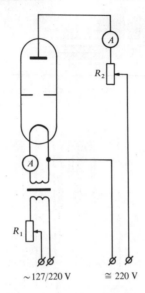

Figure 27

Supply circuit for a xenon discharge lamp.

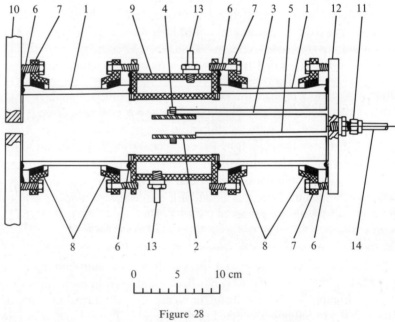

Figure 28

A hollow-cathode lamp.

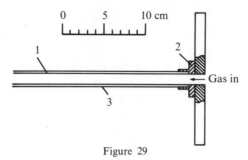

Figure 29

The cathode part of a hollow-cathode tube which prevents discharge spreading:

1) tantalum cathode,   2) aluminum cathode holder,   3) insulating tube.

Cathode sputtering is negligible, and the tube may reach service life of 10 hrs. This tube design ensures a stable discharge, facilitating photoelectric spectrum recording.

### Penning discharge [98, 99]

Penning has shown that a self-sustained discharge develops in a magnetic field for certain electrode geometry even if the inert gas pressure in the tube is very low. The electrode configuration and the magnetic field geometry are clear from Figure 30. Because of the large potential difference maintained in the Penning discharge, highly excited ions are generated in the plasma. The discharge is stable at pressures of from $10^{-2}$ to $10^{-4}$ T, the discharge current is about 1 A, the magnetic field strength is about 1 kG, the electrode voltage is 500–1000 V, depending on pressure. The cathode in Penning tubes is eroded by ion bombardment. The discharge spectrum shows the high terms of the He II Lyman series, and the Ne II, Ne III, Ne IV, Ar II, Ar III, and Ar IV lines [99].

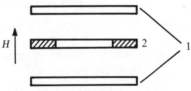

Figure 30

Electrode configuration in a Penning discharge:

1) cathodes,   2) annular anode.

### Ring discharge

A ring discharge emits a peculiar glow which is restricted to a relatively thin ring close to the tube walls. This discharge develops when the tube is placed coaxially inside the coil of a high-frequency oscillatory circuit. It is observed only for a certain relationship between the variable magnetic field in the coil and the gas pressure in the tube. The ring discharge spectrum shows lines of ions with high excitation potentials.

In vacuum spectroscopy, the ring discharge is used for the excitation of ionic argon lines. At 40 MHz frequency, 0.05 T pressure, and 500 watt power, 45 argon lines were excited at wavelengths between 600 and 2300 Å, half of them those of Ar II [100].

### Electron bombardment

Almost monochromatic radiation between 100 and 250 Å is obtained by the conventional method of X-ray excitation, namely by bombarding light-element solid targets with a beam of sufficiently fast electrons. The $K$ edge of Be corresponds to $\lambda = 110$ Å, the $L_{2-3}$ edge of Al to 170 Å, and the $L_{2-6}$ edge of Mg to 250 Å [101, 102]. These bands are some 10–20 Å wide. This method is discussed in some detail in [102].

### Atmosphere pressure arc

Vacuum ultraviolet spectroscopy uses arcs burning in an atmosphere of inert gases, nitrogen, and other gases whose absorption bands do not interfere with measurements. Boldt [103–105] used Maecker's arc [106] as a standard light source.

It is clear from Figure 31 that the arc between the two graphite electrodes is produced inside perforated water-cooled copper plates, isolated by Teflon rings from one another. Arc ignition is accomplished by a thin wire joining the cathode with the anode. The main gas is admitted through openings 1, 2, and 3. The pinched arc column rapidly expands, and because of the large distance between the third and the fourth rings, a constant-temperature homogeneous plasma is obtained behind the fourth ring. The impurity gas is admitted through the inlet $Z$.

This arc gives a stable high-current discharge: this is accomplished by the stabilizing action of the copper walls, which act as excellent heat sinks. The Teflon gaskets restrain the discharge from creeping along the walls.

Boldt used an argon arc, but the arc can be ignited in other gases also. At atmospheric pressure and 90 A current, the arc temperature is about 12,000 °K.*

A special chamber with differential pumpout was devised to enable the arc radiation to reach the slit 5 (Figure 32) without absorption. The design of this chamber is clear from the figure. The diameter of the aperture nearest the source (in chamber 1) is 0.9 mm, and all the other apertures are 1.3 mm in diameter. All the apertures are set on the optical axis of the instrument and are spaced 8 mm from one another. Each chamber 1, 2, 3, 4 is pumped out separately. Additional gas inlets 6 and 7 permit

---

* The arc temperature was calculated from the Saha equation, the electron concentration was measured from the Stark broadening of the $H_\beta$ hydrogen line. Hydrogen was present as an impurity gas.

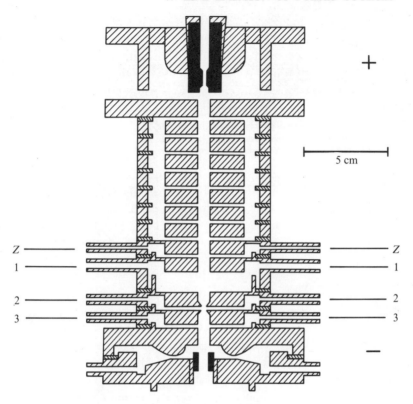

Figure 31

Diagram of a Boldt–Maecker arc.

compensating for gas losses in the source when the optical shutter 8 is opened. Lines of atomic hydrogen and arc lines of argon were observed in the arc spectrum.

## 7. LINE EMISSION OF PULSED SOURCES

### Gas discharge tubes

A gas discharge excited in a capillary by low current densities (below 30,000 A/cm$^2$) gives off high-intensity emission with a characteristic line spectrum (see Figure 6), which mainly consists of the lines of singly and doubly ionized species. Helium also shows atomic lines. The visible spectra of these flash lamps have been repeatedly recorded [107, 108]. Lee and Weissler [109, 109a] also studied the vacuum UV. This source is very popular in absorption spectroscopy. The tube design is described in [49]; aluminum electrodes are used, the capillary is 4 cm long and 2 mm in diameter. The supply circuit is shown in Figure 33. The circuit parameters are chosen to

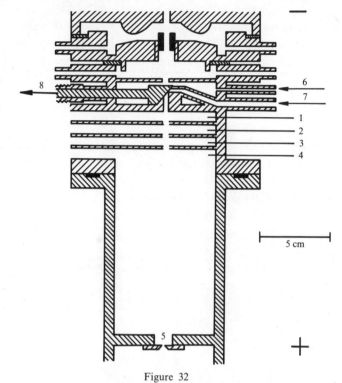

Figure 32

A chamber with differential pumpout.

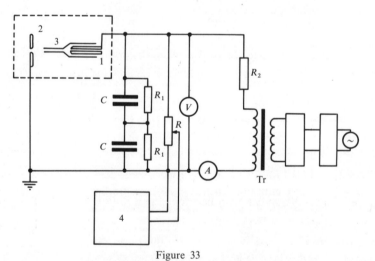

Figure 33

Supply circuit of the Lee tube:

1,2) electrodes,   3) quartz capillary,   4) oscilloscope.

ensure an aperiodic discharge with maximum current rise rate; this is conductive to a high ion concentration. Circuit parameters: $C = 0.0175 \, \mu F$, $R = R_1 = 10$ megohm, $R_2 \approx 12$ kohm, $L \approx 5 \cdot 10^{-3}$ mH, leading edge duration 0.1 μsec.

An oscilloscope is used to monitor the potential difference across the electrodes and the number of breakdowns. To achieve a stable discharge, gas purity in the tube must be rigidly controlled and the composition of the gas mixture should remain strictly constant, since otherwise the ignition potential is liable to drift. The circuit capacitance and the discharge power also greatly affect the discharge stability. A highly stable discharge is obtained in mixtures of helium with nitrogen, oxygen, dry air, or argon. The helium pressure is 0.2 T, and the ignition potential is then about 5 kV; impurities can be pumped in to lower the ignition potential to 3 kV. Stable discharge conditions are achieved by carefully watching the ignition potential. In ordinary spark circuits, the ignition potential is regulated by an additional spark gap, but this approach is not always fully effective, as the breakdown conditions may change following electrode oxidation or burnup.

Changing the capacitor voltage, we obtain atomic lines and lines of various multiply charged ions.

Between 250 and 1320 Å, several hundred lines were recorded, and their intensity remained constant to within 2%.

Another supply circuit is proposed by Hunter [110]. A thyratron in series with the discharge tube controls the ignition process. The circuit parameters: discharge repetition rate about 80 sec$^{-1}$, $C = 0.2 \, \mu F$, $L \approx 1.1 \cdot 10^{-3}$ mH, pulse current 4000 A. The discharge tube has a thick-walled quartz capillary 10 cm long and 6 mm in diameter; aluminum electrodes are used. The line intensity changes by about 3% in a few minutes, and by about 5–6% some 10–15 min after ignition. Alongside with atomic lines, the spectrum shows lines of multiply charged ions, e.g., N V. The N V lines were also excited in a low-pressure high-voltage condensed discharge described in [111].

A thyratron-controlled pulsed circuit with a capillary discharge, giving off a high-intensity line spectrum in the vacuum ultraviolet, is described in [112].

Flash sources with quartz capillaries are used in photochemical work. The lamp is filled with argon or xenon. Nelson [113] suggested substituting a sapphire capillary for quartz, as it is transparent to 1500 Å. The sapphire capillary, however, is less durable than the quartz tube, and at high discharge energies it is more readily broken [114].

An impulsive discharge can also be excited in a hollow cathode. Paschen was the first to use a pulsed hollow cathode in the visible spectrum [115], and later others adopted the same system [116–118].

In tubes with a pulsed hollow cathode, the wires soldered to the electrodes should be enclosed in a glass envelope, to prevent spurious discharges breaking through. Figure 34 shows one of the appropriate flash circuits. A 0.5 μF capacitor at 2 kV is

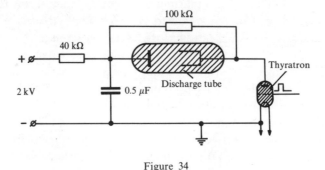

Figure 34

Supply circuit of a pulsed hollow cathode.

discharged through the tube. The breakdown voltage of the tube is controlled by a thyratron connected in series; the thyratron is triggered by single pulses from a master oscillator. In pulsed operation, the discharge is better confined inside the cathode if the electrodes are non-concentric.

The pulsed hollow cathode, as far as we know, hitherto has not been used in vacuum UV spectroscopy, although it has numerous advantages compared to the d.c. hollow cathode. The discharge conditions in the flash mode reach at least up to the lines of doubly charged atoms, and many of these lines actually fall in the vacuum UV.

Pulsed excitation can be achieved in electrodeless discharge tubes also.*

Powerful high-frequency pulsed oscillators operating at 9 and 18 MHz were applied to produce line spectra of inert gases [119–121]. The anode voltage was changed in steps between 5 and 20 kV, corresponding to pulse power of from 5 to 100 kW. The pulse duration varied from a few tens of microseconds to several milliseconds; pulse repetition rate changed from 40 to 1000 per second. The mean power released in the discharge tube was about 500 watt.

The discharge tube 3 was placed in the coil of an *LC* circuit, connected by coaxial cable 1 to the oscillator 4. The circuit was tuned to resonance with the aid of the variable capacitance 2 (Figure 35). The frequencies were matched by a wavemeter. The discharge tube was 20 cm long and 20 mm in diameter. The pressure was varied from a few hundredths to a few tenths of tor. The appearance of the spectrum changed depending on the discharge power. Maximum power excited Ar IV and Xe IV lines, and at low discharge power only the Ar I and Xe I lines were observed.

The dependence of the spectrum on the discharge power is useful for classifying the lines of the inert gases. This source revealed numerous argon and xenon lines, which had been previously unknown.

---

* Minnhagen [118a] reviewed the various excitation methods for multiply charged ions with high-frequency pulsed oscillators. An extensive bibliography is also given in [118a].

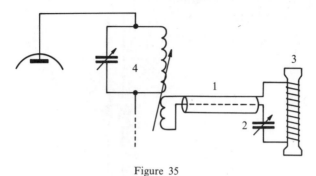

Figure 35

Resonance circuit and discharge tube.

**Vacuum spark**

Millikan [122] was the first to introduce the vacuum spark—often called a *hot spark*—into spectroscopy, and it became very popular in spectrum classification work.

The vacuum spark excites the lines of multiply ionized atoms whose ionization potentials reach hundreds and thousands of volt [123]. In particular, the lines of Cu XIX, Ti XIII, Fe XVII, Al XII, and In XXIII are excited in the vacuum spark.

The dielectric breakdown in vacuum occurs at substantially higher voltages than the breakdown in air. The breakdown voltage in vacuum may reach 100 kV/mm. A vacuum spark is therefore generated at high voltages and small interelectrode spacings. Both these factors involve a wide range of experimental difficulties: unwieldy equipment, high sensitivity to any change in the interelectrode spacing in the course of work, difficulties of source alignment on the spectroscope axis, and poor reproducibility of results. Therefore originally the vacuum spark could be used neither in analytical work nor in absorption spectroscopy.

Vodar and Astoin's introduction of a creeping spark in vacuum [124] proved highly fruitful. The properties of this source and various chamber designs are described by Vodar and co-workers [125–133].

A creeping spark is a spark discharge* between metallic electrodes joined by a solid heat-resistant dielectric (Figure 36). The dielectric is generally in the shape of a cylinder. The emission of the spark, creeping over the inner surface of the cylinder, is observed through a longitudinal slit in the cylinder. The sparking voltage of a creeping discharge is much less than for an ordinary vacuum spark. The creeping spark is also fairly stable and produces a relatively large luminous spot.

The electric circuit supplying a creeping spark is no different from the circuit of an ordinary spark. A 1 $\mu$F capacitor is charged from a high-voltage rectifier (to 20–30 kV) and is discharged through a rotary circuit breaker and a spark gap (inter-

---

* A creeping spark is also observed at pressures of the order of 1 atm [134].

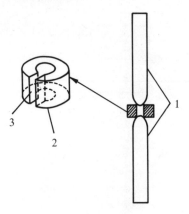

Figure 36

An insulating cylinder between electrodes:

1) electrodes,   2) insulator,   3) slit for observation.

electrode gap about 3 mm). The circuit breaker frequency determines the spark repetition rate (20 to 100 discharges per minute).

Bockasten [135] has shown that the lines in the spectrum of a creeping spark are narrower than in Millikan's "hot spark" spectrum, since the ion concentration in the creeping spark is lower. Stark shift of the spectral lines is apparently also smaller, and the source is thus more reliable for accurate measurement of wavelengths and energy level profiles.

Another means of lowering the sparking voltage is with the aid of a three-electrode spark, using the creeping spark for ignition [130, 136]. The setup is shown in Figure 37. The creeping spark is generated between electrodes 1 and 3 and the main spark is excited between electrodes 2 and 3. A circuit breaker gives up to 15–30 discharges per minute. The capacitance of the capacitor 6 can be varied from a few tenths of a microfarad to 10 $\mu$F, the capacitance of the capacitor 7 is a few tenths of a microfarad. The interelectrode gap is 10–15 mm. The discharge spectrum is determined by the material of the main anode 2.

Bockasten [135] developed a useful creeping spark chamber, shown in Figure 38. The cubic chamber has six openings: pumpout outlet, gas inlet, electrode slits, windows for photographic and visual observations.

The creeping spark excites the lines of multiply ionized atoms, in particular O VI, C1 VII, C V, and C VI. The lines of singly ionized atoms are also excited in the creeping spark. In practice, its spectrum shows the same lines as the "hot spark" spectrum. The dielectric remains virtually unexcited. The creeping spark spectrum may show a great variety of lines. An unusually crowded line spectrum is observed in a creeping spark between iron and uranium electrodes. The creeping spark may also excite a high-intensity continuum, as well as a line spectrum.

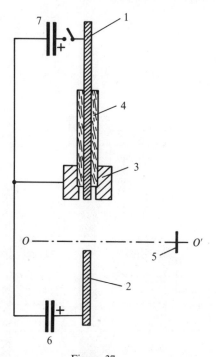

Figure 37

Spark with ignition:

1) igniting anode,   2) main anode,   3) cathode,   4) insulator,   5) spectroscope slit,   $OO'$ optical axis of the instrument,   6, 7) capacitors.

The continuum in the creeping spark spectrum extends from a few thousand angstrom to 80 Å [131, 132]. (This limit is apparently set by the properties of the spectroscopic instrument, and not by the intrinsic features of the light source.) The continuous spectrum develops near the anode and displays maximum intensity in the direction of the $OO'$ axis (see Figure 37). The bright continuum is observed only if the spark current rises rapidly to a high peak value. Circuit parameters satisfying this condition are $C = 0.5\,\mu F$, $U = 22\,kV$, $L \approx 8 \cdot 10^{-5}\,mH$, $I_{max} \approx 55,000\,Å$, $\tau = 1.25\,\mu sec$ [131, 132].

The continuous spectrum develops between heavy metal electrodes. The origin of this continuum is not clear at this stage. It may probably be used in absorption spectroscopy.

Photoelectric recording of the vacuum spark spectrum is not easy because of the low repetition rate of the sparking pulses. In most recent circuits, the repetition rate has been increased to $10–20\,sec^{-1}$, which is sufficient for photoelectric measurements [137]. These high pulse repetition rates are made possible by a certain modification of the main and the igniting spark gaps (Figure 39). The modified device contains two anodes and a cathode. The electrodes should be fairly large and water

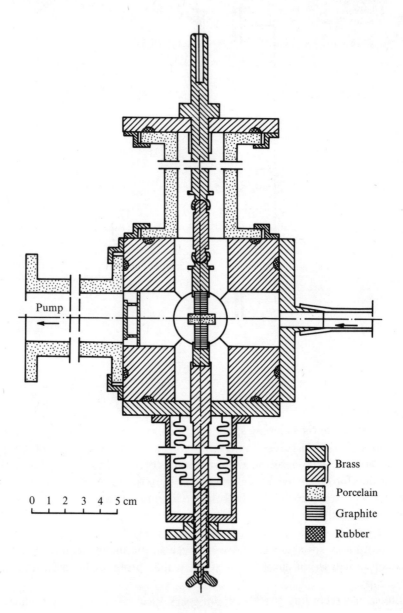

Pump

0  1  2  3  4  5 cm

Brass

Porcelain

Graphite

Rubber

Figure 38
Creeping spark chamber.

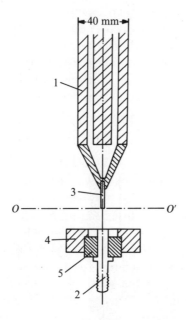

Figure 39

Electrode geometry in a high-repetition-rate spark:

1) main anode,   2) igniter anode,   3) electrode,   4) cathode,   5) refractory insulator,
$OO'$ optical axis of the instrument.

cooling is essential; the anode diameter is about 40 mm,* the anodes are made of stainless steel, and the tip of the main anode is copper. Electrode 3, inserted in the anode, is 2–3 mm in diameter; it is made of tungsten, molybdenum, or tantalum. A mechanical or an electrical circuit breaker is provided.

To prevent the discharge from being attracted to the walls, the chamber should be maintained at a vacuum of the order of $10^{-6}$ T. The capacitance should not exceed $0.2\ \mu F$.

The temperature of the creeping spark has been measured by various authors [130, 137–139]. It has been determined from the intensity ratio of two lines with sufficiently distant upper levels. The occupancy ratio of these levels is assumed to be described by the Boltzmann factor $\exp(\Delta E/kT)$, where $\Delta E$ is the energy difference of the two levels. For nonequilibrium sources (and a creeping spark is definitely nonequilibrium), $T$ is known as the excitation temperature.

The temperatures were found to vary for lines of differently charged ions. The measurements were far from faultless: they ignored the wavelength dependence of

---

* The figure only shows the tip of the auxiliary anode.

the grating reflectance [130, 138, 139] and reabsorption [139], but they nevertheless give valuable information about the temperature. The temperature of the creeping spark from the lines of various ions reaches $(3-20) \cdot 10^4$ °K. This temperature is substantially higher than the temperatures observed in ordinary sparks, $(1-2) \cdot 10^4$ °K.

The creeping spark is widely used for spectrum classification [135, 140]. This is a fairly stable source which can be used to considerable advantage in spectral analysis and in absorption spectroscopy.

### Low-voltage vacuum spark

A low-voltage source (about 300 V) driven by a low-power high-voltage igniter gives a discharge whose properties and spectrum characteristics are similar to those of the creeping spark [141–146]. Various electrical circuits have been proposed, but the best results are obtained in systems with two independent circuits: the main discharge circuit and the ignition circuit [143, 145]. If the two circuits are not separate, high power is released in the ignition stage (even in the presence of a limiting resistance), gradually destroying the auxiliary electrode and causing discharge instability in the main circuit.

Figure 40 shows an arrangement with two separate circuits [143]. When the auxiliary circuit is made, ignition occurs. The igniter electrode is mounted near the cathode, at a distance of 0.2–0.5 mm. The main discharge gap is from 1 to 20 mm wide. The igniter electrode material does not affect the spectrum composition. The low-voltage vacuum spark excites the lines of multiply ionized atoms, in particular C IV, N V, O VI, P V, S VII, Ti V, Fe IV [144]. If an additional resistance is connected to the discharge circuit, the spark will also excite atomic lines. The discharge is distinctly aperiodic; for a 8000 $\mu$F capacitor, the discharge time is about 450 $\mu$sec (considerable background is registered during the first 50–70 $\mu$sec).

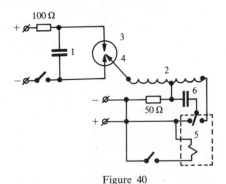

Figure 40

Circuit of low-voltage vacuum spark:

1) bank of capacitors 200–15,000 $\mu$F,   2) automobile ignition coil,   3) discharge chamber and electrodes,   4) auxiliary electrode,   5) relay,   6) 200–800 $\mu$F capacitor.

Increasing the capacitance of the discharge circuit enhances the overall intensity of the spectrum, without markedly changing its appearance. The temperature of the low-voltage vacuum spark is 20,000–30,000°C. The source is attractively simple, fairly stable, and approaches the creeping spark in its spectral characteristics. The excitation conditions in the source are adequately reproducible, and it can therefore be used for spectroscopic determination of gases in metals from lines in the vacuum ultraviolet. A serious shortcoming of this source is the low pulse repetition rate, which makes it unsuitable for photoelectric recording.

The light source proposed by Boldt [103] (Figure 41) occupies an intermediate position between the high-voltage and the low-voltage vacuum spark.

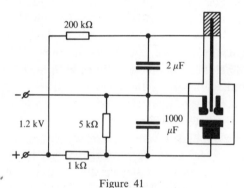

Figure 41

Boldt's flash source.

A 1000 $\mu$F capacitor charged to 1.2 kV is discharged through the main spark gap; a 2 $\mu$F capacitor is discharged through an auxiliary gap between the cathode and the inserted electrode. The inner electrode is about 2 mm in diameter; it is pressed into an iron rod. The electrodes are enclosed in porcelain tubes and are water-cooled.

The iron electrode is made to oscillate by a magnetic field, and the main spark is ignited when the two auxiliary electrodes touch. The electrodes are mounted in a vacuum chamber. The capacitor charging time is about 2.5 sec, the pulse consists of three half-waves, each of 80 $\mu$sec duration; the peak current is 30 kA. The spectrum shows the lines of C II, C III, C IV, O II, O III, O IV, O V, O VI, Si III, Si IV, Si V.

## 8. HOT PLASMA SOURCES

The hot plasma used in thermonuclear research is made up of high-energy electrons and ions. This plasma is usually formed by passing high-current impulsive discharge through a preionized gas at $10^{-4}$–$10^{-2}$ T.

The plasma is thermally insulated in most cases by magnetic fields of varied, and often highly peculiar, geometry.

Although the plasma temperatures ($10^6$–$10^7$ °K) attainable in modern machines are at least one order of magnitude lower than those needed for a self-sustained thermonuclear reaction, they are sufficiently high to excite the lines of multiply charged ions. Most of these lines lie in the vacuum ultraviolet, and thermonuclear machines may therefore be considered as sources of short-wave radiation. Some work in the spectroscopy of multiply charged ions has indeed been carried out on such installations.

Thermonuclear machines are generally known under various cryptic names or acronyms which generally provide an indication of certain distinctive properties of the machine (for example, the Russian Tokamak, designating a toroidal chamber with a magnetic field, or the British ZETA—Zero Energy Thermonuclear Accelerator). In most cases, however, the designations of these machines (e.g., OGRA, ALPHA) are proper names without any hidden meaning.

Almost all the available plasma machines have been used at one stage or another for spectroscopic studies, including the vacuum ultraviolet. The most successful results were obtained with toroidal chamber installations—ALPHA, Tokamak, TA-2000, Stellarator—where discharge plasma is formed, and machines where plasma is injected into the chamber from a special source and is subsequently confined in a magnetic bottle. Typical machines of this type are OGRA, SCYLLA, DC X.

The spark produced by a focused laser beam is also a promising source of light in the vacuum ultraviolet (it probably can be used as a standard source). The plasma of this laser spark emits ionic lines and a strong continuous spectrum [147, 148].

**BIBLIOGRAPHY**

1. CHALONGE, D. *Ann. Phys.* **1**, 123 (1934).
2. DÉJARDIN, G. and R. SCHWÉGLER. *Rev. opt.*, **13**, 313 (1934).
3. GONSALVES, V.E. *Physica*, **2**, 1003 (1935).
4. SMITH, N.D. *Phys. Rev.*, **49**, 345 (1936).
5. ANAN'EVA, L.N. and A.A. SHISHLOVSKII. *Doklady AN SSSR*, **17**, 183 (1937).
6. IVANOVA, M.K. and A.V. YAKOVLEVA. *Izvestiya AN SSSR*, phys. ser., **14**, 561 (1950).
6a. KULIKOV, S.A. and A.V. YAKOVLEVA. *Izvestiya AN SSSR*, phys. ser., **19**, 86 (1955).
7. KERN, J. *Z. angew. Phys.*, **6**, 536 (1954).
8. GLADUSHCHAK, V.I. and E.YA. SHREIDER. *Zh. Prikladnoi Spektr.*, **6**, 447 (1967).
9. SMOLKIN, M.N. and N.B. BERDNIKOV. *Optika i Spektroskopiya*, **14**, 414 (1963).
10. GONSALVES, V.E. *Metingen angaande de relatieve energieverdeeling van het continue waterstof-spectrum tusschen* 2000 *en* 3000 Å, Dissertation, Delft, 1937. (Cited in H. MAYER and E.G. SEITZ. *Ultraviolette Strahlen*, Berlin, de Gruyter. 1949.)
11. FINKELNBURG, W. and W. WEIZEL. *Z. Phys.*, **68**, 577 (1931).

12. JAMES, H.M. and A.S. COOLIDGE. *Phys. Rev.,* **55**, 184 (1939).
13. COOLIDGE, A.S. *Phys. Rev.,* **65**, 236 (1944).
14. FINKELNBURG, W. and TH. PETERS. *Kontinuierliche Spektren,* in: *Handbuch der Physik,* **XXVIII**, 179. Berlin, Springer. (1957).
15. GRANDSIRE, G. *Ann. astrophys.,* **17**, 287 (1954).
16. WOOD, R. *Phil. Mag.,* **42**, 729 (1921).
17. TOURNAIRE, A. and E. VASSY. *C. R. Acad. Sci., Paris,* **201**, 957 (1935).
18. LEVIKOV, S.I. and L.P. SHISHATSKAYA. *Optika i Spektroskopiya,* **11**, 689 (1961).
19. GROMOVA, I.I. and S.A. KULIKOV. *Optika i Spektroskopiya,* **7**, 130 (1959).
20. DIEKE, G.H. and J.J. HOPFIELD. *Phys. Rev.,* **30**, 400 (1927).
21. WARNECK, P. *Appl. Optics,* **1**, 721 (1962).
22. PACKER, D.M. and C. LOCK. *J. Opt. Soc. America,* **41**, 699 (1951).
23. VILESOV, F.I., M.E. AKOPYAN, and V.I. KLEIMENOV. *Pribory i Tekhnika Eksperimenta,* No.6, 150 (1963).
24. SHISHATSKAYA, L.P. *Optiko-mekhanicheskaya Promyshlennost',* No.12, 33 (1964).
24a. LEVIKOV, S.I. *Zh. Prikl. Spektr.,* **3**, 473 (1965).
25. JOHNSON, F.S., K. WATANABE, and R. TOUSEY. *J. Opt. Soc. America,* **41**, 702 (1951).
26. VILESOV, F.I. *Pribory i Tekhnika Eksperimenta,* No.4, 89 (1958).
27. ROBIN, S., S. ROBIN, and B. VODAR. *J. phys. et radium,* **13**, 671 (1952).
28. ROBIN, S., S. ROBIN, M. PRIOL, and J. RUPIN. *J. phys. et radium,* **24**, 167 (1963).
29. HARTMAN, P.L. and J.R. NELSON. *J. Opt. Soc. America,* **47**, 646 (1957).
30. RENDINA, J.F. *Rev. Scient. Instrum.,* **34**, 813 (1963).
31. GERASIMOVA, N.G., D.A. GUSEV, E.D. MISHCHENKO, and G.P. STARTSEV. *Optiko-mekhanicheskaya Promyshlennost',* No.7, 34 (1964).
32. SCOULER, W.J. and M. ELWIN. *Rev. Scient. Instrum.,* **35**, 489 (1964).
33. LYMAN, T. *Astrophys. J.,* **60**, I (1924); *Science,* **64**, 89 (1926).
34. ANDERSON, J.A. *Astrophys. J.,* **75**, 394 (1932).
35. HAHN, O.TH. and W. FINKELNBURG. *Z. Physik,* **122**, 36 (1944).
36. GREINER, H. *Naturwissenschaften,* **40**, 238 (1953).
37. WELTNER, K. *Z. Physik,* **136**, 631 (1954).
38. COMES, F.J. and H.G. SALZER. *Z. Naturforsch,* **18a**, 594 (1963).
39. COMES, F.J. and H.G. SALZER. *Proc. 6th Intern. Conf. on Ioniz. Phenomena in Gases, Paris,* 1963, **3**, 353.
40. UNSÖLD, A. *Physik der Sternatmosphären, mit besonderer Berücksichtigung der Sonne,* 2nd ed., Berlin, Springer (1955).
41. KRAMERS, H.A. *Philos. Mag.,* **46**, 836 (1923).
42. UNSÖLD, A. *Ann. Physik,* **33**, 607 (1938).
43. MAECKER, H. and T. PETERS. *Z. Physik,* **139**, 448 (1954).
44. REEVES, E.M. and W.H. PARKINSON. *Proc. 4th Intern. Conf. on Ioniz. Phenomena in Gases, Munich,* 1961, p. 1017.
45. PARKINSON, W.H. and E.M. REEVES. *Proc. Roy. Soc.,* **A262**, 409 (1961).
46. GARTON, W.R.S. *J. Scient. Instrum.,* **30**, 119 (1953).
47. GARTON, W.R.S. *J. Scient. Instrum.,* **36**, 11 (1959).
48. GARTON, W.R.S., I.W. CELNICK, H. HESSBERG, and J.E.G. WHEATON. *Proc. 5th Intern. Conf. on Ioniz. Phenomena in Gases, Uppsala,* 1959, p. 518.

49. WORLEY, R.E. *Rev. Scient. Instrum.*, **13**, 67 (1942).

50. GARTON, W.R.S. *Proc. 4th Intern. Conf. on Ioniz. Phenomena in Gases, Munich*, 1961, p. 1884.

51. WHEATON, J.E.G. *Appl. Optics*, **3**, 1247 (1964).

52. WILLIAMS, S.E., M.R. MEHARRY, V.W. MASLEN, and R.L. FALCONER. *J. Opt. Soc. America*, **44**, 654 (1954).

53. KRASAVIN, V.V., S.A. KULIKOV, E.D. MISHCHENKO, and G.P. STARTSEV. *Zh. Prikl. Spektr.*, **2**, 546 (1965).

54. NORRISH, R.G.W. and G.A. OLDERSCHAW. *Proc. Roy. Soc.*, **A249**, 499 (1959).

55. SHUKHTIN, A.M. and V.S. EGOROV. *Optika i Spektroskopiya*, **2**, 543 (1957).

56. MORLAIS, M. and S. ROBAIN. *C.R. Acad. Sci., Paris*, **258**, 862 (1964).

56a. KULIKOV, S.A., V.G. NIKITIN, Yu.L. SNIGIREV, and G.P. STARTSEV. *Optiko-mekhanicheskaya Promyshlennost'*, No.2, 26 (1965).

57. HUFFMAN, R.E., Y. TANAKA, and J.C. LARRABEE. *J. Opt. Soc. America*, **52**, 851 (1962).

58. HUFFMAN, R.E., Y. TANAKA, and J.C. LARRABEE. *J. Quant. Spectr. Rad. Trans.*, **2**, 451 (1962).

58a. HUFFMAN, R.E., L.C. LARRABEE, and Y. TANAKA. *J. Opt. Soc. America*, **55**, 101 (1965).

59. HOPFIELD, J.I. *Astrophys. J.*, **72**, 133 (1930).

60. TANAKA, Y. *Sci. Pap., Inst. Phys. Chem. Res., Tokyo*, **39**, 465 (1942).

61. TANAKA, Y., A.S. JURSA, and F.J. LE BLANC. *J. Opt. Soc. America*, **48**, 304 (1958).

62. HUFFMAN, R.E., Y. TANAKA, and J.C. LARRABEE. *Appl. Optics*, **2**, 617 (1963).

63. HUFFMAN, R.E., J.C. LARRABEE, and D. CHAMBERS. *Appl. Optics*, **4**, 1145 (1965).

64. HUFFMAN, R.E., Y. TANAKA, and J.C. LARRABEE. *Proc. 6th Intern. Conf. on Ioniz. Phenomena in Gases, Paris*, 1965, **1**, 145.

65. NEWBURGH, R.G., L. HEROUX, and H.E. HINTEREGGER. *Appl. Optics*, **I**, 733 (1962).

66. METZGER, P.H. and G.R. COOK. *J. Opt. Soc. America*, **55**, 516 (1965).

67. HUFFMAN, R.E., W.W. HUNT, Y. TANAKA, and R.L. NOVACK. *J. Opt. Soc. America*, **51**, 693 (1961).

68. TANAKA, Y. and M. ZELIKOFF. *J. Opt. Soc. America*, **44**, 254 (1954).

69. WILKINSON, P.G. and Y. TANAKA. *J. Opt. Soc. America*, **45**, 344 (1955).

70. TANAKA, Y. *J. Opt. Soc. America*, **45**, 710 (1955).

71. WILKINSON, P.G. *J. Opt. Soc. America*, **45**, 1044 (1955).

72. WILKINSON, P.G. and E.T. BYRAM. *Appl. Optics*, **4**, 581 (1965).

73. TANAKA, Y. and A.S. JORSA. *J. Opt. Soc. America*, **50**, 1118 (1960).

74. IVANENKO, D.D. and I.YA. POMERANCHUK. *Doklady AN SSSR*, **44**, 343 (1944).

75. SCHWINGER, J. *Phys. Rev.*, **75**, 1912 (1949).

76. TOMBOULIAN, D.H. and P.L. HARTMAN. *Phys. Rev.*, **102**, 1423 (1956).

77. KOROLEV, F.A. and O.F. KULIKOV. *Optika i Spektroskopiya*, **8**, 1 (1960).

78. ELDER, F.R., R.V. LANGMUIR, and H.C. POLLOCK. *Phys. Rev.*, **74**, 52 (1948).

79. CODLING, K. and R.P. MADDEN. *J. Appl. Phys.*, **36**, 380 (1965).

80. MEGGERS, W.F. and F.O. WESTFALL. *J. Res., Nat. Bur. Standards*, **44**, 447 (1950).

81. OKABE, H. *J. Opt. Soc. America*, **54**, 478 (1964).

82. GROTH, W., W. PESSARA, and H.J. ROMMEL. *Z. phys. Chem.*, **32**, 192 (1962).

83. SCHLAG, E.W. and F.J. COMES. *J. Opt. Soc. America*, **50**, 866 (1960).

84. SPARAPANY, J.J. *Appl. Optics*, **4**, 303 (1965).

85.  YAKOVLEV, S.A. *Optika i Spektroskopiya,* **14**, 716 (1963).

86.  COMES, F.J. and E.W. SCHLAG. *Z. phys. Chem.,* **21**, 212 (1959).

87.  HARTECK, P. and F. OPPENHEIMER. *Z. phys. Chem.,* **B16**, 77 (1931).

88.  GROTH, W. *Z. phys. Chem.,* new ser. **1**, 300 (1954).

89.  COMES, F.J. *Z.f. Instrum.,* **68**, 69 (1960).

90.  BECKEY, H.D., W. GROTH, H. OKABE, and H.J. ROMMEL. *Z. Naturforsch.,* **19a**, 1511 (1964).

91.  FEATES, F.S., B. KNIGHT, and E.W.T. RICHARDS. *Spectrochim. acta,* **18**, 485 (1962).

92.  JENSEN, C.A. and W.F. LIBBY. *Phys. Rev.,* **135**, 1247A (1964).

93.  HARRISON, G., R. LORD, and J. LOOFBOUROW. *Practical Spectroscopy.* N.Y., Prentice–Hall. 1948.

94.  ZAIDEL', A.N., N.I. KALITEEVSKII, L.V. LIPIS, and M.P. CHAIKA. *Emissionnyi spektral'nyi analiz atomnykh materialov (Emission Spectrum Analysis of Atomic Materials).* Fizmatgiz. 1960.

95.  TOLANSKY, S. *High-Resolution Spectroscopy.* London, Methuen and Co. 1947.

96.  PASCHEN, F. *Sitzungsber. d. Berl. Akad. d. Wiss.,* **5**, 536 (1928).

97.  NEWBURGH, R.G. *Appl. Optics,* **2**, 864 (1963).

98.  PENNING, F. *Physica,* **4**, 71 (1937).

99.  DESLATES, R.D., T.J. PETERSON, and D.H. TOMBOULIAN. *J. Opt. Soc. America,* **53**, 302 (1963)

100. PLATO, M. *Z. Naturforsch,* **19a**, 1324 (1964).

101. BEDO, D.E. and D.H. TOMBOULIAN. *Rev. Scient. Instrum.,* **32**, 184 (1961).

102. BLOKHIN, M.A., Editor. *Rentgenovskie luchi (X-Rays),* p. 368.—A collection of Russian translations. IL. 1960.

103. BOLDT, G. *Quant. Spectr. Rad. Trans.,* **2**, 705 (1962).

104. BOLDT, G. *Proc. 4th Intern. Conf. on Ioniz. Phenomena in Gases, Munich,* 1961, **1**, 925.

105. BOLDT, G. and W.S. COOPER. *Z. Naturforsch.,* **19a**, 968 (1964).

106. MAECKER, H. *Z. Naturforsch.* **11a**, 457 (1956).

107. VUL'FSON, K.S. *Izvestiya AN SSSR,* phys. ser., **9**, 239 (1945); *Elektrichestvo,* No.11, 16 (1946).

108. LAPORTE, M. *Les lampes à éclaire lumière blanche et leurs applications.* Paris. 1949.

109. PO LEE and G.L. WEISSLER. *J. Opt. Soc. America,* **42**, 80 (1952).

109a. PO LEE. *J. Opt. Soc. America,* **55**, 783 (1965).

110. HUNTER, W.R. *Proc. 10th Colloq. Spectr. Intern. Conf., Washington,* 1963. p. 247.

111. TILFORD, S.G. *J. Opt. Soc. America,* **53**, 1051 (1963).

112. KULIKOV, S.A., V.G. NIKITIN, YU.A. SNIGIREV, and G.P. STARTSEV. *Pribory i Tekhnika Eksperimenta,* No.2, 157 (1965).

113. NELSON, L.S. *J. Opt. Soc. America,* **46**, 768 (1956).

114. NELSON, L.S. and D.A. RAMSAY. *J. Chem. Phys.,* **25**, 372 (1956).

115. PASCHEN, F. *Ann. Physik,* **71**, 142 (1923).

116. GARTLEIN, C.W. and R.C. GIBBS. *Phys. Rev.,* **38**, 1907 (1931).

117. WITTKE, H. *Z. Phys.,* **116**, 547 (1940).

118. GLAD, S. *Arkiv fys.,* **10**, 291 (1956).

118a. MINNHAGEN, L. *J. Res., Nat. Bur. Standards,* **68C**, 237 (1964).

119. MINNHAGEN, L. and L. STIGMARK. *Arkiv fys.,* **8**, 471 (1954).

120. MINNHAGEN, L. and L. STIGMARK. *Arkiv fys.*, **13**, 27 (1958).

121. MINNHAGEN, L., B. PETERSSON, and L. STIGMARK. *Arkiv fys.*, **16**, 541 (1960).

122. MILLIKAN, R.A. and R.A. SAWYER. *Phys. Rev.*, **12**, 167 (1918).

123. EDLÉN, B. *Physica*, **13**, 545 (1947).

124. VODAR, B. and N. ASTOIN. *Nature*, **166**, 1029 (1950).

125. ASTOIN, N. *C.R. Acad. Sci., Paris*, **234**, 2055 (1952).

126. ROMAND, J. and G. BALLOFFET. *J. phys. et radium*, **16**, 489 (1955).

127. ROMAND, J., G. BALLOFFET, and B. VODAR. *Spectrochim. acta*, No.6, 454 (1959).

128. ASTOIN, N., J. ROMAND, and B. VODAR. In: *Na poroge v kosmos.*—A collection of Russian translations, B.A. BAGARYATSKII, Editor, p. 178. IL. 1960.

129. ROMAND, J. *Quant. Spectr. Rad. Trans.*, **2**, 691 (1962).

130. BALLOFFET, G. *Ann. phys.*, **5**, 1243 (1960).

131. BALLOFFET, G., J. ROMAND, and B. VODAR. *C.R. Acad. Sci., Paris*, **252**, 4139 (1961).

132. BALLOFFET, G., J. ROMAND, and J. KIEFFER. *Sprectrochim. acta*, **18**, 791 (1962).

133. VODAR, B. *Proc. 10th Colloq. Spectr. Intern. Conf., Washington*, 1963, p. 217.

134. FÜNFER, E. *Z. angew. Phys.*, **1**, 295 (1949).

135. BOCKASTEN, K. *Arkiv fys.*, **9**, 457 (1955).

136. MORLAIS, M. and S. ROBIN. *C.R. Acad. Sci., Paris*, **259**, 1489 (1964).

137. BALLOFFET, G. *J. phys., Paris*, **25**, 73A (1964).

138. LEBEDEV, S.V., S.L. MANDEL'SHTAM, and G.M. RODIN. *ZhETF*, **37**, 349 (1959).

139. AKIMOV, E.M. and I.P. MALKOV. *Optika i Spektroskopiya*, **6**, 96 (1959).

140. TORESSON, Y.G. *Arkiv fys.*, **17**, 179 (1960).

141. PEDOS, F.Z. and N.S. SVENTITSKII. *Optika i Spektroskopiya*, **4**, 407 (1958).

142. PEDOS, F.Z., N.S. SVENTITSKII, and Z.I. SHLEPKOVA. *Optika i Spektroskopiya*, **6**, 815 (1959).

143. KAPORSKII, L.N. and N.S. SVENTITSKII. *Izvestiya AN SSSR*, phys. ser., **26**, 857 (1962).

144. KAPORSKII, L.N., F.Z. PEDOS, N.S. SVENTITSKII, and Z.I. SHLEPKOVA. *Izvestiya AN SSSR*, phys. ser., **26**, 968 (1962).

145. KAPORSKII, L.N. *Optiko-mekhanicheskaya Promyshlennost'*, No.3, 23 (1963).

146. KAPORSKII, L.N., I.S. LINDSTROM, and Z.I. SHLEPKOVA. In: *Problemy povysheniya tochnosti, pravil'nosti i chuvstvitel'nosti emissionnogo spektral'nogo analiza*, p. 26. Moscow, Dom Nauchno-Tekh. Propagandy. 1964.

147. FAWCETT, B.C., A.H. GABRIEL, F.E. IRONS, N.I. PEACOCK, and P.A.H. SAUNDERS. *Proc. Phys. Soc.*, **88**, 1051 (1966).

148. EHLER, A.W. and G.L. WEISSLER. *Appl. Phys. Lett.*, **8**, 89 (1966).

# CHAPTER II

# Optical Materials

## 9. TRANSPARENT MATERIALS

The optical components of the apparatus for vacuum UV spectroscopy, including the optics of the spectroscopic instrument, should be transparent to radiation of relevant wavelengths. Mirror optics and diffraction gratings require materials of sufficiently high reflectance.

In addition to these fundamental requirements, the optical materials should also meet a number of other specifications: they should be homogenous, easily machined (especially polished), readily accessible, and their properties should be immune to the effects of radiation at the relevant wavelengths.

As we advance deeper into the short-wave region, the range of suitable optical materials diminishes, and in fact not a single bulky solid is transparent at wavelengths shorter than 1000 Å. Reflecting and transparent thin films, on the other hand, have found wide uses in vacuum UV spectroscopy. The properties of a number of films and coatings are considered in the following sections.

The crystals of $CaF_2$, $BaF_2$, LiF, and leucosapphire ($\alpha$-$Al_2O_3$) are transparent in the vacuum ultraviolet. Minor impurities, however, may substantially lower their transmittance, and it is the short-wave absorption that increases to the greatest extent [1]. Considerable reduction of transmittance in the short-wave region is mostly associated with the absorption of radiation by a thin surface film, and not by the crystal proper. This harmful film may form when the crystal is machined, or it may be a reaction production of some active medium which attacked the crystal

47

during storage or normal service life; another source of these surface films is adsorption, e.g., condensation of vacuum oil on the crystal. This invisible film coating the surface of the crystal readily absorbs short-wave radiation. The current preference is for mirror (reflection) optics, and refracting prisms are only occasionally used at wavelengths greater than 1800–1700 Å.

The prisms are manufactured from fluorite and lithium fluoride. Figure 42 plots the refractive index of the LiF and $CaF_2$ crystals as a function of wavelength [2].

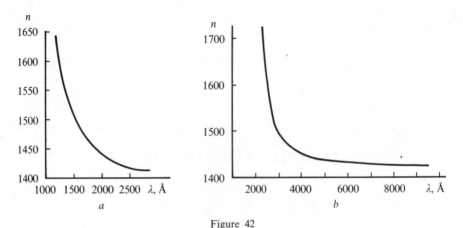

Figure 42

Dispersion curves of lithium fluoride (a) and fluorite (b).

Quartz, sapphire, fluorite, and lithium fluoride are used as window material for cuvettes and discharge tubes in absorption and emission spectroscopy in the long-wave part of the vacuum ultraviolet.

## Quartz

Ordinary crystalline quartz starts absorbing noticeably near 2000 Å; some specimens absorb even longer wavelengths. Specially selected crystals may remain transparent down to 1800 Å. At shorter wavelengths, quartz is opaque. Fused quartz is even worse in this respect, but thin films of this material remain transparent to 1440 Å [3, 4].

## Fluorite

Natural fluorite is used, as well as vacuum-grown crystals. Fluorite is normally transparent to 1250 Å, and the best specimens may even prove transparent to $L_\alpha$ (1216 Å) [5]. The transmittance vs. wavelength curves of fluorite may change from one specimen to the next, but at wavelengths longer than 1500 Å, the transmittance is generally over 50% for specimens 1–2 mm thick. Figure 43 shows the transmittance curve (1) of one such specimen [6]. The transmittance falls off fairly slowly at wavelengths above 1300 Å, but more steeply at shorter wavelengths. The transmittance of fluorite, like that of most solids, depends on temperature. Figure 44 shows the transmittance curves of fluorite plates at various temperatures [7, 8]. At −196°C, the short-wave cutoff shifts to 1170 Å.

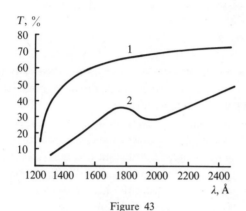

Figure 43

Transmittance of fluorite vs. wavelength before (1) and after (2) irradiation.

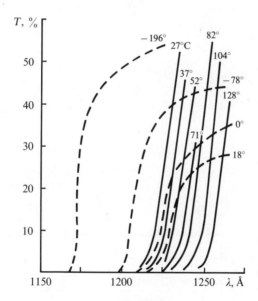

Figure 44

Transmittance of fluorite at various temperatures. The solid curves correspond to a specimen 1.22 mm thick, dashed curves to a specimen 0.71 mm thick.

The transparency of fluorite changes following irradiation in vacuum. The transmittance of a fluorite plate was found to diminish after exposure to a hydrogen lamp (curve 2, Figure 43). Polishing partly restores the transmittance of fluorite.

### Lithium fluoride

The short-wave cutoff of cleaved LiF crystals is near 1100–1050 Å [6, 9]. Ordinary polishing of crystals shifts this limit to 1400 Å [101], and only special polishing methods ensure a less pronounced decrease of transmittance. For example, polishing by Thorne's method [10] lowered the transmittance of LiF at 1216 Å from 50 to 25%. According to Thorne's method, the crystal is polished with aluminum oxide on a parraffin wax disk; the surface is then cleaned with an organic solvent, the specimen is heated at 300°C, and the finishing is done with dry aluminum oxide.

LiF plates of higher transparency are obtained by cleavage. The transmittance of cleaved LiF crystals diminishes during exposure to atmospheric air (Figure 45) [11]. Eventually, the downward trend stops but this may take a few hundred hours.

The decrease of crystal transparency is associated with the formation of a surface film of atmospheric moisture. Therefore, the higher the air humidity, the sooner is the steady-state transmittance attained. If freshly cleaved LiF crystals are stored in an atmosphere of dry gas or in vacuum, the transmittance hardly diminishes.

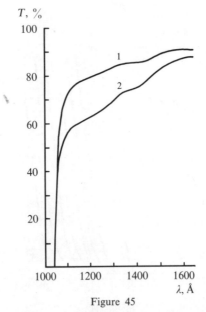

Figure 45

Transmittance of lithium fluoride vs. wavelength:

1) fresh crystal,   2) same crystal after 97 days in the air.

Radiation, like moisture, has a detrimental effect on the transparency of LiF crystals [12–14]. In particular, the transparency of LiF windows in discharge tubes deteriorates under the effects of short-wave UV radiation.

Detailed study of the effects of radiation on the transmittance of lithium fluoride was carried out by Shishatskaya [13] and Warneck [14]. Hydrogen emission hardly affected the transmittance of lithium fluoride, as long as the crystal was protected against charged particles from the discharge. A certain deterioration of the transmittance is caused by radiation below 1100 Å; longer wavelengths do not alter the optical properties of LiF. For example, the transmittance of LiF is not lowered by a discharge in xenon or krypton.

The transmittance of lithium fluoride is partly restored by repeated polishing and almost completely restored by heating [15]. Irradiation of LiF produced color centers, which are directly responsible for the reduction of transmittance. Heating to 450–500°C destroys these color centers, and the transmittance is completely restored.

In cases when the reduction of LiF transmittance is associated with the adsorption of an oil film and its denaturation by the short-wave radiation, the initial transmittance can be restored simply by washing the discharge tube window with petroleum ether [16].

The transmittance of lithium fluoride is a function of temperature and the short-wave cutoff at low temperatures is shifted toward shorter wavelengths [7] (Figure 46). At the dry ice temperature and especially at the liquid nitrogen point, LiF is expected to remain transparent to 1000 Å.

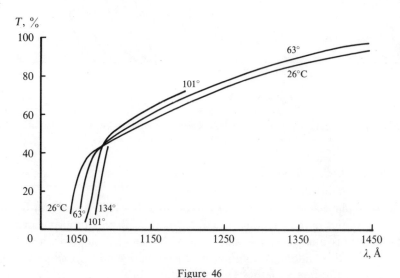

Figure 46

Transmittance of lithium fluoride (1.55 mm thick) at various temperatures.

The effect of Co[60] gamma radiation on the optical properties of lithium fluoride may be utilized to make a filter isolating the 1849 Å line from the mercury spectrum. The transmittance at 2537 Å diminishes to 0.1% of the initial value following exposure to gamma radiation, whereas the transmittance at 1849 Å remains fairly high [17].

### Sapphire and other materials

The best grades of *sapphire* are transparent to 1425 Å [18] (transmittance of over 10% for 0.5 mm thickness), but the transmittance falls off steeply and at wavelengths shorter than 1415 Å it is less than 1%. Figure 47*a* shows the transmittance curve of sapphire [19]. The transmittance of sapphire markedly decreases on heating (Figure 47*b*).

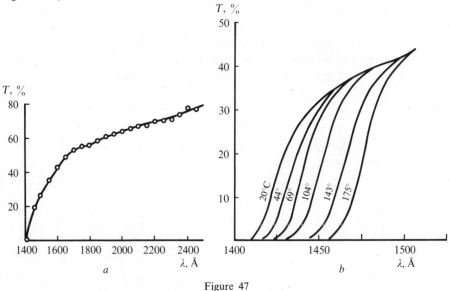

Figure 47

*a* Transmittance of sapphire vs. wavelength for a specimen 0.8 mm thick. *b* Transmittance of sapphire (specimen 0.32 mm thick) at various temperatures.

*Barium fluoride* crystals are transparent to 1350 Å and can be used, say, as windows for ionization chambers.

*Magnesium fluoride* crystals are transparent to 1400–1200 Å and can be used for polarization optics in the vacuum ultraviolet, as they display birefringence.

Some solutions and gases are also transparent in the vacuum ultraviolet, and they can be used as filters. A solution of 9,10-dimethylanthracene in cyclohexane has a high transmittance for the 1849 Å mercury line and is virtually opaque at 2537 Å [20].

The "oxygen filter" is fairly common. A cell 2 cm long, with LiF windows, is filled with oxygen at atmospheric pressure. Although the absorbance of oxygen between 1050 and 1750 Å is on the whole fairly high (see §39, Figure 211c), it has seven narrow transmission bands in this region and one of them covers $L_x$ [21].

## 10. TRANSPARENT FILMS

Normally opaque materials may prove to be transparent if taken as a sufficiently thin film. The selection of thin transparent films for cell windows or filters is determined by the absorbance at the relevant wavelengths and by the mechanical properties of the materials. Films a few hundred or thousand angstroms thick are used. Methods of preparation of such films and absorbance measurements have been developed in nuclear physics and electron microscopy [22–24].

Transparent thin films are beginning to be used in vacuum UV and X-ray spectroscopy [25–28].

Organic, and in particular celluloid, films are the easiest to prepare. The absorbance of celluloid films was measured between 4000 and 200 Å; maximum absorption was observed at 850 Å [29, 30] (Figure 48). These films, however, quickly deteriorate on heating.

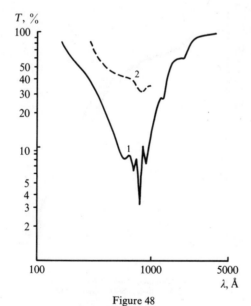

Figure 48

Transmittance of organic films:

1) a 270 Å nitrocelluloid film,   2) a 100 Å celluloid film.

Aluminum oxide films can withstand much greater heating and a substantially higher pressure gradient than the organic films. For example, a film 2 mm in diameter with a surface density of $10^{-4}$ g/cm$^2$ resists pressures of a few torr. Various pure elements also turn to be transparent in the vacuum ultraviolet if used in these films, e.g., Al [30–38], Sn [31, 33, 39], Pb [40], Cd [31, 41], Be [34, 35, 37], Mg [34, 42], C [43, 44], Ti [35, 37, 45], Se [46, 47], Te [37, 45, 46, 48], Ag [31, 37], Au [31, 37], In [30, 31, 33], Bi [30, 31], Cr [49, 50], Sb [37, 45], Mn, Fe, Co, Ni, Cu, Zn, Ga [50], Ge [30, 50], Si [30, 50].

There are reports of transparent SiO films [51, 52], whose absorbance has been measured [36].

Figures 49–62 show the transmittance curves of various thin films. As we see from the curves, each metal has a certain characteristic frequency at which the transmittance reaches a maximum. Theoretical considerations also point to the existence of a peak on the transmittance curve of metals [53–55].

## Film preparation

All films are fairly brittle, break in moderate pressure gradients, and are insufficiently resistant to heating.

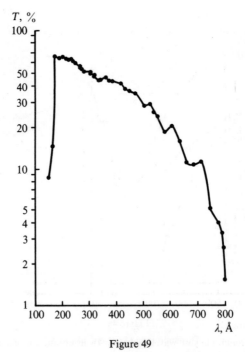

Figure 49

Transmittance of aluminum film 800 Å thick vs. wavelength.

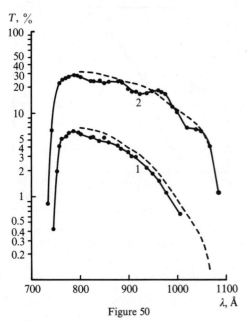

Figure 50

Transimittance of indium films vs. wavelength:

1) 3650 Å film,   2) 1560 Å film; dashed curve—
theoretical.

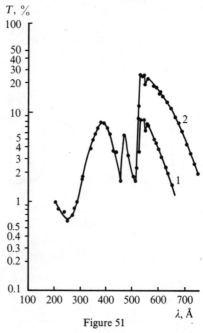

Figure 51

Transmittance of bismuth films vs. wavelength:

1) 1990 Å film,   2) 950 Å film.

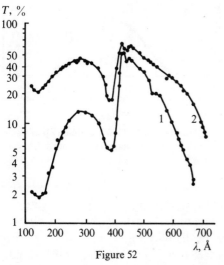

Figure 52

Transmittance of germanium films vs. wavelength:

1) 1380 Å film,   2) 700 Å film.

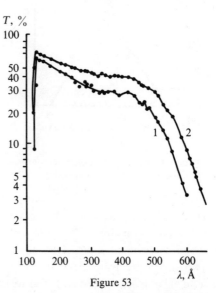

Figure 53

Transmittance of silicon films vs. wavelength:

1) 2040 Å film,   2) 1250 Å film.

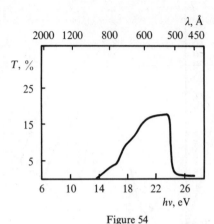

Figure 54

Transmittance of a 1020 Å tin film vs.
wavelength and photon energy.

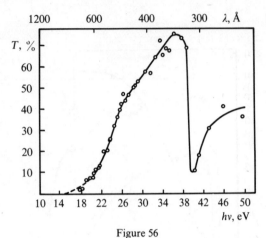

Figure 56

Transmittance of a 550 Å tellurium film vs.
wavelength and photon energy.

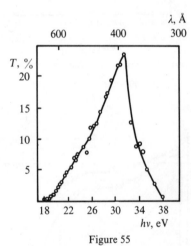

Figure 55

Transmittance of a 525 Å titanium film vs.
wavelength and photon energy.

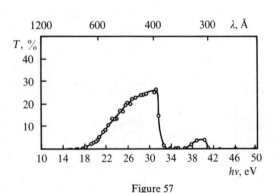

Figure 57

Transmittance of a 1000 Å antimony film vs.
wavelength and photon energy.

To prepare films from Zapon (a cellulose nitrate varnish, collodion, or celluloid), the solid component is dissolved in amyl acetate to make a 1–3% solution, and one or two drops are transferred to the surface of distilled water in a wide-mouthed cuvette. The drops spread over the water surface forming a thin film, which rapidly dries and can be picked out with a frame. Generally a better procedure is to grow double films, especially when the total film thickness should be less than 1000 Å.

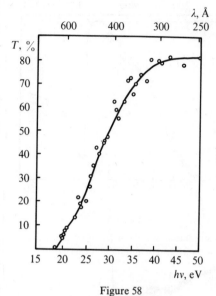

Figure 58

Transmittance of a 875 Å beryllium film vs.
wavelength and photon energy.

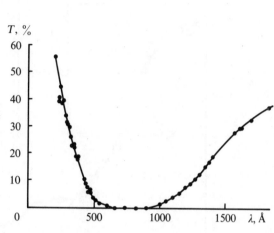

Figure 59

Transmittance of a 270 Å carbon film vs. wavelength.

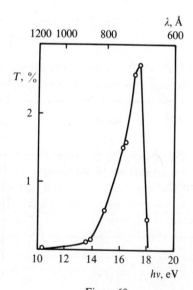

Figure 60

Transmittance of a 1000 Å lead film vs.
wavelength and photon energy.

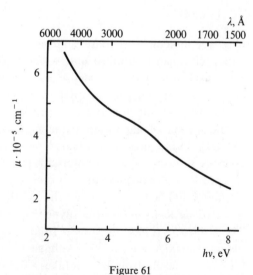

Figure 61

Absorption coefficient of cadmium vs.
wavelength and photon energy.

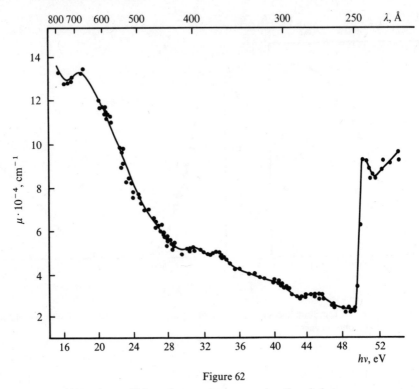

Figure 62

Absorption coefficient of magnesium vs. wavelength and photon energy.

It is very difficult to prepare sufficiently strong individual films of such thickness. Zapon films can be applied onto a fine grating (about 25 lines/mm), which stiffens them mechanically [24, 25, 56]. Metallic films are prepared by vaporizing the metal in vacuum. They are generally deposited on a special base, such as Zapon, Formvar, Mylar, Teflon, collodion, polystyrene [34].

Preparation of aluminum oxide films has been described by various authors [57–60]. These films are obtained by electrolytic oxidation of aluminum foil in aqueous solution of ammonium citrate. (Before the electrolysis, the foil must be checked for holes or punctures: it is examined against a strong source of light.) The aluminum foil acts as an anode; the foil thickness is a few tens of microns. The foil is placed vertically in the electrolytic bath, where an aluminum rod acts as a cathode. The electrode voltage is chosen from considerations of oxide film thickness. To obtain a 1000 Å film, a 70 V voltage is needed with a current density of about 0.1 A/cm$^2$; the electrolysis then takes a few minutes.

The aluminum foil is oxidized on both sides along the four edges, and the central part is oxidized only on the top side. The oxidized foil is attached onto a slightly larger frame and is lowered vertically into concentrated hydrochloric acid, with a few crystals of $CuCl_2$ added. The hydrochloric acid dissolves the unoxidized aluminum at the center and we thus obtain an oxide film with thicker oxide-coated aluminum foil running along its four edges (Figure 63).

Figure 63

Geometry of aluminum oxide layers on aluminum foil.

Although the preparation of these films is a fairly simple procedure, it is not easy to obtain a high-quality film. The purity of aluminum and various uncontrollable technological factors probably play a decisive role. Thin films which are transparent in the vacuum ultraviolet have thicknesses of a few hundred angstrom. These films are always partly permeable to gas. Apparently they should be used under the same conditions as the organic films: either in small pressure gradients or in cases when slight leakage is not critical. So far, aluminum oxide films have not been used in vacuum UV spectroscopy.

## Film uses

The main application of thin films is as partitions between different parts of the system. Films limit the thickness of the absorbing layer in the cell, separate the radiation source from the spectrograph, etc. Metallic films are used as filters reducing light scattering in monochromators and spectrographs or unravelling superimposed spectra of various orders.

These films also can be used as narrow-band monochromatic filters. In solar spectrum studies, Be films isolate the 110–200 Å region, and Sn films isolate the 500–700 Å region [61]. In conjunction with photocathodes which are sensitive at wavelengths below 2000 Å (see §23), metallic filters will even isolate individual spectral lines. Thus the 584 Å line can be isolated from the helium spectrum using an aluminum filter and a barium fluoride photocathode [33].

## 11. REFLECTING LAYERS

The absence of sufficiently transparent materials leads to an ever growing use of reflection optics in the short-wave ultraviolet. Plane and spherical mirrors are used fairly seldom, and the main spectroscopic instrument is a concave reflecting diffraction grating, whose efficiency is completely conditioned by its surface reflectance. Considerable efforts therefore have been devoted to the search for high-reflectance materials in the vacuum ultraviolet [62].

The reflection properties of a whole range of materials were studied in detail by Sabine [63], and this probably remained the only study on the subject up to the 1950's. The technique of reflection measurements for various metals was substantially improved by Banning [64]. He measured the reflectance immediately after film preparation.

Film deposition techniques, vaporization methods, and vaporization conditions have been developed to a considerable extent. Madden [65] gives a comprehensive literature review on this subject. He also lists the reflection coefficients of various materials in the vacuum ultraviolet.

Figures 64 through 97 show the reflection properties of the main materials used in vacuum UV spectroscopy. The reflection coefficient is highly sensitive to the incidence angle of radiation, and this effect is particularly noticeable at wavelengths below 1000 Å.

If the incidence angle is not indicated, the reflection coefficients have been measured for normal incidence.

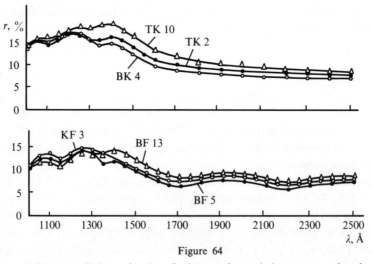

Figure 64

Reflection coefficients of various Soviet manufactured glasses vs. wavelength.

The reflection of most materials is generally poor at small incidence angles, and sufficiently strong spectra can be obtained only for nearly normal incidence; the reflection coefficient markedly increases for 90° incidence.

In experimental work the incident radiation is always assumed to be unpolarized, although in fact the light reflected from the diffraction grating is partly polarized, especially for large incidence angles.

## Glass

The reflection coefficient of glass in the vacuum ultraviolet is very low even for normal incidence. Figure 64 plots the reflection coefficient of various glasses for 45° incidence. The reflection coefficient of glass between 400 and 2000 Å fluctuates from 20 to 8% [66]. The curves for different grades of glass naturally do not coincide. The actual position of the maxima on these curves is determined by the content of silicon, lead, and barium oxides in the glass.

## Quartz

The reflection coefficients of fused and crystalline quartz were measured by various authors [3, 6, 63, 66–68]. The measurements were made at incidence angles of 45, 60, 75, and 85° between 1609 and 910 Å. At 45° incidence, the reflection coefficient varied from 26 to 9% [3]. The reflection coefficient of quartz between 1100 and 1900 Å was studied in [68], between 1100 and 2500 Å in [66],* and between 1000 and 1800 Å in [6]. Figure 65 plots the reflection coefficient of crystalline quartz vs. wavelength. Quartz has a high reflection coefficient at 1300–1000 Å (nearly 30%) and a fairly low reflection coefficient in the visible and the near ultraviolet (6–7%).

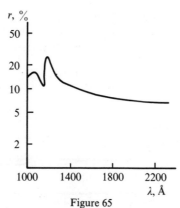

Figure 65

Reflection coefficient of crystalline quartz vs. wavelength.

* References to earlier literature are also given in [66].

## Lithium fluoride

The reflection coefficient of lithium fluoride was measured in [9, 68–71]. It is highly variable, depending on surface preconditioning. A surface left untreated after cleavage gives a lower reflection coefficient than a polished surface. Figure 66 plots the reflection coefficient of LiF vs. wavelength (20° incidence).

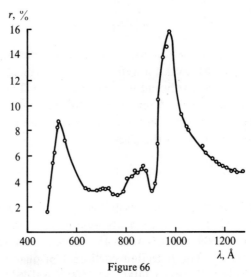

Figure 66

Reflection coefficient of lithium fluoride vs. wavelength.

## Fluorite

The reflection coefficient of fluorite between 900 and 1600 Å was measured in [6, 68, 72]. Figure 67 plots the reflection coefficient as a function of wavelength for 45° incidence.

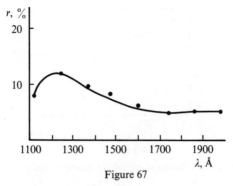

Figure 67

Reflection coefficient of fluorite vs. wavelength.

## Aluminum [31, 63, 73–85]

The reflection properties of aluminum have been studied experimentally by numerous authors, as aluminum films are very often used to coat mirrors and diffraction gratings. The reflection coefficient of aluminum is highest for normal incidence at wavelengths above 1000 Å. We see from Figure 68*a* that the reflection coefficient of aluminum layers soon after deposition is fairly constant between 1000 and 2000 Å, reaching over 85%. The reflection coefficient of aluminum film was found to change

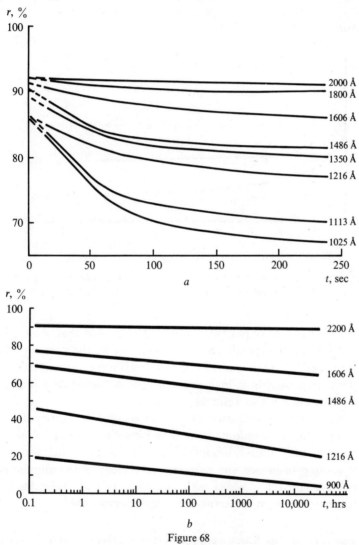

Figure 68

Effect of aging on reflection coefficient of aluminum film.

with time; only freshly deposited layers show high reflection (compare Figures 68*a* and 68*b*). Two years after deposition, the reflection coefficient of an aluminum film at 1160 Å was found to be about 2% for 30° incidence [85]. These sharp changes in reflection coefficient are not observed only at wavelengths above 2000 Å.

The gradual reduction of the reflection coefficient is associated with the oxidation of aluminum. For this reason, the reflection coefficient remains virtually constant in a nitrogen atmosphere, and falls off markedly in an oxygen atmosphere. The process of oxidation is speeded up by ultraviolet radiation (Figure 69). The original value of the reflection coefficient is restored if the mirror is exposed to ultraviolet light in a hydrogen atmosphere [6].

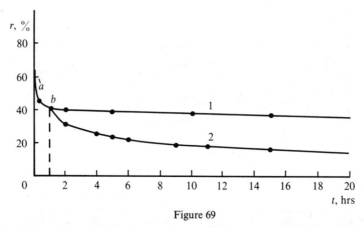

Figure 69

Effect of aging on aluminum film before exposure to UV light (curve 1) and after exposure (curve 2) ($\lambda = 1216$ Å). Air bleeding begins at point *a*, UV illumination at point *b*.

The reflection coefficient of pure aluminum is higher than that of aluminum with impurities (Figure 70). It depends on the temperature of the substrate during the vaporization (Figure 71), on the rate of vaporization (Figure 72), and on the vacuum. Aluminum films deposited in a high vacuum have a higher reflection coefficient than films deposited at a higher residual gas pressure.

The aluminum grating, as we see from Figure 73, is highly ineffective. This is associated with the formation of aluminum oxide film. We see from Figure 74 that different parts of the grating may differ substantially in terms of their efficiency [79].

In case of grazing incidence, the reflection coefficient of the aluminum grating is a nonmonotonic function of wavelength, and this may lead to considerable errors in energy measurements even in narrow spectrum intervals [84].*

---

* Nonmonotonic variation of the reflection coefficient with wavelength has also been observed for glass between 70 and 130 Å [86].

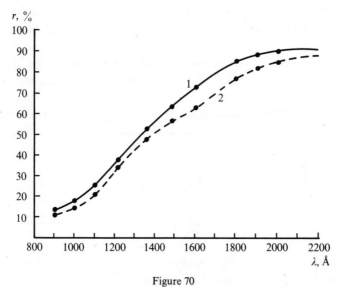

Figure 70

The effect of purity on the reflection coefficient of aluminum film:

1) 99.99 % Al,   2) 99.5 % Al.

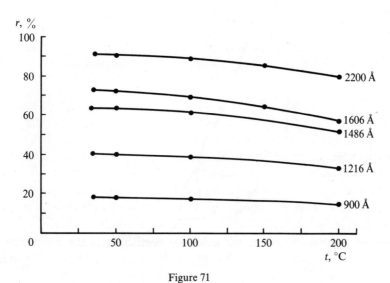

Figure 71

The effect of substrate temperature on the reflection coefficient of aluminum film.

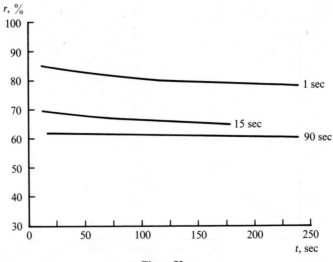

Figure 72

The effect of vaporization rate on the reflection coefficient of aluminum film ($\lambda = 1216$ Å).

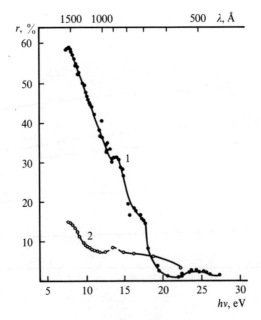

Figure 73

Reflection coefficient of aluminum (curve 1) and grating efficiency (curve 2) vs. photon energy (25° incidence).

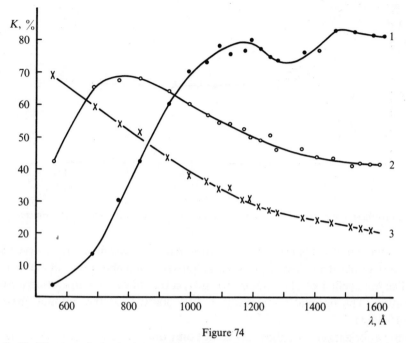

Figure 74

Ratio $K$ of line intensity in the first order to the overall intensity of the other orders vs. wavelength for left (curve 1), middle (curve 2), and right (curve 3) parts of the grating.

## Platinum [68, 80–82, 87–90]

The reflection coefficient of platinum is higher than that of the other metals, especially at wavelengths below 1000 Å for normal incidence. Figure 75 plots the reflection coefficient of platinum vs. wavelength. The effect of film thickness on the reflection coefficient of platinum has been studied separately. To this end, the reflection coefficient at 584 Å has been determined (Figure 76). The reflection coefficient slightly

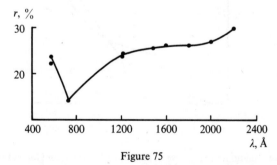

Figure 75

Reflection coefficient of platinum vs. wavelength (film thickness 90–140 Å).

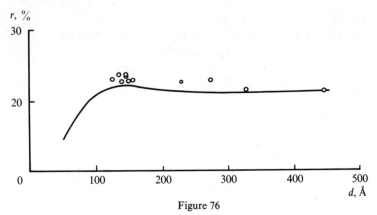

Figure 76

Reflection coefficient of platinum vs. film thickness $d$ (curve—theoretical, points—experimental).

decreases as the film is made thicker. The highest reflection coefficient is observed for films 120–140 Å thick deposited on glass; these films transmit about 10% in the visible.

The reflection coefficient of platinum depends on the substrate temperature during the deposition. The optimal temperature is 250–300°C, and the optimal growth rate is 5–15 Å/sec.

Platinum vaporization should be carried out only once, as repeated, and especially multiple, vaporization greatly reduces the reflection coefficient. The reflection coefficient as a function of the angle of incidence at 584 Å is plotted in Figure 77.

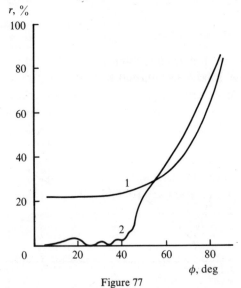

Figure 77

Reflection coefficient of a platinum film (curve 1) and an aged aluminum film (curve 2) vs. the incidence angle $\phi$.

For 80° incidence the reflection coefficient markedly increases, reaching 65%. However, it is still lower than the reflection coefficient of aluminum.

The reflection coefficient of platinum is not affected by aging. This constitutes a fundamental advantage of platinum films over aluminum coatings (Figure 78). During one year, the reflection coefficient drops merely by 1–2%. Since platinum is used to coat diffraction gratings ruled on aluminum, the effect of aging was separately studied for platinum films deposited on aged aluminum surfaces (and not on glass substrate). Again, the reflection coefficient did not change with time.

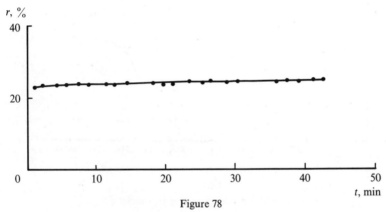

Figure 78

Effect of film aging on the reflection coefficient of platinum ($\lambda = 584$ Å).

Figure 79 plots the efficiency of a platinized grating. Platinizing clearly leads to a substantial improvement of the grating properties only if the low efficiency of the grating is associated with a low reflection coefficient, but not with structural defects. The beneficial effect of platinizing was apparently first noted by Watanabe [89].

**Rhodium** [68, 75, 80, 81, 91]

Rhodium, like platinum, has a high reflection coefficient in the vacuum ultraviolet, and may therefore be used as a coating for diffraction gratings. Figure 80 plots the reflection coefficient of rhodium vs. wavelength. The reflection coefficient of rhodium is lower than that of platinum between 800 and 1500 Å and higher at longer wavelengths. Rhodium has no advantages compared to platinum as a coating for diffraction gratings.

**Gold** [31, 36, 68, 82, 88, 90]

The reflection coefficient of gold in the vacuum ultraviolet is fairly high. It has been studied between 450 and 2000 Å (Figure 81). The curve in Figure 91 is incon-

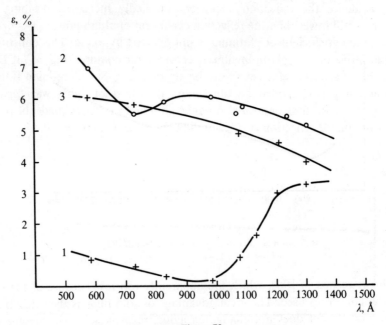

Figure 79

Efficiency of platinized grating vs. wavelength:

1) uncoated,    2 and 3) platinized.

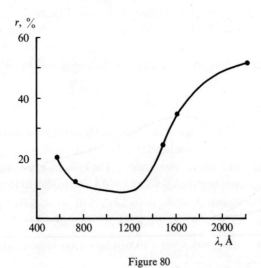

Figure 80

Reflection coefficient of rhodium film vs. wavelength.

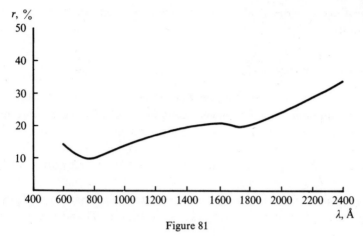

Figure 81

Reflection coefficient of gold vs. wavelength [82].

sistent with the results of [90], which are apparently too low because of the poor quality of the gold films used. The great advantage of gold films is their durability: the reflection coefficient does not change on aging, regardless of whether the film is kept in air or in vacuum.

High-efficiency gratings can be ruled on gold. We see from Figure 82 that near

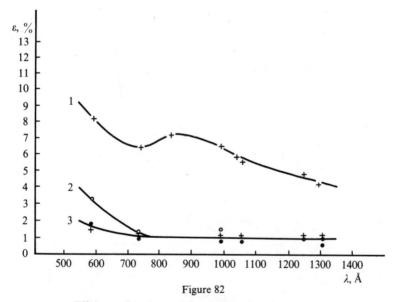

Figure 82

Efficiency of gratings ruled on gold surface vs. wavelength:

1, 2) uncoated grating,   3) grating 2 after platinizing.

500 Å the grating efficiency is almost 10%, which is higher than the efficiency of a platinized grating.

## Germanium [65, 82, 92–94]

The reflection coefficient of germanium films does not fall off with aging quite as fast as that of aluminum films, but nevertheless the effect of aging is substantial. The reflection coefficient of germanium is dependent on the vaporization temperature. The higher the vaporization temperature, the higher the reflection coefficient. The reflection coefficient of opaque germanium films at 1216 Å and normal incidence is over 50%.

Madden [65] gives curves of the reflection coefficient of germanium and germanium oxide vs. the angle of incidence at 735 and 584 Å (Figures 83 and 84).

## Tungsten, tantalum, molybdenum, and rhenium [65, 95]

Tungsten has a high reflection coefficient between 500 and 1000 Å, which is even higher than that of platinum. Between 580 and 1220 Å, the reflection coefficient of tungsten is almost constant, a highly convenient feature in some cases. The reflection coefficients of tungsten, tantalum, nolybdenum, and rhenium between 500 and 2000 Å were measured for 15° incidence (Figure 85) [95].

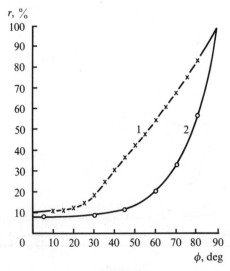

Figure 83

Reflection coefficient of germanium film (curve 1) and germanium oxide film (curve 2) vs. angle of incidence ($\lambda = 735$ Å).

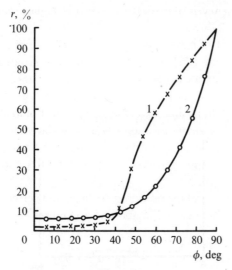

Figure 84

Reflection coefficient of germanium film (curve 1) and germanium oxide film (curve 2) vs. angle of incidence ($\lambda = 584$ Å).

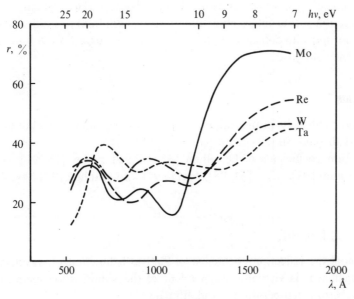

Figure 85

Reflection coefficients of molybdenum, rhenium, tungsten, and tantalum vs. wavelength.

## Cadmium [31, 96]

The reflection coefficient of cadmium at 3000 Å is 48%, and at 1500 Å and 1200 Å it is 8 and 3%, respectively [96]. The reflection coefficient of cadmium film 1000 Å thick at 20° incidence was measured between 560 and 2000 Å (Figure 86).

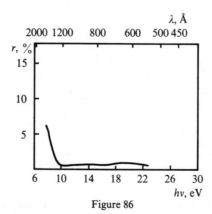

Figure 86

Reflection coefficient of cadmium film vs. wavelength.

## Silicon [93, 97]

The reflection coefficient of silicon is highly sensitive to surface structure. Figure 87 plots the reflection coefficient as a function of wavelength from two different surfaces: curve 2, for an optically polished single-crystal surface; curve 1, for a fused and then slightly polished surface.

## Other elements

The reflection coefficients of tin, indium, and bismuth vs. the wavelength are plotted in Figures 88 through 90 (20° incidence).

The reflection coefficients of beryllium [65, 68, 91], nickel [68, 91], chromium [68, 90], selenium [93], silver [31, 98] (Figure 91), and graphite [99] have also been studied.

## Zinc sulfide [75, 100, 101]

Figure 92 plots the reflection coefficient of ZnS as a function of wavelength. The reflection coefficient is virtually independent of the vaporization conditions, film thickness, substrate temperature*, and film age.

* The substrate temperature during vaporization should not be less than 150°C.

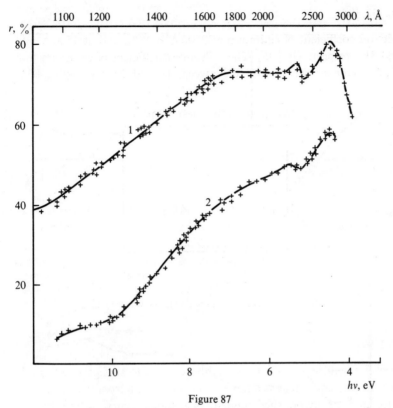

Figure 87

Reflection coefficient of silicon vs. wavelength.

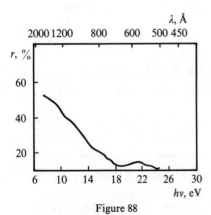

Figure 88

Reflection coefficient of tin vs. wavelength
and photon energy.

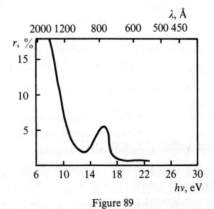

Figure 89

Reflection coefficient of indium vs. wavelength
and photon energy

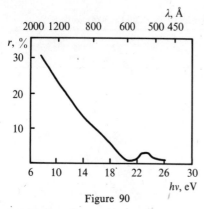

Figure 90

Reflection coefficient of bismuth vs. wavelength and photon energy.

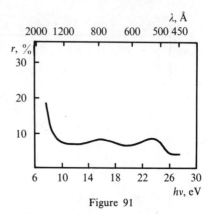

Figure 91

Reflection coefficient of silver vs. wavelength and photon energy.

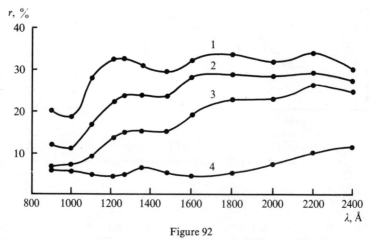

Figure 92

Reflection coefficient of zinc sulfide after exposure to UV light for 2 hours (curve 2), 4 hrs (curve 3), and 24 hrs (curve 4). Curve 1 corresponds to an unexposed specimen.

Therefore for wavelengths below 1250 Å, zinc sulfide films have considerable advantages compared to aged aluminum films. The older the aluminum film, the more pronounced these advantages are. However, zinc sulfide films have a very distinct shortcoming: their reflection coefficient falls off following exposure to ultraviolet radiation (see Figure 92).

The dependence of the reflection coefficient on the incidence angle at various wavelengths is plotted on Figure 93. This dependence is more pronounced at short wavelengths.

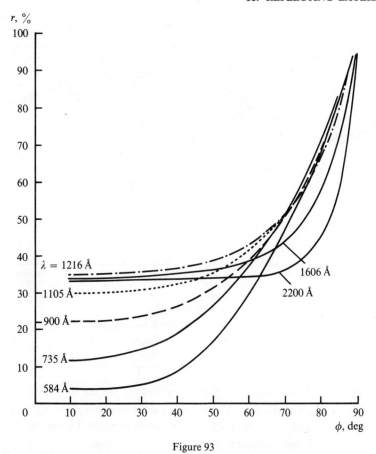

Figure 93

Reflection coefficient of zinc sulfide vs. angle of incidence at various wavelengths.

## Aluminum layers coated with MgFe and LiF [65, 69, 75, 81, 83, 102–105]

As we have noted before, the reflection coefficient of an aluminum layer rapidly decreases in the air. To prevent the formation of the oxide film, which readily absorbs short-wave radiation, the aluminum surface may be coated with an $MgF_2$ film, which protects the metal against oxidation. If the film thickness is appropriately chosen, constructive interference will enhance the reflection coefficient, as in ordinary multilayer coatings.

Figure 94 plots the reflection coefficient of aluminum coated with films having various refractive indices. These curves were obtained by theoretical calculation. The refractive index of magnesium fluoride is $n \approx 1.7$, and the theoretical curves predict an enhancement of the reflection coefficient. This is indeed observed in practice.

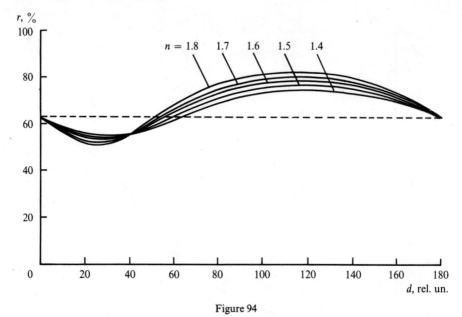

Figure 94

Reflection coefficient of an aluminum layer coated with films of various refractive indices $n$
(theoretical curves, $\lambda = 1216$ Å).

Figure 95 plots the reflection coefficient of a freshly prepared aluminum surface which is coated with an $MgF_2$ film. All the three curves were obtained using specimens which had been coated one day before the measurements began. $MgF_2$-coated films do not age, and their optical properties remain constant.

We see from Figure 95 that at short wavelengths (from 1000 to 1300 Å), the reflection coefficient is higher for thin $MgF_2$ films. This is so because magnesium fluoride absorbs at these wavelengths. In practice, magnesium fluoride films should not be used at wavelengths shorter than 1100 Å.

The reflection coefficient of $MgF_2$-coated aluminum was studied as a function of the angle of incidence for films of various thicknesses [65]. We see from Figure 96 that for the optimal thickness (250 Å) the reflection coefficient drops to 50% as the angle of incidence is increased to 85°.

$MgF_2$ can be advantageously replaced with LiF. Lithium fluoride gives a higher reflection coefficient between 1000 and 1200Å. The reflection coefficient of aluminum film coated with lithium fluoride depends on film thickness (Figure 97). At 1025 Å, the highest reflection coefficient is obtained for films 140–180 Å thick.

LiF film ages in air with humidity of over 50%. The film should therefore be coated with a very thin protective layer of $MgF_2$. The thickness of the $MgF_2$ film need not exceed 15 Å, so that it should not cause noticeable absorption. Suitable deposition

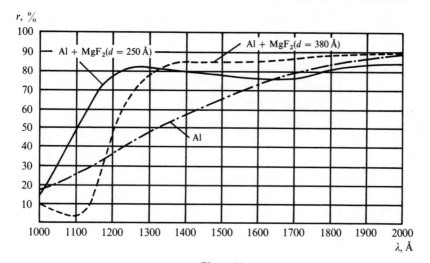

Figure 95

Reflection coefficient of pure aluminum and aluminum coated with magnesium fluoride films of different thicknesses.

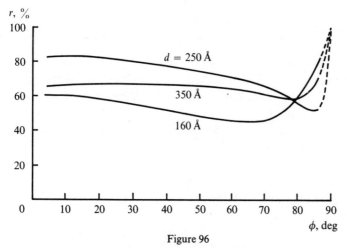

Figure 96

Reflection coefficient of aluminum film coated with different thicknesses of magnesium fluoride vs. angle of incidence (1216 Å).

techniques are described in [65, 75, 102]. Alongside with experiments intended to measure the reflection coefficients of $MgF_2$-coated aluminum surfaces, special tests of diffraction grating efficiencies were carried out [103].

A grating with a peak near 5500 Å was coated with aluminum layer 1000 Å thick and an $MgF_2$ film 265 Å thick. The effect of these coatings on grating efficiency was

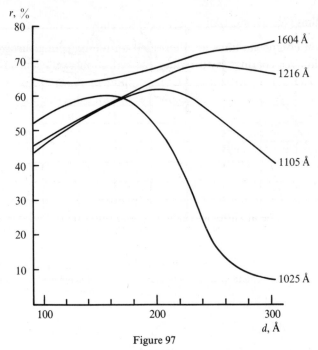

Figure 97

Reflection coefficient of an Al + LiF coating vs. thickness of LiF layer at various wavelengths.

studied; the efficiency in the fourth order at 1335 Å was found to increase by a factor of 12.5, and the efficiency in the fifth order at 1216 Å increased by a factor of 20. The distribution of energy between the various orders at 1335 Å was also studied. The efficiency data of this grating are shown in Table 2 (the efficiency of the coated grating in the fourth order was taken as 100).

We see from the table that the efficiency markedly increases only near the blaze angle; at other incidence angles it remains low.

Image quality deteriorates when the grating is coated with $MgF_2$.

Table 2

| Spectrum order | $\phi$, deg | Grating efficiency, rel. units | Spectrum order | $\phi$, deg | Grating efficiency, rel. units |
|---|---|---|---|---|---|
| IV | 19.13 | 8.0* | IV | 19.13 | 100 |
| II | 9.22 | 6.2 | V | 23.60 | 5.7 |
| III | 13.91 | 3.8 | VI | 28.73 | 3.2 |

\* Efficiency before coating.

**Multilayer films** [75, 81, 83, 106]

In some cases, composite films are deposited on the reflecting surface; the purpose of these multilayer coatings is to reduce the reflection coefficient in the long-wave region and to suppress the scattered light component. A layer of germanium topped by a zinc sulfide layer is an example of films of this kind. Germanium is first deposited onto aluminum substrate. The thickness of the germanium layer is chosen so that at 4000 Å the reflection coefficient is 50%. ZnS is deposited on top of the germanium layer until the reflection coefficient at this wavelength falls to zero.

Figure 98 plots the reflection coefficient of this double layer between 900 and 4800 Å. The decrease of the reflection coefficient above 2900 Å is associated with the partial transparency of zinc sulfide in this region, which causes destructive interference. ZnS is opaque at short wavelengths, and only the outer layer reflects.

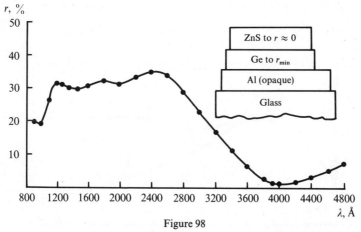

Figure 98

Reflection coefficient of Al + Ge + ZnS coating vs. wavelength.

A useful multilayer film is made up of aluminum and zinc sulfide (Figure 99). A dense layer of aluminum is deposited on a glass substrate; it is then topped by a ZnS layer, which lowers the reflection coefficient at 4000 Å to 5%; after that a thin semitransparent layer of aluminum is applied, which increases the reflection coefficient to 25%, and then again a layer of ZnS until the reflection coefficient at 4000 Å is zero. The curve on Figure 99 has two reflection minima near 2700 and 4000 Å.

The scattered light is suppressed by a double ZnS + $MgF_2$ layer (the thickness of the magnesium fluoride layer is $d = 250$ Å). Figure 100 plots the reflection coefficient of ZnS coated with an $MgF_2$ film. The reflection coefficient increases between 1100 and 1300 Å and falls off at longer wavelengths. At 2000 Å the reflection coefficient is about 8%, and at 4000 Å it is close to 6%. This coating has a maximum reflection coefficient

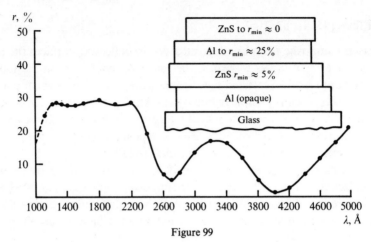

Figure 99

Reflection coefficient of Al + ZnS + Al + ZnS coating vs. wavelength.

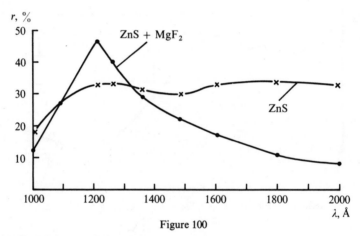

Figure 100

Reflection coefficient of zinc sulfide and of a double ZnS + MgF$_2$ layer vs. wavelength.

at 1216 Å, and it is therefore used as a reflection filter for $L_\alpha$ [83] (Figure 101a). Another coating that can be used as a reflection filter for $L_\alpha$ is Al + MgF$_2$ + Al + MgF$_2$ (Figure 101b).

Double layers of Al$_2$O$_3$ and SiO are also used. The thickness of the two layers is chosen so that the reflection coefficient at 3000 Å is virtually zero. Al$_2$O$_3$ is the outer layer, because of its fairly high reflection coefficient in the vacuum UV (Figure 102).

Multilayer coatings do not ensure a substantial improvement of the reflection coefficient from an aluminum surface in the vacuum ultraviolet (compared to one-layer coating).

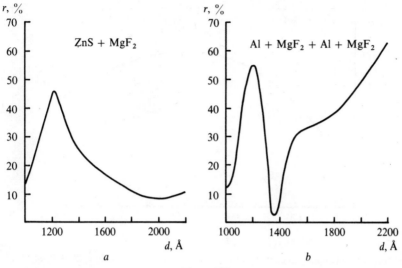

Figure 101

Filters isolating the $L_\alpha$ line ($\lambda = 1216$ Å).

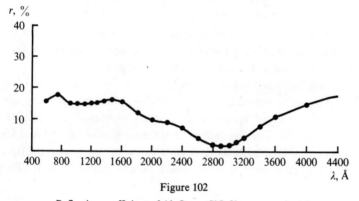

Figure 102

Reflection coefficient of $Al_2O_3$ on SiO film vs. wavelength.

Certain coatings ensure a high reflection coefficient between 500 and 950 Å. For example, coating a platinum film with a thin layer of aluminum should markedly increase the reflection coefficient. The theoretical curve calculated for 735 Å is shown in Figure 103. In practice, however, this pronounced increase of the reflection coefficient was not observed. To this day, we have no special film coatings which can substantially improve the reflection coefficient of platinum.

As we have mentioned above, the results of different authors on reflection coefficients are often contradictory. This is apparently due to inevitable changes in film deposition conditions, rather than to gross experimental errors.

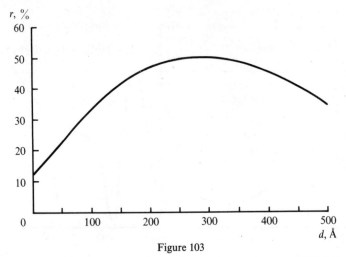

Figure 103

Reflection coefficient of aluminum-coated platinum film vs. film thickness at $\lambda = 735$ Å (theoretical curve).

A grating is coated only after it is ruled. The choice of the grating material is thus determined by various considerations pertaining to ruling, and not by the reflection coefficient. A surface coating should not effect the resolving power of the grating. The choice of the coating, on the other hand, is definitely decided by the reflection coefficient of the material in the relevant spectral region.

The best coating for wavelengths above 1000 Å is Al + MgF$_2$ or Al + LiF (see above). For wavelengths between 500 and 1000 Å, platinum displays obvious advantages compared to other coatings for normal incidence; for incidence angles greater than 55°, the reflection coefficient of aluminum oxide at 584 Å is higher than that of platinum (see Figure 77). This is so because no internal reflection arises in the platinum film at these angles of incidence (where the aluminum film is totally reflecting).

**BIBLIOGRAPHY**

1. SOIFER, L.M., M.I. SHAKHNOVICH, A.I. CHUBENKO, and A.B. BLANK. *Zh. Prikl. Spektr.,* **2**, 26 (1965).
2. BOMKE, H. *Vakuumspektroskopie.* Leipzig, Barth. 1937.
3. TOUSEY, R. *Phys. Rev.,* **57**, 1060 (1940).
4. BOYCE, J. *Revs. Mod. Phys.,* **13**, 1 (1941).
5. SCHNEIDER, E.G. *Phys. Rev.,* **45**, 152 (1934).
6. GERASIMOVA, N.G. and S.A. KULIKOV. *Optiko-mekhanicheskaya Promyshlennost',* No. 1, 17 (1958).

7. LAUFER, A.H., J.A. PIROG, and J.R. MCNESBY. *J. Opt. Soc. America*, **55**, 64 (1965).
8. KNUDSON, A.R. and J.E. KUPPERIAN. *J. Opt. Soc. America*, **47**, 440 (1957).
9. SCHNEIDER, E.G. *Phys. Rev.*, **49**, 341 (1936).
10. PERY-THORNE, A. *J. Quant. Spectr. Rad. Trans.*, **2**, 427 (1962).
11. PATTERSON, D.A. and W.H. VAUGHAN. *J. Opt. Soc. America*, **53**, 851 (1963).
12. SCHNEIDER, E.G. *J. Opt. Soc. America*, **27**, 72 (1937).
13. SHISHATSKAYA, L.P. *Optiko-mekhanicheskaya Promyshlennost'*, No.12, 33 (1964).
14. WARNECK, P. *J. Opt. Soc. America*, **55**, 921 (1965).
15. NADEAU, J.S. and W.G. JOHNSTON. *J. Appl. Phys.*, **32**, 2563 (1961).
16. TAYLOR, R.G., T.A. CHUBB, and R.W. KREPLIN. *J. Opt. Soc. America*, **55**, 1078 (1965).
17. WEEKS, J.L., S. GORDON, and G.M.A. MEABURN. *Nature*, **191**, 1186 (1961).
18. FRIEDMAN, H. *The Sun's Ionizing Radiations*, J.A. Ratcliffe, Editor, p. 133. New York–London, 1960.
19. YAKOVLEV, S.A. *Pribory i Tekhnika Eksperimenta*, No.2, 175 (1962).
20. WOLF, C.M. and R. PETEL. *J. Opt. Soc. America*, **54**, 1168 (1964).
21. BRACKMANN, R.T., W.L. FITE, and K.E. HAGEN. *Rev. Scient. Instrum.*, **29**, 125 (1958).
22. LEBEDEV, A.A., Editor, *Elektronnaya mikroskopiya (Electron Microscopy)*, p. 497. Gostekhizdat 1954
23. SIEGBAHN, K. *Beta- and Gamma-Spectroscopy*, Amsterdam, North-Holland Publishing Co. 1955.
24. DARGENT, R. *Metaux (Corros.-Inds.)*, **32**, 135 (1957).
25. BAKER, D.J., D.E. BEDO, and D.H. TOMBOULIAN. *Phys. Rev.*, **124**, 1471 (1961)
26. EDERER, D.L. and D.H. TOMBOULIAN. *Phys. Rev.*, **133A**, 1525 (1964).
27. DITCHBURN, R.W. *Proc. Roy. Soc.*, **A229**, 44 (1955).
28. LUKIRSKII, A.P., M.A. RUMSH, and L.A. SMIRNOV. *Optika i Spektroskopiya*, **9**, 505 (1960).
29. O'BRYAN, H.M. *J. Opt. Soc. America*, **22**, 739 (1932).
30. HUNTER, W.R., D.W. ANGEL, and R. TOUSEY. *Appl. Optics*, **4**, 891 (1965).
31. WALKER, W.C., O.P. RUSTGI, and G.L. WEISSLER. *J. Opt. Soc. America*, **49**, 471 (1959)
32. BORISOV, M.D., I.I. DEMIDENKO, and V.G. PADALKA. *Optika i Spektroskopiya*, **11**, 769 (1961)
33. SOROKIN, O.M. *Optika i Spektroskopiya*, **16**, 139 (1964)
34. TOMBOULIAN, D.H. and D.E. BEDO. *Rev. Scient. Instrum.*, **26**, 747 (1955).
35. RUSTIGI, O.P. *J. Opt. Soc. America*, **54**, 1387 (1964).
36. ASTOIN, N. and B. VODAR. *J. phys. et radium*, **614**, 424 (1953).
37. RUSTGI, O.P. *J. Opt. Soc. America*, **55**, 630 (1965).
38. TOMBOULIAN, D.H. and E.M. PELL. *Phys. Rev.*, **83**, 1196 (1951).
39. RUSTGI, O.P. and G.L. WEISSLER. *J. Opt. Soc. America*, **55**, 456 (1965).
40. WALKER, W.C. *J. Phys. Chem. Solids*, **24**, 1667 (1963).
41. JERIC, S., J. ROBIN, and S. ROBIN-KANDARE. *J. phys. et radium*, **23**, 957 (1962).
42. KROGER, H. and D.H. TOMBOULIAN. *Phys. Rev.*, **130**, 152 (1963).
43. SAMSON, J.A.R. *J. Opt. Soc. America*, **54**, 1491 (1964).
44. SAMSON, J.A.R. and R.B. CAIRNS. *Appl. Optics*, **4**, 915 (1965).
45. RUSTGI, O.P., W.C. WALKER, and G.L. WEISSLER. *J. Opt. Soc. America*, **51**, 1357 (1961).
46. GIVENS, M.P., C.J. KOESTER, and W.L. GOFFE. *Phys. Rev.*, **100**, 1112 (1955).
47. VAŠKO, A. *J. Opt. Soc. America*, **55**, 894 (1965).

48. WOODRUFF, R.W. and M.P. GIVENS. *Phys. Rev.,* **97**, 52 (1955).
49. AXELROD, N.N. and M.P. GIVENS. *Phys. Rev.,* **120**, 1205 (1960).
50. TOMBOULIAN, D.H., D.E. BEDO, and W.M. NEUPERT. *J. Phys. Chem. Solids,* **3**, 282 (1957).
51. HASS, G. and N.W. SCOTT. *J. Opt. Soc. America,* **39**, 179 (1949).
52. SAWYER, G.A. *Rev. Scient. Instrum.,* **23**, 604 (1952).
53. BOHM, D. and D. PINES. *Phys. Rev.,* **82**, 625 (1951).
54. PINES, D. and D. BOHM. *Phys. Rev.,* **85**, 338 (1952).
55. BOHM, D. and D. PINES. *Phys. Rev.,* **92**, 609 (1953).
56. EDERER, D.L., D.J. BAKER, and D.E. BEDO. *Bull. Amer. Phys. Soc.,* **6**, 284 (1961).
57. HAUSER, U. and W. KERLER. *Rev. Scient. Instrum.,* **29**, 380 (1958).
58. HARRIS, L. *J. Opt. Soc. America,* **45**, 27 (1955).
59. STROHMAIER, K. *Z. Naturforsch.,* **6a**, 508 (1951).
60. HOFFMAN, O. *Z. Phys.,* **143**, 147 (1955),
61. EFREMOV, A.I., A.L. PODMOSHENSKII, I.M. PRIBYLOVSKII, and V.S. PETROV. *Optiko-mekhanicheskaya Promyshlennost',* No.3, 28 (1964).
62. LEVITINA, E.I. and A.V. YAKOVLEVA. *Optiko-mekhanicheskaya Promyshlennost',* No.5, 38 (1961).
63. SABINE, G.B. *Phys. Rev.,* **55**, 1064 (1939).
64. BANNING, M. *J. Opt. Soc. America,* **32**, 98 (1942).
65. MADDEN, R.P. *Physics of Thin Films. Advances in Research and Development,* **I**, 123. G. Hass, Editor. New York–London, Academic Press. 1963.
66. GERASIMOVA, N.G., S.A. KULIKOV, and A.V. YAKOVLEVA. *Optiko-mekhanicheskaya Promyshlennost',* No.11, 12 (1958).
67. JOHNSON, F.S., H.H. MALITSON, J.D. PURCELL, and R. TOUSEY. *Astrophys. J.,* **127**, 80 (1958).
68. ROBIN, S. *Rev. opt.,* **33**, 377 (1954).
69. FABRE, D., J. ROMAND, and B. VODAR. *Optica acta,* **9**, 73 (1962).
70. KATO, R. *J. Phys. Soc. Japan,* **16**, 1476, 2525 (1961).
71. WALKER, W.C. *J. Opt. Soc. America,* **52**, 223 (1962).
72. TOUSEY, R. *Phys. Rev.,* **50**, 1057 (1936).
73. MADDEN, R.P., L.R. CANFIELD, and G. HASS. *J. Opt. Soc. America,* **53**, 620 (1963).
74. HASS, G., W.R. HUNTER, and R. TOUSEY. *J. Opt. Soc. America,* **47**, 1070 (1957).
75. HASS, G. and R. TOUSEY. *J. Opt. Soc. America,* **49**, 593 (1959).
76. IVANOVA, M.K., T.N. LOMONOSOVA, and A.V. YAKOVLEVA. *Optika i Spektroskopiya,* **4**, 535 (1959).
77. ASTOIN, N., B. VODAR, and J. ROMAND. *J. phys. et radium,* **16**, 491 (1955).
78. HASS, G., W.R. HUNTER, and R. TOUSEY. *J. Opt. Soc. America,* **46**, 1009 (1956).
79. SAMSON, J.A.R. *J. Opt. Soc. America,* **52**, 525 (1962).
80. MADDEN, R.P. and L.R. CANFIELD. *J. Opt. Soc. America,* **51**, 838 (1961).
81. BERNING, P.H., G. HASS, and R.P. MADDEN. *J. Opt. Soc. America,* **50**, 586 (1960).
82. HASS, G. and R.W. HUNTER. *J. Quant. Spectr. Rad. Trans.,* **2**, 637 (1962).
83. HUNTER, W.R. *Optica acta,* **9**, 255 (1962).
84. CRISP, R.S. *Optica acta,* **8**, 137 (1961).
85. PURCELL, J.D. *J. Opt. Soc. America,* **43**, 1166 (1953).

86. LUKIRSKII, A.P., E.P. SAVINOV, O.A. ERSHOV, I.I. ZHUKOVA, and V.A. FOMICHEV. *Optica i Spektroskopiya,* **19**, 425 (1965).
87. JACOBUS, G.F., R.P. MADDEN, and L.R. CANFIELD. *J. Opt. Soc. America,* **53**, 1084 (1963).
88. REEVES, E.M. and W.H. PARKINSON. *J. Opt. Soc. America,* **53**, 941 (1963).
89. WATANABE, K. *J. Opt. Soc. America,* **43**, 318 (1953).
90. ROBIN, S. *C.R. Acad. Sci., Paris,* **236**, 674 (1953).
91. ROBIN, S. *J. phys. et radium,* **14**, 427 (1953).
92. RANDARE, S. *C.R. Acad. Sci., Paris,* 245, 1716 (1957).
93. VODAR, B. *J. Quant. Spectr. Rad. Trans.,* **2**, 406 (1962).
94. PHILIPP, H.R. and E.A. TAFT. *Phys. Rev.,* **113**, 1002 (1959).
95. LE BLANC, L.J., J.S. FARRELL, and D.W. JUENKER. *J. Opt. Soc. America,* **54**, 956 (1964).
96. ROBIN-KANDARE, S., J. ROBIN, and S. KANDARE. *C.R. Acad. Sci., Paris,* **257**, 1605 (1963).
97. ROBIN-KANDARE, S., M.H. DAMANY, and L. TERTIAN. *J. phys. et radium,* **20**, 504 (1959).
98. TAFT, E.A. and H.R. PHILIPP. *Phys. Rev.,* **121**, 1100 (1961).
99. CARTER, J.G., R.H. HUEBNER, R.N. HAMM, and R.D. BIRKHOFF. *Phys. Rev.,* **137A**, 639 (1965).
100. COX, J.T., J.E. WAYLONIS, and W.R. HUNTER. *J. Opt. Soc. America,* **49**, 807 (1959).
101. COX, J.T., J.E. WAYLONIS, and W.R. HUNTER. *J. Opt. Soc. America,* **48**, 281 (1958).
102. ANGEL, D.W., W.R. HUNTER, R. TOUSEY, and G. HASS. *J. Opt. Soc. America,* **51**, 913 (1961).
103. WILKINSON, P.G. and D.W. ANGEL. *J. Opt. Soc. America,* **52**, 1120 (1962).
104. FABRE, D. and J. ROMAND. *J. phys. et radium,* **22**, 324 (1961).
105. BENNET, H.E., J.M. BENNET, and E.J. ASHLEY. *Appl. Optics,* **2**, 156 (1963).
106. HASS, G., H.H. SCHROEDER, and A.F. TURNER. *J. Opt. Soc. America,* **46**, 31 (1956).

CHAPTER III

# Spectral Instruments

## 12. GENERAL INFORMATION

The range of spectral instruments for the vacuum ultraviolet is substantially more limited than for other, better studied, spectral regions. Research workers often have to use instruments of their own design, custom built in their laboratories. Mass-produced instruments have appeared only recently on the market, and they are mainly intended for spectroscopic analysis.

The difficulties in the manufacture of spectral instruments for the short-wave region stem from the exacting precision requirements to be met by the optical and the mechanical components intended for use at short wavelengths, as well as from the overall decrease in transmission and reflection coefficients of most materials in the ultraviolet.

The sharpness of the image depends on the relative departure of the actual surfaces from the ideal theoretical profiles, measured in number of wavelengths. Therefore, in the long-wave region, in the IR spectrum, say, fairly crudely finished gratings and lenses are quite acceptable, whereas the optical components in the short-wave vacuum ultraviolet are expected to meet much more exacting precision standards.

An additional difficulty is associated with the vacuum that must be maintained in work with short-wave radiation. This not only places definite restrictions on the design of the body of the instrument, but also substantially complicates various routine operations, such as instrument adjustment and source alignment. It is relatively difficult to create a sufficiently high vacuum in a large volume. To avoid

88

the tedious pumpdown stage, some authors tried to fill the instrument with a gas that was transparent at the relevant wavelengths, such as argon or helium. However, to eliminate the effect of residual gases, the instrument had first to be evacuated nevertheless. Therefore, in our opinion, the only advantage of filling the instrument with an inert gas at a pressure slightly higher than atmospheric is that it enables the operator to do away with small leaks in his system (the excess pressure of the inert gas prevents air leakage into the system). This method is very seldom used nowadays, on account of the considerable advances in vacuum techniques.

Back in the 1930's, spectroscopic instruments with a fluorite prism and fluorite focusing optics were in common use. By now, these instruments have been almost completely displaced by diffraction gratings: concave reflection gratings and replica gratings are quite common and readily available.

In terms of the recording device, the spectral instruments are divided into *spectrographs*, which employ photographic plates to produce a permanent record of the spectrum, and *spectrometers*, which use a photoelectric recording or measuring system. Spectrometers also include instruments with a variety of other detectors, such as ionization chambers, photochemical radiation detectors, etc. Photoelectric multichannel spectrometers with a discrete energy scale are generally called *quantometers*. Instruments whose only function is to isolate one or several spectral regions are called *monochromators* or *polychromators*, respectively. These are standard components of any single-channel or multichannel spectrometer.

This is not an exact classification, especially as some instruments have two or more working modes, e.g., the Soviet SP-99 model which will function as a spectrograph, spectrometer, or monochromator.

Spectral instruments for the vacuum ultraviolet almost invariably use concave reflection gratings, first introduced in this region by Lyman [1].

Plane gratings are seldom used, although they have a unique advantage: they produce a strictly stigmatic spectrum. These gratings, however, require concave focusing mirrors, and the additional light losses severely limit their uses.

At wavelengths shorter than 500 Å, the angle of incidence of light on the grating is generally greater than 80°. This is the only way to ensure sufficient energy in the diffracted beam. The corresponding instruments are known as *grazing-incidence gratings* [2].

At wavelengths above 1000 Å, small incidence angles are generally used (0–30°). These are so-called *normal-incidence* instruments. Between 500 and 1000 Å, instruments of both kinds can be used, depending on the particular problem on hand and the available equipment.

## 13. CONCAVE REFLECTION GRATING

**Properties of concave gratings**

Consider a spherical mirror of radius $R$ (Figure 104) with a number of equidistant lines or grooves ruled on its surface. The distance between the lines is $d$ (measured along the chord), the total number of lines is $N$, and the length of each line is $l$. A circle of radius $R/2$ tangent to the surface of the grating at its center and lying in a plane perpendicular to the direction of the grooves is called the *Rowland circle*.

If the slit $S$ is aligned with the Rowland circle, the spectrum is observed on the surface of a cylinder whose cross section is this circle (Figure 104).

The geometrical theory of the concave grating was mainly developed by Rowland [3], and later by other authors in more detail [4–13]. The elementary theory can be found in general monographs [14–15]. Following is a brief résumé of the principal properties of the concave grating.

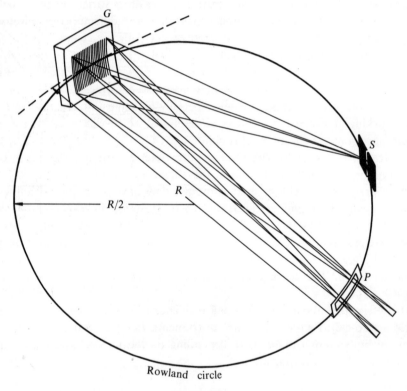

Figure 104

The relative position of the principal components in a diffraction spectrograph.
*S* slit, *P* film holder, *G* grating.

1. The concave grating is astigmatic, and the magnitude of astigmatism depends on the angles of incidence and diffraction. The length of the image of any point of the slit in the focal plane is expressed by the relation

$$Z = (\sin^2 \beta + \sin \alpha \tan \alpha \cos \beta)l. \tag{1}$$

Here $\alpha$ is the angle of incidence, $\beta$ is the angle of diffraction.

The astigmatism was calculated by Beutler [9], and also by Namioka [11, 12].

The theory of image formation for grazing incidence ($\alpha$ close to 90°) was also considered in some detail by Kastner and Neupert [13]. Figure 105 plots the calculated astigmatism values, and Figure 106 gives the corresponding curves for grazing incidence specifically. We see from equation (1) that the astigmatism is particularly large when $\alpha \rightarrow 90°$, i.e., for grazing incidence.

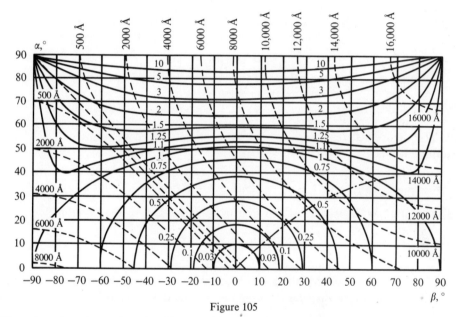

Figure 105

The astigmatism of a grating per unit groove length. The dashed curves relate the angles of incidence and diffraction for a grating with 1200 lines/mm.

The condition of maxima, the resolving power, and the dispersion of a concave grating are determined in the same way as for a plane diffraction grating. The condition of maxima is thus

$$k\lambda = d (\sin \alpha + \sin \beta) \tag{2}$$

(here $k$ is the order of the spectrum).

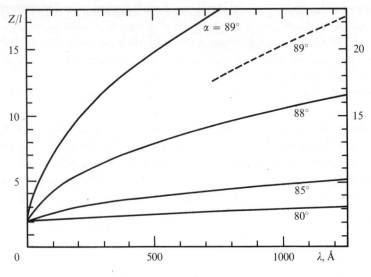

Figure 106

The astigmatism of a grazing-incidence grating per unit groove length (the right-hand scale corresponds to the dashed curve).

2. The theoretical resolving power of a grating, defined in terms of Rayleigh's criterion, is

$$\mathscr{R} = \frac{\lambda}{d\lambda} = kN .$$  (3)

3. The angular dispersion of the grating is expressed by the equality

$$\frac{d\beta}{d\lambda} = \frac{k}{d \cos \beta}.$$  (4)

4. If the distances between the grooves are measured along the arc $S$ of the Rowland circle, the linear dispersion is expressed by the relation

$$\frac{ds}{d\lambda} = \frac{kR}{d \cos \beta}.$$  (5)

5. Even if the geometrical conditions of Figure 104 are satisfied, the image of a spectral line is not free from aberrations. Astigmatism is not the only distortion: the lines are also somewhat broadened. This is so because in calculating the focusing conditions, one generally ignores the high orders of the ratio of the grating width and the groove height to the grating–slit distance. These high-order terms introduce a definite aberration, which increases as the grating becomes wider and the grooves higher.

The resolving power defined in terms of the Rayleigh criterion is therefore attainable only with fairly small gratings used under normal-incidence conditions. In grazing incidence, the aberrations are by no means ignorable and they markedly reduce the resolving power of the grating. This often limits the width of the grating, a point discussed in what follows.

The theory of the concave grating shows that spectra of different orders are focused on one curve. Shenstone [16] has noted, however, that for one of his gratings (radius of curvature 6.4 m, 1200 lines/mm) the spectra of second and third order are not focused on the same curve, whereas the spectra of fourth and fifth order are free from any anomalies. This effect is apparently associated with certain deviation of grating properties from the ideal properties, and it must be taken into consideration whenever observed. The relative shift of the focal surfaces for the spectra of different orders is apparently not very large. Other authors apparently failed to notice this effect.

## Choice of grating

Normal-incidence instruments in the vacuum ultraviolet ($\lambda > 500 \text{ Å}$) will take the same gratings as in the visible spectrum. The quality of the grating used in the vacuum ultraviolet on the whole should be substantially higher than the quality of the grating for longer wavelengths. Aluminized gratings are mostly used, ruled with 600 or 1200 lines/mm. Recently, gratings have been ruled with 3600 lines/mm [17].

Some authors distinctly prefer using gratings specially developed for the short-wave spectrum. These gratings are characterized by very shallow lines.

Figure 107a shows the profile of a shallow-groove grating. The light is reflected from the flat strips between the grooves. Ruling normal-depth grooves on a soft aluminum surface, we can obtain "blazed" gratings which give mirror reflection from the groove sides (Figure 107b) and correspondingly increase the reflected energy in the short-wave part of the spectrum in one of the first orders. There are differences of opinion as to which of the two grating types is to be preferred [18].

Replica gratings are very popular: these are plastic mold replicas of ordinary diffraction gratings, and the corresponding production technology has reached a stage of considerable sophistication. Replica gratings are coated with a reflecting layer, and their spectra are often in no way inferior to the spectra produced by the original gratings. Most mass-produced instruments are therefore equipped with replica gratings, which can be safely substituted for the unique and costly individually ruled gratings. The ruling machine in this case produces matrices from which the cheap replicas are made.

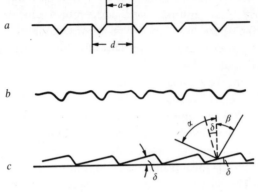

Figure 107

Cross section of grooves of a diffraction grating:

*a* shallow, *b* deformed, *c* step formation.

### Grating efficiency

In a grazing-incidence grating, the surface defects of the sphere on which the grating is ruled are acutely felt, and all aberrations rapidly increase as the incidence angle approaches 90°. This effect greatly interferes with spectroscopic work, and gratings should therefore be used as far as possible at small incidence angles. To this end, the grating should be coated with a layer which gives satisfactory reflection in the vacuum ultraviolet at angles far from 90°. One of the common coatings used for this purpose is $MgF_2$ on aluminum surface (see Chapter II).

The reflection coefficient of a mirror in grazing incidence can be estimated from the equations of the electromagnetic theory of light, which relate the angle of the total internal reflection to the concentration of electrons in the reflecting medium. (We are naturally referring to electrons which take part in dispersion.) At a given wavelength, the critical angle is found to increase as $C^{1/2}$ ($C$ is the electron concentration). In other words, as $C$ increases for a given angle of incidence, radiation of progressively shorter wavelengths can be observed. It follows from these considerations that in grazing incidence, the grating is best coated with platinum or gold, which have high $C$ values. Conversely, the $C$ of hydrocarbons is low, and the reglection coefficient of the grating decreases when vacuum oil vapor is deposited on the surface. Mercury diffusion pumps should thus be preferred to oil pumps [18a].*

The angles of total internal reflection calculated from the electromagnetic theory are consistent with the experimental values.

---

* Always assuming that mercury vapor does not give an amalgam with the grating material.

Edlén formulated a simple empirical rule, which states that the grating efficiency diminishes rapidly at wavelengths (expressed in Å) which are 10 times greater than the grazing angle $\theta = 90° - \alpha$ expressed in degrees. The shortest observable wavelength is found to be some 25% shorter than Edlén's predicted value [19]. Thus, for incidence angles of 80, 85, 89°, the corresponding wavelengths are 100, 50, and 10 Å, and Edlen's $\lambda_{min}$ is 75, 38, and 7.5 Å. This rule is adequately observed for angles of incidence greater than 80°, for gratings ruled on glass and on a special mirror alloy (speculum). These relations, however, do not apply to "blazed" gratings.

Wood has shown that blazed gratings substantially increase the energy for certain values of incidence and diffraction angles [19a]. Such blazed gratings with controlled groove shape for the infrared spectrum are known as *echelettes*. Blazed gratings which give high-order spectra in the visible and the ultraviolet are called *echelles*.

For the grating shown in Figure 107c, we may write

$$k\lambda = d (\sin \alpha + \beta) = 2d \sin (\alpha - \delta) \cos \delta, \qquad (6)$$

where $\delta$ is the slope angle of the reflecting surface of the groove.

Thus, given $d$, $\delta$, $\alpha$, and $k$, we can find the wavelength at which concentration of reflected energy is observed. This wavelength is generally given for autocollimation geometry ($\alpha = -\beta$). From equation (6) we can then find the wavelength of light concentration for any other (non-collimating) grating geometry. The angle $\beta$ which produces the strongest spectrum is called *blaze angle*. For an unblazed grating $\delta = 0$ and the maximum intensity is observed in zero order.

Grooves of controlled shape can be ruled on aluminum or on glass. The ruling of blazed gratings for the vacuum ultraviolet is naturally a much more difficult undertaking than for the visible spectrum, but the technique has nevertheless been mastered. Various aspects of grating production are discussed in detail in [20–22].

Reflection coefficients and energy distribution in various orders of diffraction for unblazed gratings are calculated in [23]. The theoretical equations have often been borne out experimentally. The inconsistencies that are occasionally observed are due to the complex groove shape [24, 25].

Consider the following example of energy distribution in different orders at 110 Å: for a grazing angle of 4° 38′, the first-order spectrum carries 5.4% of the incident energy, and the second-order spectrum 1.5% of the incident energy [23].

In general (and especially for grazing incidence), the angles of incidence differ for different parts of the grating. The blaze angle of any given grating is therefore different for different parts; this effect lowers the luminosity of the instrument and complicates its energy calibration. This difficulty is currently avoided by manufacturing gratings which consist of several parts ruled at a different angle. The ruling angle is chosen to give a nearly constant blaze angle for the different parts of the grating [26].

### Echelette, echelle, and Michelson–Williams echelon

The terms echelette and echelle indicate that these are varieties of the Michelson echelon grating, which is made up of a number of plane-parallel transparent plates in step formation (Figure 108$a$). The echelon spectrum is the result of constructive interference between light beams passing through a different number of plates. The phase difference between two neighboring beams is

$$\delta = \frac{2\pi(n-1)d}{\lambda},$$

where $n$ is the refractive index of the plate and $d$ is the plate thickness.

Williams devised a reflection echelon (Figure 108$b$) using mirror surfaces. The phase difference between successive beams in case of normal incidence is evidently

$$\delta = \frac{4\pi d}{\lambda}.$$

This echelon can be used as a high-resolution spectral instrument in the vacuum ultraviolet.

As for a normal diffraction grating, the resolving power of the echelon is $\mathscr{R} = kN$, where $N$ is the number of echelon plates, $k$ is the order of the spectrum.

Taking $d = 5$ mm as the plate thickness and $N = 10$, we obtain at $\lambda = 2000$ Å, $k = 5 \cdot 10^4$ and $\mathscr{R} = 5 \cdot 10^5$. The region free from overlapping is thus $\Delta\lambda = \lambda^2/2d = 0.02$ Å. The different orders are therefore very densely spaced, and this, together with the high cost of the echelon, constitutes the principal shortcoming of the instrument.

The blazed grating, echelle, and echelon, all function on the same principle. For ruled gratings, the number of grooves is $N \approx 10^4$–$10^5$ and the order of the spectrum is $k \approx 1$–10; for the echelle, $N \approx 10^3$–$10^4$ and $k \approx 10$–100; for the echelon, $N \approx 10$–50 and $k \approx 10^4$–$10^5$.

The echelle and the echelon ensure a high resolving power despite their relatively small size. The grating, on the other hand, gives a wider spectral region free from overlapping. The Michelson–Williams echelon so far has been used on a very limited scale (see Chapter V).

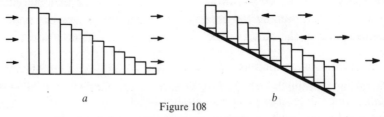

a          b

Figure 108

Michelson echelon ($a$) and Michelson–Williams echelon ($b$).

## Aspherical gratings

A significant shortcoming of a concave spherical grating is its astigmatism, so that the energy transmitted through the slit is distributed over an image area which may prove to be substantially higher than the height of the illuminated part of the slit. The image illuminance correspondingly decreases and the photographic exposure has to be increased. Photoelectric recording calls for efficient detection of the entire luminous flux transmitted by the instrument, but because of astigmatism the slit image may be too large to be entirely accommodated by the photocathode. In either case, the effect is highly detrimental. Moreover, astigmatism interferes with the production of comparison spectra and lowers the resolving power (even if the slit makes a very small angle with the grating grooves). The various mountings intended to reduce the astigmatism in the visible spectrum (e.g., Wadsworth's mounting [27]) are seldom applicable to the vacuum ultraviolet, as they require additional optics.

The astigmatism can be reduced for certain points of the focal plane if the grating is ruled on a toroidal [28, 29] or an ellipsoidal [12, 30, 31] surface. The theory of gratings ruled on surfaces of more complex geometry, with a single plane of symmetry, has also been considered [32, 33]. Gratings of this kind have two points of zero astigmatism, and the astigmatism is on the whole very small over a fairly wide range on either side of these points (sometimes reaching 1000 Å). Aspherical gratings substantially reduce other aberrations, as well as astigmatism, so that the effective width of the grating and the luminosity of the spectroscopic instrument are increased accordingly.

Gratings of this geometry, however, are not very popular because of technical production difficulties. In some cases, the requisite surface can be formed by a certain mechanical deformation of a spherical grating in its setting (by an arrangement of screws, say) [34].

Only one report has been published, describing a grating ruled on a specially designed toroidal mirror [34a]. The principal radii of curvature of the torus are $R_1 = 489$ mm and $R_2 = 330$ mm. The grating was ruled with 1150 lines/mm.

## 14. SEPARATION OF OVERLAPPING SPECTRA
## OF SUCCESSIVE ORDERS

### Overlapping of successive orders

Gratings reflecting in a wide spectral region lead to a certain overlapping of successive orders. The overlapping occurs because different wavelengths correspond to the same diffraction angle; these corresponding wavelengths are related by the standard equality $k_1\lambda_1 = k_2\lambda_2$, where $k_1$ and $k_2$ are the spectrum orders.

This overlapping is generally undesirable even in the first and second order, but it is very difficult to avoid in high-order spectra. The lines of successive orders in high-order overlapping spectra are very closely spaced, since for $k_2 = k_1 + 1$ we have

$$\lambda_1 - \lambda_2 = \lambda_2 / k_1. \tag{7}$$

The usual methods which prevent overlapping in the visible call for the use of filters, preliminary dispersion elements, crossed-dispersion instruments, selective-transmission systems, and selective detectors. Selective transmission and selective detection techniques are suitable only for the first orders. All these methods are applicable to the vacuum ultraviolet also, but there are a number of specific difficulties, such as shortage of transparent materials for interference filters, astigmatism, etc.

### Prisms

Brix and Herzberg [35] worked with orders 4 through 6 of a blazed grating in the region between 1000 and 1500 Å. The overlapping of the successive orders was prevented with the aid of an LiF prism with one cylindrical surface whose generator was parallel to the spectrograph slit (Figure 109). This prism gave the spectrum in the plane of the slit. The resolving power in this spectrum had to be very low, so as to isolate the light from the overlap-free spectral interval.

The resolution in this case is determined by the angular size of the source. This method of spectrum separation is limited by the transmission of lithium fluoride.

### Mirrors and films

At shorter wavelengths the successive orders can be separated by truncating the spectrum from the short-wave direction by reflection from a mirror [36, 37]. Metallic

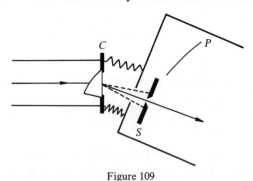

Figure 109

Application of a cylindrical prism to separate spectra of successive orders.
*C* aperture with a prism,   *S* slit,   *P* photographic plate.

films acting as filters can also be used to this end. They often give a sufficiently narrow transmission band.

## Gratings

Herzberg et al. proposed preliminary dispersion gratings for the separation of successive orders [38, 39]. A preliminary dispersion grating is mounted so that it eliminates the overlapping and also largely suppresses the astigmatism introduced by the principal grating. The first grating should be aligned so that it collects the light on the Rowland circle. The luminosity of the instrument is increased following the reduction in the length of the spectral lines and the resulting increase in the quantity of energy reaching the detector. A better utilization of the grating area is also accomplished.

Two gratings satisfying this focusing condition should be mounted so that they satisfy the following relations [40]:

$$\left. \begin{array}{c} R\left[(\cos \alpha - \sin \beta \tan \beta)^{-1} - \cos \alpha\right] = R'\left[\cos \beta' - (\cos \beta' - \sin \alpha' \tan \alpha')^{-1}\right], \\ d(\sin \alpha + \sin \beta) = k\lambda, \\ d'(\sin \alpha' + \sin \beta') = \lambda. \end{array} \right\} \quad (8)$$

All the primed quantities refer to the preliminary dispersion grating, which is used in the first order; the unprimed quantities correspond to the main grating. The angles $\alpha'$ and $\beta'$ are taken close to 90° to ensure adequate reflection coefficients. When using a preliminary dispersion grating as a measure against overlapping of orders, one should remember that the first order contains short-wave lines from the higher orders produced by this grating. This overlapping effect, however, generally can be corrected for without difficulty.

## 15. GRATING MOUNTINGS

Concave grating mountings mainly differ in terms of the kinematics of the different system components, which include the slit, the grating, and the detector (the exit slit with a photomultiplier or a photographic emulsion). By kinematics we mean the motion of the components necessary to scan the various wavelengths of the spectrum. In this section we will briefly describe only those systems which are currently used in the vacuum ultraviolet. The various aspects of this problem are discussed in greater detail in [41, 42, 43] and in review papers dealing with the mounting of concave gratings [12, 43a].

In almost all the existing systems, the entrance and the exit slit (or the photographic plate) are mounted on the Rowland circle. The only exceptions are the Seya–Namioka system and the Johnson–Onaka system.

### Paschen–Runge mounting [44]

All the optical elements are arranged on the Rowland circle (Figure 110). In case of photoelectric recording, the exit slit moves along the Rowland circle. Positive orders are obtained when the exit slit is on the same side of the normal as the entrance slit, and negative orders when the two slits lie on the two sides of the normal. Positive orders are characterized by a lower astigmatism than negative orders.

### Eagle mounting [45]

*a. Planar mounting (Figure 111)*

The angle of incidence is approximately equal to the diffraction angle, and the astigmatism is correspondingly small. Scanning is achieved by moving the grating along the line A—A and at the same time turning it around the axis 5 (at right angles to the plane of the drawing). When photographic recording is used, the plate holder should also be rotated, so that the photographic emulsion always remains on the Rowland circle.

*b. Spatial mounting*

Exact equality of the angles $\alpha$ and $\beta$ is achieved by moving the entrance and the exit slit above and below the plane of the Rowland circle. This spatial arrangement in general gives a poorer resolution than the planar Eagle mounting, but calculations and experimental results show that the loss in resolution is negligible if the angle

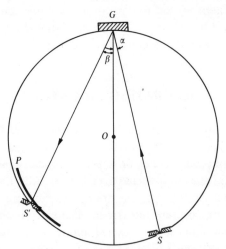

Figure 110

Paschen–Runge mounting (spectrograph and monochromator).

S   entrance slit,   S′   exit slit,   P   photographic plate,   G   grating.

Figure 111

Eagle mounting (spectrograph and monochromator):

1) Rowland circle, 2) exit slit, 3) entrance slit, 4) plate, 5) axis, 6) grating.

between the straight lines joining the center of the grating to the center of the entrance slit and the center of the spectrum is not greater than 2° [45a]. In practice, this requirement implies that the spatial system can be used for gratings with a radius of curvature of at least 3 m. For smaller radii of curvature, the slit and the film holder should be set too close to each other.

### Seya–Namioka mounting [11, 46]

This system is commonly used for monochromators. The optical elements are slightly displaced from the Rowland circle, as shown in Figure 112a. The grating turns about an axis which is tangent to its surface at the center and is parallel to the grating lines. This mounting ensures manageable aberrations for sufficiently large turning angles of the grating [11]. The monochromator design is thus greatly simplified, as the only degree of freedom is the angle of rotation of the grating about its axis. The Seya–Namioka mounting, however, is plagued by a high astigmatism, and the optimal grating width is small. This mounting can nevertheless be conveniently used in cases when only moderate monochromatization is required and the grating resolution is only partly utilized. Application of ellipsoidal gratings will markedly improve monochromators using this mounting.

### Johnson–Onaka mounting [47, 48]

The monochromator using this mounting is almost as simple as the Seya–Namioka monochromator. The system is illustrated in Figure 112b. The entrance and the exit slits are stationary. The grating rotates about the vertical axis through the point C.* The two slits and the grating lie on the Rowland circle only in one position. To find the rotation axis through the point N which lies halfway along the arc SS', we draw the diameter NM. A straight line is passed through the point M and the

---

* The terms "vertical" and "horizontal" axis and plane refer to the usual mounting of the instruments in the laboratory, when the grooves of the grating are vertical.

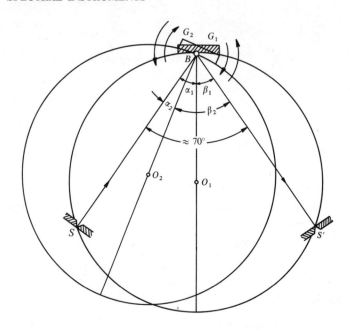

Figure 112a

Seya–Namioka monochromator.

S and S' slits, $G_1$ and $G_2$ two positions of the grating, B the axis of rotation of the grating.

center of the grating, and a segment $d$ is laid off this line, which fixes the point $C$:

$$d = \frac{2R \sin \theta}{2 - \tan \phi (\tan \alpha_1 - \tan \beta_1)}. \qquad (9)$$

All the angles are indicated in Figure 112.

The astigmatism of a Johnson–Onaka monochromator is lower than that of the Seya–Namioka monochromator. However, it is applicable only in a relatively narrow spectral region (1000 Å). Moreover, when the grating turns around an axis which does not pass through its center, the grating is translated and, for a stationary source, the effective illuminated area changes. Both these factors, and especially the latter, may prove quite troublesome.

## Wadsworth mounting [27]

An additional concave mirror eliminates the astigmatism at one point of the spectrum and markedly lowers the astigmatism over a certain range of wavelengths on either size of this point. The geometry of the system is shown in Figure 113. The

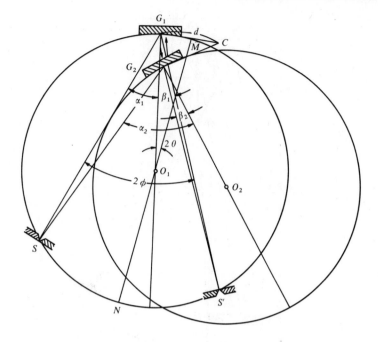

Figure 112*b*

Johnson–Onaka monochromator.

*S* and *S'* slits, $G_1$ and $G_2$ two positions of the grating.

spectrum is obtained near the normal to the grating. The linear dispersion is half the dispersion attained with the same grating in the Paschen–Runge mounting. The main shortcoming of this system are the light losses due to reflection from the additional mirror. Another drawback is that only a narrow spectral is sharply focused for photographic recording: aberrations increase rapidly as one moves away from the normal.

### Sirks's construction for compensation of astigmatism

There exists a point in front of the slit such that the edges of a horizontal slit passing through this point are sharply imaged by the grating (with vertical grooves) on the Rowland circle.

Sirks has shown [48a] that if the spectrum is formed near the normal to the grating, the distance of this point from the instrument slit can be found by a simple geometrical construction, which is explained on Figure 114.

The edges of the slit lying along *AB* are sharply imaged on the focal surface.

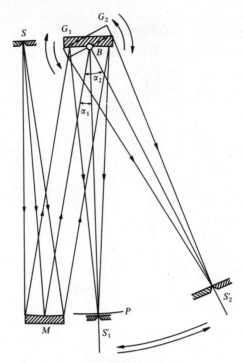

Figure 113

Wadsworth mounting (monochromator and grating).
$P$ photographic plate, $S$ entrance slit, $S'_1$, $S'_2$ two positions of the exit slit, $G_1$, $G_2$ two positions of the grating, $B$ the axis of rotation of the grating.

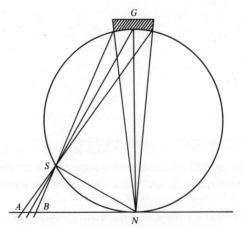

Figure 114

Sirks's construction.
$S$ slit, $GN$ normal to the grating.

This construction makes it possible to photograph comparison spectra and standard density markings by arranging diaphragms or filters along the line *AB*, as in an ordinary stigmatic instrument.

## 16. THE MAGNIFICATION OF A SPECTRAL INSTRUMENT

The ratio of the width of the slit image to the actual slit width can be defined as the longitudinal magnification of the instrument, and the corresponding height ratio if the transverse magnification. For most spectral instruments, both the longitudinal and the transverse magnification are close to unity. However, this is not always so for concave gratings. The transverse magnification in this case is determined by the astigmatism of the grating, and it can be calculated using the curves of Figure 105. Longitudinal magnification depends on instrument design, and it is particularly large for grazing-incidence-spectrographs. From equation (2) we can readily calculate the ratio of the angular dimensions of the slit and its image:

$$\frac{\Delta \alpha}{\Delta \beta} = \frac{\cos \beta}{\cos \alpha}.$$

Seeing that $\Delta \alpha = s/R \cos \alpha$ and $\Delta \beta = s'/R \cos \beta$, we find $s = s'$, i.e., the slit width is equal to the width of the slit image.

It is assumed in this analysis that the plane of the entrance slit and the plane of the exit slit are both perpendicular to the respective beam directions. This slit geometry is indeed used in monochromators of numerous designs, and the longitudinal magnification in these instruments is thus 1 regardless of the angle of incidence of the light on the grating.

On the other hand, the slit image width $s'$ for a spectrograph whose focal surface makes an angle $90°$, $\beta$ with the beam is related to the actual slit width $s$ by the equality

$$s' = \frac{s}{\cos \beta}$$

For normal-incidence instruments, $\cos \beta$ is close to 1 and the transverse magnification is small. At $85°$ incidence, however, the slit width is $s' \approx 9s$, and for $\alpha = 89°$, $s' = 57s$.

As a result, the image of the exit slit at incidence angles close to $90°$ is always so wide that the resolving power of the photoemulsion cannot be fully utilized.

The broadening of the spectral lines associated with the magnification of the slit image leads to a marked drop in the illumination of the photographic emulsion. Therefore, when concentrating on a very narrow spectral region, e.g., the contour of a spectral line, it is advisable to set the emulsion at right angles to the incident beam at the point where the diffracted beam crosses the Rowland circle (rather than align the emulsion with the surface of the Rowland circle).

## 17. TYPES OF SPECTRAL INSTRUMENTS

**Prism instruments**

Schumann's original spectrograph had a 60° fluorite prism and two fluorite lenses 16 mm in diameter, with an average focal distance of 150 mm. The reciprocal dispersion of Schumann's spectrograph at 1400 Å was 4 Å/mm [49]. Subsequently, similar spectrographs and monochromators were designed and used by other authors [50–57].

The size of the fluorite spectrographs was initially limited by the high cost and the great rarity of large natural crystals of optical fluorite. The situation has changed, however, and artificial crystals of calcium fluoride and lithium fluoride are being grown successfully in laboratory. Thus, although diffraction gratings have virtually displaced prism spectrographs in the vacuum ultraviolet, prism instruments nevertheless find limited uses because of their natural advantages, such as total absence of astigmatism and no overlapping of successive orders [58–61].

As an example, we would like to mention the work of Yakovleva et al. [58], who described a spectrograph with a 60° fluorite prism 20 mm high and two fluorite lenes. The relative aperture (at 1600 Å) was 1:10. In another source [51], a prism vacuum monochromator using Wadsworth's constant deflection mounting is described (Figure 115). The prism has a 60° refraction angle. The refracted beam is reflected from an aluminized mirror. Plane-convex fluorite lenses 15 mm in diameter serve as the objectives; the lenses are displaced synchronously with prism rotation. The relative aperture is about 1:12.

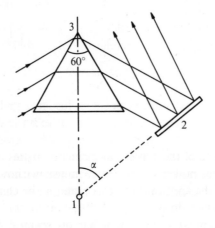

Figure 115

Prism in Wadsworth mounting:

1) axis of rotation of the prism with the mirror,   2) mirror,   3) prism.

### Normal-incidence instruments

These are the commonest instruments for wavelengths between 1000 and 2000 Å. Concave gratings are used with radii of curvature ranging from 40–50 cm to 10 m. Large spectrographs preferably use the Eagle mounting, which ensures a fairly compact arrangement of the components and hence simplifies the design of the vacuum envelope. Medium-sized spectrographs use either the Paschen–Runge or the Eagle mounting. Monochromators are best designed along the lines of Seya–Namioka and Johnson–Onaka systems.

Multichannel photoelectric instruments generally use the Paschen–Runge mounting. Plane gratings are sometimes used, mostly in combination with concave mirrors. A number of commercial and experimental normal-incidence instruments are described in what follows.

The largest known normal-incidence spectrograph is apparently the one built by Douglas and Potter [62], which uses the Eagle mounting. The dispersing element is a replica grating with a radius of curvature of 10.685 m ruled with 600 lines/mm. The ruled area covers $198 \times 100$ mm (the total number of lines is about 120,000). The wavelength corresponding to the blaze angle (in the first order) is 11,600 Å. The instrument thus covers the range between 1000 and 2000 Å in orders 5 through 10. The spectra of successive orders are separated by a cylindrical LiF prism described on p. 98.

The main difficulty in designing a large instrument is how to protect the optical components from misalignment and vibrations. In smaller instruments, all the optical elements are generally mounted on a common chassis, which is then enclosed in the vacuum envelope; alternatively, the components are fixed to the envelope itself. In large instruments, however, neither technique is applicable. The grating, the slit, and the plate holder are mounted on a rail, which is held by thick steel rods fitted into concrete sockets, well insulated from the floor. These rods are connected to a metallic envelope 1115 cm long and about 10 cm in diameter by bellows couplings.

Figure 116 shows the mounting at one end of the large spectrograph. The effective length of the film holder is 93 cm, the height of the slit is 5.7 cm. The instrument is aligned and focused without breaking the vacuum. The film-holder part of this spectrograph comprises a small container partitioned off from the main part of the instrument. The film is charged via the container, also without breaking the vacuum in the main part of the system; as a result, a plate can be changed in 5 min, whereas the pumpdown time of the entire system is 12 hrs (starting with atmospheric pressure). The spectrograph incorporates an option for obtaining comparison spectra from a lamp with an iron hollow cathode.

Essentially, this system is a large and very expensive fixed instrument which cannot be removed from the laboratory where it has been built. Instruments of this

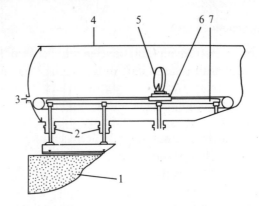

Figure 116

A cross section through the 10-m spectrograph:

1) foundation, 2) rods 5 cm in dia. with bellows coupling, 3) window for adjustment, 4) body, 5) grating, 6) grating table, 7) rail.

size are exceedingly sensitive to temperature fluctuations and therefore require excellent thermostating.

Wilkinson [45a] described a high-resolution spectrograph using higher order spectra from a grating with $R = 6$ m and 1200 lines/mm. The blaze angle of the grating corresponded to 5000–6000 Å in the first order. In the vacuum ultraviolet, those orders are used for which the relevant wavelength is near the blaze angle. The entire system is mounted in a steel pipe about 6 m long and 40 cm in diameter; the pipe is provided with thermal insulation and rests on three concrete supports. The slit is set horizontally, and the Rowland circle therefore lies in the vertical plane. The slit and the focal surface were displaced by about 25 cm one relative to the other, so that the Rowland circle passed approximately half-way between them.

To work the instrument to its full capacity, it should be thermostated to within 0.05°; this requirement mainly applies to the temperature of the grating. Figure 117 is a microphotometric tracing of the self-reversed O I triplet (1302–1306 Å) photographed in fourth order. The resolving power measured from the width of the triplet components was found to be about 300,000. This is apparently the highest resolution ever attained in the vacuum ultraviolet.

Commonly used instruments, however, are of more humble dimensions, with gratings of 2–3 m radius of curvature. An interesting specimen of this class is the very-high-resolution spectrograph described by Brix and Herzberg [35]. It uses Eagle mounting with a grating of 1200 lines/mm, 40 × 90 mm ruled area, and radius of curvature of 3 m. The blaze angle of this grating corresponds to 6000 Å in the first order. The vacuum ultraviolet region extending to the transmission threshold of LiF was studied in spectra of orders 4 through 6. The spectra of successive

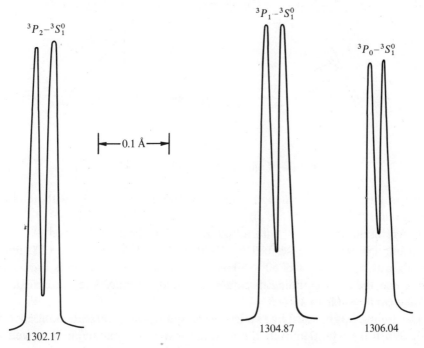

Figure 117

The O I resonance triplet.

orders were again separated with a cylindrical lithium fluoride prism. The dispersion was 0.65 Å/mm in fourth order and 0.4 Å/mm in sixth order. The effective resolution of the spectrograph in these orders was around 200,000.

The same spectrograph was also used with a preliminary dispersion grating, which separated between successive orders [39]. The arrangement of the optical elements is shown in Figure 118. The preliminary dispersion grating $R_1$ had the same radius of curvature as the main grating $R_2$ (3 m), but it only held 135 lines/mm. It was set so that the wide slit $S_1$ between the source and the grating (perpendicular to the slit $S_2$) was sharply imaged in the focal plane $P$.

Beutler's formula [9] gives the condition for which the astigmatism at a given wavelength and a given incidence angle is compensated:

$$D = R \left[ (\cos \alpha - \sin \beta \tan \beta)^{-1} - \cos \alpha \right]. \tag{10}$$

Here $\alpha$ is the angle of incidence, $\beta$ is the diffraction angle, $D$ is the distance between slits $S_1$ and $S_2$ in the direction of the beam. With the preliminary dispersion grating, a change in wavelength from 400 to 1400 Å entailed a change in $\alpha$ from 81.5 to 84°; the angle $\beta$ correspondingly varied from 80 to 77° and the distance $D$ from 94.9 to 96.6 mm. In practice, choosing some fixed average distance between the slits, we

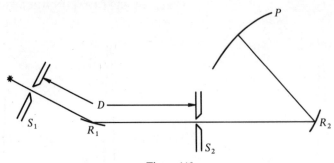

Figure 118

Separation of successive orders with an auxiliary grating.

can scan the different wavelengths simply by turning the grating, without changing the distance $D$. The results are quite adequate in this case.

A very useful instrument with a 2-m grating for photographic and photoelectric recording (SP-99) was described by Kulikov et al. [63]. It has a 1200 lines/mm grating with a ruled area of $60 \times 80$ mm. The first order spectrum is used in actual work, and the corresponding dispersion is about 4 Å/mm. The blaze angle of the grating corresponds to 1500 Å.

The grating $G$ is coupled by two levers $OD$ and $OS$ with the plate holder $P$ (Figure 119). When the axis $O$ moves, the grating turns and simultaneously travels along the optical axis and the plate is rotated. The spectrograph covers the region from 400 to 3000 Å; the grating turns through $11°30'$ and travels along $SD$ over a distance of 41 mm.

A photograph of this instrument is shown in Figure 120$a$. It is equipped with vacuum systems pumping down the source, the working volume of the instrument, and the plate holder chamber. Spectra of excellent quality are obtained, although the theoretical resolving power of the grating apparently is not fully attained. The instrument is very simple to use and is highly reliable. This appears to be the best Soviet-made spectrograph so far available for the 400–2000 Å region.

A somewhat smaller normal-incidence spectrograph, covering the 500–4000 Å region, is manufactured in the Soviet Union under the trade-name of DFS-29 (Figure 120$b$). The Eagle planar mounting is used. The grating parameters are $R = 1$ m, 1200 lines/mm, ruled area $60 \times 50$ mm. The spectrum is photographed on 35-mm film. Film spool length 180 mm, so that a spectrum of 1500 Å can be photographed in one run. Different wavelengths are scanned without breaking the vacuum. The film is also charged without letting any air in.

Chulanovskii's small vacuum spectrograph [64, 65] also uses the Eagle mounting. This is a highly successful design using a grating with a 1 m radius of curvature. The resolving power is apparently the highest attained for instruments of this class. A small normal-grazing spectrograph has been described by Shenstone [66].

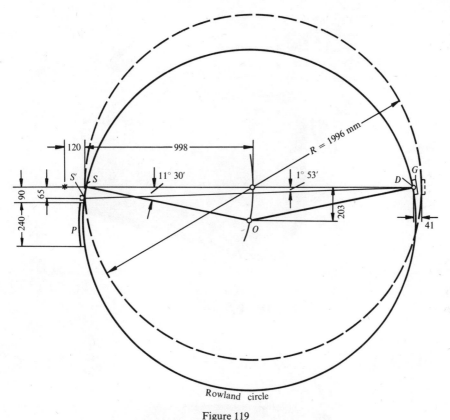

Figure 119

The optical systems of the SP-99 spectrograph.

## Monochromators and spectrometers

As we have mentioned previously, a monochromator is the heart of any spectrometer. We will now describe the different instruments, using in each case the name originally assigned by the author. Only normal-incidence systems are treated.

The first monochromator for the vacuum ultraviolet was apparently described by Powell in 1934 [67]. This is a concave-grating photoelectric instrument using the Eagle mounting.

Later Tousey et al. [68] described a normal-incidence monochromator with the grating automatically gliding along the Rowland circle. The authors aimed at maximum simplicity of the monochromator kinematics, and therefore chose to depart from the conditions of best focusing [69]. In one of the probable solutions, the Eagle mounting is used with the grating turning about an axis near its center, while the entrance and exit slits remain fixed. The spectrum quality is somewhat

Figure 120*a*

The SP-99 spectrograph.

Figure 120*b*

The DFS-29 spectrograph.

affected by the rotation of the grating, but the resolving power is quite adequate for most purposes. A 1-m grating 50 mm wide ensures a resolution of nearly 1000 between 1000 and 2100 Å in this system.

Later authors considered various monochromator designs from the point of view of best focusing and maximum resolving power, without sacrificing the simple kinematics [11, 46, 47, 70, 71]. The Seya–Namioka mounting [11, 12, 46] apparently provides the best solution in this respect.

A Soviet-made VM-70 monochromator using the Seya–Namioka mounting is described by Gerasimova and Startsev [72].

A simple and useful vacuum monochromator was designed by Vilesov et al. [73]. It also uses the Seya–Namioka mounting, with a distance of about 41 cm from the grating center to the slits. A concave grating with $R = 0.5$ m and 1200 lines/mm has a ruled area of 50 + 40 mm. For these parameters, the theoretical slit defocusing is about $\pm 0.05$ mm as the wavelength varies from 0 to 2850 Å. The instrument is adapted to continuous recording, with scanning rates of 25 and 150 Å/min. The scale of the instrument enables wavelengths to be read to within 0.2–0.3 Å. The instrument will resolve bandwidths of at most 1.5 Å between 1050 and 4500 Å.

A different model of a vacuum monochromator (Soviet-made SP-68) is described in [74]. It uses a 1-m grating. The angle between the incident and the diffracted beam is 8°36′, the grating turns through 4°18′. The defocusing is compensated by displacing the slit over 2.7 mm.

An entrance attachment converts the SP-68 monochromator into a double-beam spectrophotometer [75]. In this attachment, the radiation leaving the monochromator is split into two beams by a mirror; one of the beams is passed through the sample, and the other is used as a comparison beam. The beams are detected with sodium salicylate screens, and a chopper alternately exposes the same photomultiplier to signals from the two screens. The amplified signal is recorded by a pen-and-ink device. The resolving power of the instrument is fairly low (effective slit width 0.5–1 mm, which corresponds to a passband of 10 Å).

A similar instrument was previously described by James [76] (Figure 121). Part of the beam leaving the monochromator is reflected from mirror 1 to hit the fluorescent screen 2, whose light is picked up by photomultiplier 3. The other part of the beam is passed through the absorption cell 4 and then hits the fluorescent screen of photomultiplier 5. The signal ratio of the two photomultipliers is measured. The shortcoming of this system is that it uses two photomultipliers (and not one, as the first system); this involves additional errors associated with different effects of temperature, voltage, etc., on the responses of the two photomultipliers.

Kulikov et al. [77] described a VM-140 monochromator using a constant deflection angle (140°). The grating is ruled with 600 lines/mm, $R = 1$ m. Scanning is achieved by turning the grating around an axis through its center. Defocusing is compensated by moving one of the slits synchronously with the rotation of the

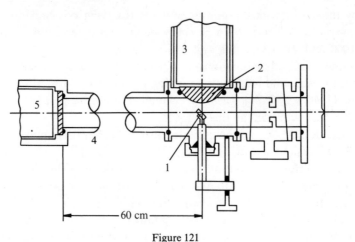

Figure 121
Photometric attachment.

grating. This arrangement clearly involves certain difficulties as compared to Seya–Namioka monochromators.

Gerasimova and Kulikov described a normal-incidence vacuum monochromator with a 1-m grating [78]. The grating rotates around an axis through its center and synchronously travels along the instrument axis. Improved focusing is achieved by displacing the exit slit over some 3 mm. The wavelengths are fixed to witnin 1 Å.

A small vacuum monochromator with a replica grating (0.5 m radius of curvature, 1200 lines/mm, 40 × 50 mm ruled area) was described by Kokin [49].

A combined spectrograph–monochromator with a half-meter grating was described by Reich [80]. The turntable with the light source and the entrance slit is mounted on the Rowland circle, while the grating, the exit slit with the photomultiplier, and the film are mounted on radial levers (Figure 122a). Appropriate rotation of the system components gives one of the three alternative geometries: normal incidence (a), grazing incidence (b), and Seya–Namioka (c).

A normal-incidence vacuum monochromator VMR-2 manufactured in the Soviet Union (Figure 122 b) covers the wavelengths from 500 to 2500 Å. The grating parameters are $R = 1$ m, 600 lines/mm ruled area 60 × 50 mm, linear dispersion about 16.5 Å/mm. A photomultiplier with a fluorescent screen is used as a detector. The signal is read off a microammeter.

**Multichannel spectrometers**

A whole range of multichannel photoelectric instruments is available for spectral analysis in the vacuum ultraviolet (see Chapter XI). These instruments generally

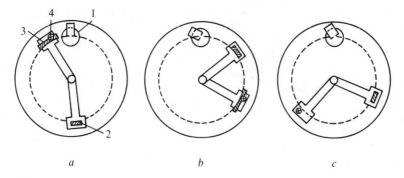

Figure 122*a*

Combined spectral instrument:

1) source and entrance slit,   2) grating,   3) photographic plate,   4) exit slit with photomultiplier.

Figure 122*b*

VMR-2 monochromator.

provide a simultaneous recording of lines between 3500 and 1500 Å, and thus meet all the immediate needs of the spectral analysis of metals.

One of the common Soviet-made multichannel spectrometers is DFS-31, covering the wavelength region from 1600 to 3300 Å. The optical system is shown in Figure 123. The image of the source 1 is projected by the condenser 2 onto the entrance slit 3. The light diffracted from the grating 4 passes through exit slits 5 lying on the

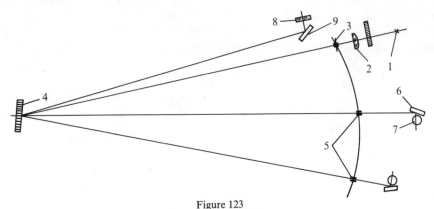

Figure 123

The optical system of the DFS-31 spectrograph.

Rowland circle (the figure shows two of the ten exits of the spectrometer); it is then reflected from the mirror 6 and hits quartz-window photomultipliers after passing through the windows 7. Eight of the ten photomultipliers record lines with wavelengths greater than 2000 Å; these photomultipliers are set behind quartz plates covering the windows 7. Two photomultipliers intended for lines between 2000 and 1600 Å are attached by vacuum seals directly to apertures in the spectrometer envelope.

The spectrometer has a 1-m grating with 1200 lines/mm. Grating illumination area is monitored using the green part of the spectrum, by means of mirror 9 and window 8.

The instrument is evacuated by a forevacuum pump to 0.01 T. This vacuum is quite sufficient for instruments of this size in the relevant spectral region.

Similar instruments are also manufactured by Western firms. As an example, we will consider two instruments, Spectrowide (Philips, Holland) and Quantovac-31000 (ARL). The Spectrowide has a replica grating with $R = 1.5$ m and 1200 lines/mm, $40 \times 78$ mm ruled area. The instrument uses the Paschen–Runge mounting with incidence angle of $17°36'$. Dispersion, about 5.5 Å/mm. Wavelength coverage 1600–3500 Å. The resolving power of the grating is not fully exploited: a $50 \mu$ exit slit gives a bandwidth of about 0.3 Å.

The images of the entrance slits are focused by cylindrical mirrors on cathodes of 24 photomultipliers, of which 18 are intended for the near ultraviolet, 5 for the vacuum ultraviolet, and 1 records the zero-order spectrum. The instrument is thermostated to within 0.1°C.

The other multichannel spectrometer, Quantovac-31000, is equipped with interchangeable 1-m gratings. One grating (2160 lines/mm) covers wavelengths from 1700 to 4070 Å with a dispersion of 4 Å/mm. The other grating (1440 lines/mm, 6.9 Å/mm) is intended for the 1900–5470 Å region.

The instrument contains up to 80 photomultipliers and is thermostated to within 3°C.

Similar instruments are manufactured by other firms, e.g., *Optica Milano* (Italy), *Jobin* (France), *Shimotsu* (Japan).

Somewhat less sophisticated multichannel instruments are used in plasma work. The main distinguishing feature of these instruments is a recording part with a much smaller time constant, so that they can record processes with overall duration as short as 0.1 $\mu$sec. Specimen recordings of time-swept spectra taken with one of these instruments are shown in Figure 124 [37].

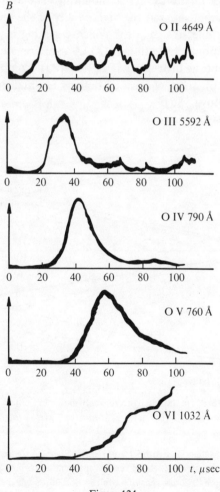

Figure 124

Variation of the intensity of oxygen lines in an impulsive discharge.

### Plane-grating instruments

At wavelengths longer than 1000–1200 Å, mirrors with a sufficiently high reflection coefficient are available. Plane gratings thus can be used, their main advantage being the virtually complete absence of astigmatism. The commonly used mounting of a plane grating was proposed by Ebert in 1889 [81]. Later this mounting was applied by Rozhdestvenskii [82] and his school [83], who built excellent spectrographs using Ebert's system exclusively. Ebert's mounting was also used by Fastie [84].*

Ebert's system is shown in Figure 125. Although a planar geometry is described in the figure, the entrance or the exit slit can be mounted above or below the grating in a spatial arrangement, not unlike the Eagle mounting. The availability of large plane gratings, their low astigmatism, and the high quality of the image often make these monochromators more effective than the concave-grating instruments, despite the drawback of two additional reflections [18]. A spectrometer of this system was actually used in rocket-borne instruments (see § 48) [85]. Comparative evaluations of plane-grating monochromators of various designs at small incidence angles were carried out by Gerasimova [86].

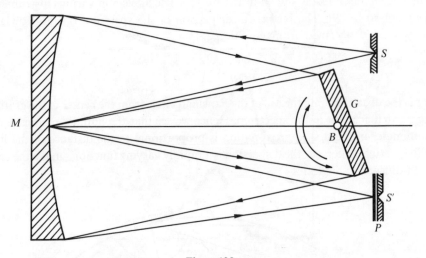

Figure 125

Ebert's mounting (spectrograph–monochromator).

S, S′ slits, P photographic plate, G grating, M mirror, B axis of rotation of the grating.

* In Western literature this system is often referred to as the Ebert–Fastie mounting, and Soviet authors call it the Rozhdestvenskii system. Rozhdestvenskii apparently was not familiar with Ebert's work, and Fastie did not know of Rozhdestvenskii's contribution, although the latter built his instrument and described it in literature four years before Fastie. We have retained the originator's name and call this system Ebert's mounting.

Startsev et al. have recently described a SP-104 instrument [87] with a plane grating and one concave mirror with a focal distance of 1 m and relative aperture of 1 : 10. The instrument has options for photographic and photoelectric recording between 1100 and 6000 Å.

A high-speed spectrophotometer with a plane grating for absorption measurements between 1700–2400 Å was also built using Ebert's mounting. It comprises a plane grating (65 × 75 mm, 1200 lines/mm) and a concave mirror 120 mm in diameter with a focal distance of 600 mm. The mirror curvature is compensated by using slits. A Cu–Be photomultiplier with a sapphire window is used as detector [88].

During scanning, the bandwidths of the entrance and the exit slit are maintained constant. The scanning rates are 5, 10, 15, and 20 Å/mm. The short-wave threshold of the instrument is determined by the transparency of its windows. The instrument described by Riemann also uses Ebert's mounting [89].

### Grazing-incidence instruments

In grazing-incidence geometry, the principal optical elements of the spectral instrument are mounted as shown in Figure 126. The angle $\alpha$ in various instruments varies from 80 to 89°. The reciprocal dispersion of the spectrum on the Rowland circle is readily obtained from equation (5):

$$\frac{d\lambda}{ds} = \frac{d}{kR} \cos\left(\alpha - \frac{s}{R}\right). \tag{11}$$

Here $s$ is the distance along the arc of the Rowland circle from the center of the grating to the particular point in the spectrum. Hence we see that the number of angstroms per millimeter in the first approximation is proportional to the distance of the line from the grating center, i.e., the dispersion is a rapidly varying function, unlike the case of small diffraction angles.

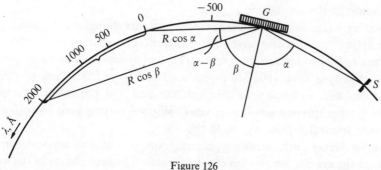

Figure 126

A grazing-incidence geometry.

S slit, G grating.

For large gratings, the theoretical resolution decreases in grazing incidence because of large aberrations, and a certain optimal grating width exists which ensures maximum resolution without appreciable loss of illumination in the spectrum [90]. This optimal width $w$ depends on the angles of incidence and diffraction $\alpha$ and $\beta$, and on the radius of curvature $R$ of the grating:

$$w = 2.42 \left[ \lambda R^3 \frac{\cos \alpha \cos \beta}{(1 - \cos \alpha \cos \beta)(\cos \alpha + \cos \beta)} \right]^{1/4}. \tag{12}$$

Table 3 gives the optimum widths of a 1-m grating with 600 lines/mm at various wavelengths of the first order for incidence angles of 80 and 88° ($s$ is the optimum slit width).

Table 3

| $\lambda$, Å | $\alpha = 80°$ | | $\alpha = 88°$ | |
|---|---|---|---|---|
| | $w$, cm | $s$, $\mu$ | $w$, cm | $s$, $\mu$ |
| 10 | 0.77 | 0.13 | 0.53 | 0.19 |
| 100 | 1.40 | 0.7 | 1.03 | 0.97 |
| 1000 | 2.65 | 3.8 | 1.88 | 5.3 |

More detailed calculations of the optimum grating width were carried out by Namioka [11, 12]. His results are plotted in Figure 127.

We see from the table that at short wavelengths, only small portions of the grating can be effectively utilized. To attain the resolving power which corresponds to this grating width, the slit width should be chosen from the relation

$$s_{\text{opt}} = \lambda R/W. \tag{13}$$

The slit widths calculated from this formula are also given in Table 3. Since in practice slits cannot be made narrower than $1-2$ $\mu$, the slit is in fact the limiting factor for resolution in the short-wave region.

The grating width in grazing-incidence instruments should not be much greater than the optimum. Otherwise, asymmetric distortion of the lines is observed, which may naturally lead to appreciable errors. This was vividly demonstrated by Edlen, whose photographs from [90] are reproduced in Figure 128. These spectra were photographed with a grating with 1183 lines/mm and $R = 1$ m, incidence angle $\alpha = 84.4°$. The grating aperture was symmetrically stopped varying from 76 to 10 mm. (In the relevant spectral region, $w_{\text{opt}} = 18$ mm.

Grazing-incidence instruments are generally equipped with an adjustable aperture which stops the grating area to the required width. The final choice of the exposed area is made by trial and error, or by reaching a certain compromise solution in terms of resolving power and luminosity.

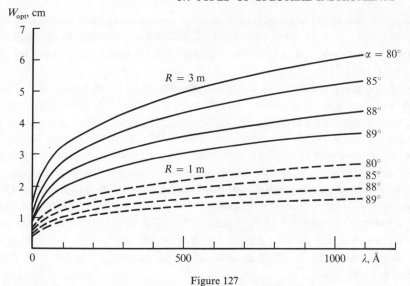

Figure 127

Optimal grating width vs. wavelength for various incidence angles and radii of curvature $R$ of the grating (600 lines/mm grating).

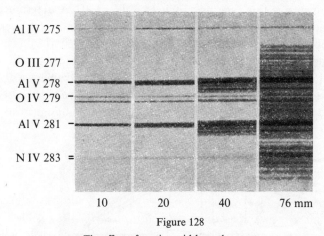

Figure 128

The effect of grating width on the spectrum.

It is clear from the diagram in Figure 126 that the distance from the entrance slit to the part of the focal surface where the spectrum is observed decreases with increasing incidence angle; at incidence angles close to 90°, this distance may be much smaller than the radius of curvature of the grating. Grazing-incidence spectrographs are therefore relatively small-sized (even those with gratings of a large radius of curvature). For example, a spectrograph with a grating with $R = 5$ m and 1200 lines/mm working between 0 and 250 Å is 100 cm long and 20 cm wide [91].

The application of gratings with very shallow grooves and large incidence angles considerably extended the short-wave limit of spectroscopy toward the characteristic X-ray radiation. Wavelengths of a few angstrom are currently being recorded with diffraction gratings [19, 92].

Grazing-incidence instruments use gratings with radii of curvature from 0.4 to 13 m. A 13-m grating is employed in the largest grazing-incidence spectrograph known to-day, the one described by Kirkpatrick [93]. The glass grating of this instrument is ruled with 576 lines/mm. It is not coated with any reflecting layers. The angle of incidence is 89°9', which in accordance with the previous calculations (see §13) gives a spectrum beginning at 6 Å. The plate holder will cover the region from 5 to 120 Å. The spectrograph dispersion is from 0.038 Å/mm at 5 Å to 0.15 Å/mm at 110 Å. The photographic plate is placed in a holder covering the entire spectral region, over a length of 139 cm. The commonly used plates are about 50 cm long and 2.5 cm wide. A normal X-ray film was used for preliminary adjustment and testing. The adjustment of this large instrument involves certain difficulties, and the procedure is briefly described in [93].

Smaller instruments have been used for a long time now. They all have minor distinctive features in their design; the incidence angles and the particular range of wavelengths also slightly differ from one instrument to another. One of the first most successful instruments of this type was built by Edlén [90]. A diagram of Edlén's instrument is shown in Figure 129. It uses a 1-m grating with 600 lines/mm. Slit attachments adapted the instrument to incidence angles from 60 to 85°. This spectrograph first advanced the short-wave limit to 50 Å.

Gabriel et al. [94] measured plasma emissions using an instrument with a vertical Rowland circle, a glass grating ($R = 2$ m, 600 lines/mm) and two slit positions corresponding to incidence angles of 86 or 89°. The instrument is designed to cover the

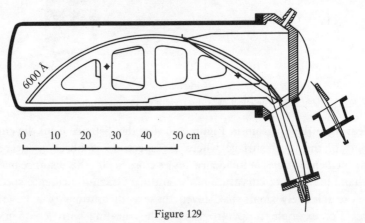

Figure 129

A cross section through a grazing-incidence spectrograph.

spectral region from 12 to 1000 Å with reciprocal dispersion varying from 3 Å/mm to 0.5 Å/mm.

Later, an improved version of the instrument was used at incidence angles of 88° [92]. A platinized replica grating (600 lines/mm) with blaze angle of 1.5° was employed. The spectrum of a hot plasma [95] and the emission of an X-ray tube were studied under these conditions. The shortest attainable wavelength was 4.7 Å (the chlorine $K$ line). The corresponding part of the spectrum was apparently very weak, since this $K$ line is indistinguishable on the photograph published in [95]. The shortest wavelength which is clearly visible on the spectrogram corresponds to the $M$ line of gold (about 5.5 Å).

A grazing-incidence spectrograph with a 2-m grating and 1200 lines/mm for the 30–2300 Å region was described by Alexander et al. [96].

A grazing-incidence monochromator–spectrograph with a variable incidence angle was described by Landon [97]. The grating has $R = 1$ m, 1200 lines/mm, and the incidence angle is variable from 80 to 86° in 1° steps (a total of 7 positions). The optical system and the driving mechanism are shown in Figure 130a. The instrument has an option for continuous scanning: this is done by turning the screw $N$, which moves the rods joining the exit slit with the grating; alternatively, the spectrum is photographed on a plate. The instrument was built for hot plasma spectroscopy on the Stellarator.

Grazing-incidence instruments are now being commercially manufactured. The ARL grazing-incidence spectrographs have 3-m gratings. The Soviet-made DFS-6 is a 1-m model. The angle of incidence on the glass grating (600 lines/mm) is 86°. The film holder accommodates the spectrum from 50 to 2000 Å. Some of the bugs can be ironed out in actual practice. Thus, a serious shortcoming is that the instrument is not equipped with a cassette, so only one spectrum can be photographed at a time. New

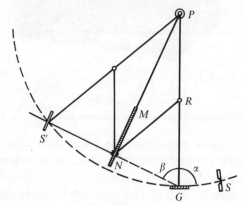

Figure 130a

A grazing-incidence monochromator.

$S$ entrance slit, $G$ grating, $S'$ exit slit, $M$ precision screw, $N$ nut.

film can be charged in normal light if a hood of opaque black material is attached to the instrument. If a moving diaphragm is mounted in front of the plate holder, 2–3 spectra can be photographed on one frame, e.g., the test spectrum and a comparison spectrum. The vacuum system of DFS-6 also requires some radical improvements, since its pumping speed is not high enough.

A newer model is DFS-26 (Figure 130*b*) which uses a 3-m grating with 600 lines/mm. The incidence angle is 85°. The spectrum covers from 100 to 2200 Å. Scanning is achieved by moving the film holder (60 × 240 mm) along the Rowland circle. If the film holder is moved at right angles to the dispersion, several spectrograms can be photographed on the same plate. The film can be moved without breaking the vacuum. The pumps reach a vacuum of $5 \cdot 10^{-5}$ T. Figure 130*c* is a diagram of the vacuum system of the instrument. The source chamber, the film holder chamber, and the main space are evacuated by independent pumps.

Figure 130*b*

DFS-26 spectrograph.

Jeaglé [98, 99] proposed a high-dispersion grazing-incidence spectrograph using two concave diffraction gratings with equal radii of curvature (Figure 131). The two gratings are set on the same Rowland circle. The light diffracted by the first grating $G_1$ is reflected from a concave mirror $M$ with the same radius of curvature and is then diffracted from the second grating $G_2$. The dispersion of the entire system is determined by the dispersion of each grating and depends on the particular order used.

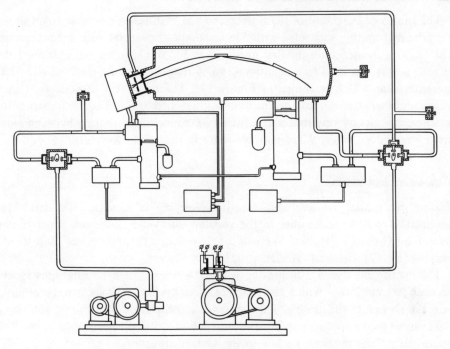

Figure 130c

Schematic diagram of the vacuum system of the DFS-26 spectrograph.

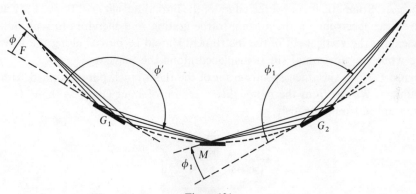

Figure 131

A two-grating spectrograph ($\phi$ is the grazing angle).

If the grating constants are $d_1$ and $d_2$, respectively, we have for the angular dispersion

$$\frac{d\phi'_1}{d\lambda} = \left(\frac{k_1}{d_1} - \frac{k_2}{d_2}\right)\frac{1}{\sin\phi_1}. \tag{14}$$

Here $k_1$ and $k_2$ are the spectrum orders.

The radius of curvature of the mirror and the gratings in this spectrograph was 2 m; the first grating was ruled with 576 lines/mm, the second with 1152 lines/mm. The angle of incidence on the first grating was 80° and spectrum of order − 1 (left of zero order) was used (see equation (14)). A magnified photograph of the Al IV spectrum near 130 Å is shown in Figure 132. The reciprocal dispersion at these wavelengths was 0.63 Å/mm, the line halfwidth reached 0.03 Å. The luminosity of this instrument is clearly very low, and it took 1500 capacitor discharges between aluminum electrodes (50 kV, 0.5 $\mu$F) to photograph the spark spectrum.

### Time-sweep instruments

Various techniques are available for time-sweeping of spectra [100, 101]. The application of these techniques in the vacuum ultraviolet, however, involves considerable technical difficulties. We will briefly describe the instrument built for this purpose by Gabriel and Waller [102].

The instrument uses a 1-m grating with 1200 lines/mm; it photographs spectra between 500 and 2500 Å with a dispersion of about 8 Å/mm. The spectrum is obtained near the normal to the grating. Time sweep is accomplished by a mirror rotating at right angles to the spectrograph dispersion. A horizontal slit positioned at the Sirks point (see p. 103) restricts the line in the vertical direction.

A trihedral mirror made of special steel is mounted between the grating and the film; it turns at 1000 rev/sec. The particular geometry ensures a sweep rate of 3 mm/$\mu$sec. Stigmatic image of the edges of the horizontal slit is obtained only at one point of the spectrum, on the normal to the grating, and therefore to scan different wavelengths the vertical slit of the instrument should be moved along the Rowland circle while the horizontal slit is displaced along the tangent.

Figure 133 is a specimen spectrogram of the theta-pinch photographed with this instrument. We see from the figure that a region of somewhat less than 1000 Å is photographed simultaneously.

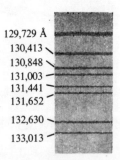

129,729 Å
130,413
130,848
131,003
131,441
131,652
132,630
133,013

Figure 132

A spectrum photographed with a two-grating spectrograph.

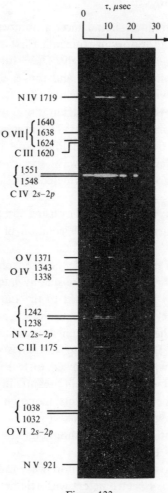

Figure 133
Time sweep of a spectrum.

Another method of time sweep in spectroscopy uses multichannel photoelectric instruments with a small time constant, so that the spectra can be recorded at a fairly high rate.

## 18. ROCKET-BORNE INSTRUMENTS

The first measurements outside the Earth's atmosphere were made from rockets starting in the late 1940s; since 1957 (the year when Sputnik I was launched) these measurements are routinely made from artificial Earth satellites. Spectral instruments mounted on rockets and satellites should meet a number of specific requirements which are not applicable to laboratory instruments. First and foremost, rocket-borne instruments should be compact and light-weight. Their sturdiness and stiffness should ensure steady focusing despite overloading and rocket vibrations.

The main object of study with rocket-borne instruments is the Sun, whose average luminosity in the long-wave part of the spectrum is 4–6 orders of magnitude higher than the luminosity in the vacuum ultraviolet. This presents considerable difficulties associated with the elimination of scattered long-wave radiation, which is strong enough to overcome completely the short-wave spectrum. The suppression of the long-wave scattering is therefore one of the principal optical problems in the design of rocket-borne instruments.

The scattered light intensity can be reduced by using additional dispersing elements, filters, selective-reflective mirrors with focal isolation of long-wave radiation, and selective detectors [103].

Measurements of the solar spectrum outside the atmosphere are made with spectrometers and spectrographs. Spectrometers are mainly launched with satellites. The spectroscopic information is then telemetered to the Earth. Spectrographs, on the other hand, are used in rocket flights. After exposure the payload is parachuted back to the Earth. In either case, the spectral instrument is evacuated spontaneously as it is lifted into the outer space. This approach to vacuum spectroscopy requires light-proof compartments from which air is allowed to leak out without considerable resistance, so as to ensure rapid equalization of pressure inside and outside the rocket [34]. The application of spectral instruments mounted on rockets and satellites requires high-precision setting of the optical axis (or projection mirror) relative to the observed object. The orientation of the axis should remain fixed during the exposure, despite precission and yaw of the rocket.

The bulk of information available on the short-wave radiation of the Sun has been obtained with spectrographs. Spectrometers with telemetered transmission are less accurate at short wavelengths than the spectrograms. This naturally interferes with the identification of spectra recorded photoelectrically.

Some spectrometers and spectrographs used in solar spectroscopy are described in what follows.

Bruns and Prokof'ev described a grazing-incidence spectrometer mounted on a Soviet spaceship-satellite for measuring the intensity of the He II 303.8 Å line in the solar spectrum [104]. This instrument scanned a small spectral region (30 Å) centered around the relevant He II line. A diagram of the instrument is shown in Figure 134. The sunlight passed through slit $A$ to be diffracted by the replica grating $R$ ($R = 0.5$ m, 1200 lines/mm). The diffracted light passing through slit $B$ and exit aperture $S$ hit a photomultiplier with Cu–Be photocathode and dynodes. Scanning was achieved by rolling the slit with cam $C$ and tooth $T$ of the beam $F$, which supported the slit $B$ and the quartz prism $P$. In one of the extreme positions of the beam $F$ the prism $P$ produces

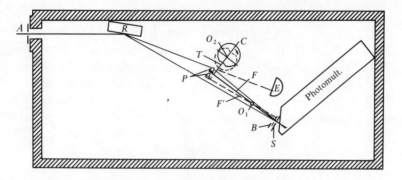

Figure 134

Schematic diagram of a spectrometer for the 304 Å line.

A entrance slit, B scanning slit, S exit slit, R replica, C cam, F beam, T tooth, E trap, P quartz prism O$_1$ and O$_2$ rotation axes of the beam and the cam.

the zero-order spectrum, which provides the calibration signal. As the beam sweeps through other intermediate positions (between F and F'), the instrument scans through the entire spectrum. The zero-order wavelengths are then absorbed in trap E.

Hinteregger described a grazing-incidence monochromator, shown diagramatically in Figure 135 [105–107]. This instrument uses 2-m gratings with 86° angle of incidence. The instrument has three interchangeable gratings of 300, 600, and 1200 lines/mm. The 300 lines/mm grating covers the spectrum from 1300 to 250 Å, and the 1200 lines/mm grating scans the region between 325 and 62 Å. The 1200 lines/mm grating is ruled on gold; its blaze angle is 4° [107]. Scanning is achieved by means of an electric motor which pulls a thin steel strip with exit slits along the surface of the Rowland cylinder.

A fixed strip with nine slits was later built into this instrument. The slits alternately opened and closed during the flight by means of shutters driven by electronic control switches [108]. A special photomultiplier with a tungsten cathode is virtually insensitive to radiation with wavelengths greater than 1300 Å (see §23) and thus effectively suppresses the long-wave scattered component. The photomultiplier cathode is fairly large to intercept the radiation in the entire spectral region. The photomultiplier functioned in the counting mode. Energy calibration was done with the aid of a second monochromator, in series with the first (see §34). A specimen telemetered recording of the spectrum taken on 29 January 1960 is given in Figure 136.

A similar monochromator was mounted on the US satellite orbited on 7 March 1962 [103]. The instrument was intended for a systematic study of the variations in the short-wave solar radiation. The monochromator comprised a 1-m grating ruled on glass (576 lines/mm). Incidence angle 88°; reliable results were obtained between 170 and 400 Å. For a 50 micron slit, the passband halfwidth is 1.7 Å. The instrument is

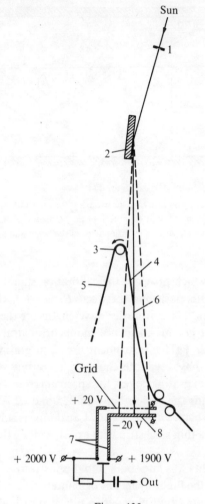

Figure 135

A grazing-incidence solar monochromator:

1) entrance slit,   2) grating   3) strip drive,   4) Rowland circle,   5) steel strip,   6) exit slit,
7) photomultiplier,   8) tungsten cathode.

shown schematically on Figure 137. The main distinctive feature of this monochromator is that the photomultiplier is moved with the exit slit along the spectrum.

A high-resolution spectrophotometer (0.01 Å resolution) with an echelle and two
concave gratings for focusing and separation of different orders was also described
[109].

The solar spectrum has been studied with a variety of spectrographs of different

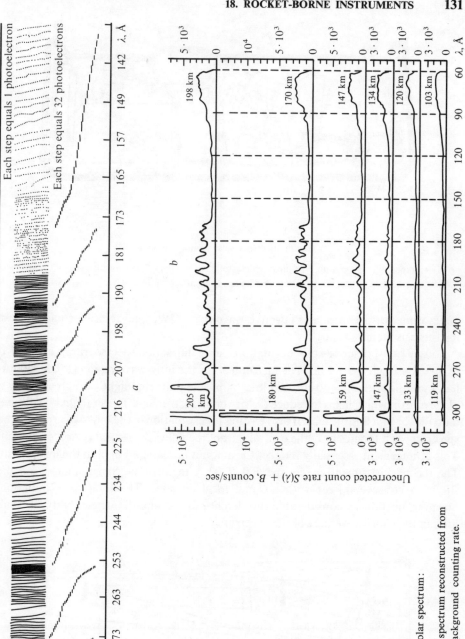

Figure 136

Photoelectric tracing of the solar spectrum:

*a* telemetered recording, *b* spectrum reconstructed from recordings. *B* is the total background counting rate.

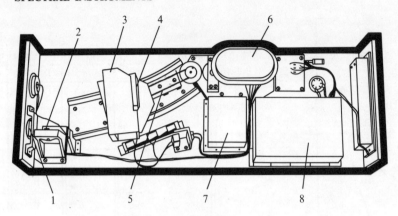

Figure 137

A grazing-incidence solar monochromator:

1) entrance slit,   2) grating,   3) moving detector,   4) amplifier,   5) transmission,   6) motor,
7) power unit,   8) electronics.

luminosities, dispersions, and effective wavelengths. We will describe some of these instruments here.

Tousey [110] describes two normal-incidence diffraction spectrographs assembled in one housing (Figure 138). The instrument for the long-wave region (1500–3500 Å) has a grating with $R = 40$ cm, 600 lines/mm. The diffracted light is intercepted by a plane mirror, which helps to reduce the size of the instrument. The sunlight is projected onto the slit by a fluorite lens. It also ensures focal isolation of the long-wave part of the spectrum, as it focuses only the central part of the relevant spectral region on the slit. This arrangement essentially reduces the amount of scattered light in the instrument. The second instrument covers the 500–2500 Å region. The Sun is imaged on the slit by a concave mirror with 200 mm focal distance. The long-wave radiation, however, introduces considerable interference and limits the detectability of weak lines in the short-wave part of the spectrum.

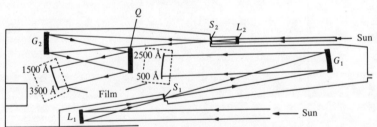

Figure 138

Instrument combining two spectrographs in one housing.
$G_1$, $G_2$ gratings, $Q$ deflecting mirror, $S_1$, $S_2$ slits, $L_1$ mirror condenser, $L_2$ fluorite condenser.

Other multipurpose instruments are similarly designed. For example, Figure 139 is a diagram of a normal-incidence spectrograph and a spectroheliograph assembled as one instrument [110]. Both components use a grating with $R = 40$ cm, 600 lines/mm. The Sun is imaged on the spectrograph slit by an aspherical mirror which compensates the astigmatism of the grating in such a way that the image of the spectrum is stigmatic relative to the Sun. In the spectroheliograph, the concave grating $G_2$ images the Sun in the plane $A$, on a circular diaphragm whose diameter corresponds to the diameter of the Sun's image in $L_\alpha$ light (diaphragm bandwidth 50 Å). The second grating $G_3$ produces a magnified image of the Sun in $L_\alpha$ light in its focal plane $F$. The entire system is stigmatic, as the first grating is appropriately deformed. The dispersions of both gratings are perpendicular to one another.

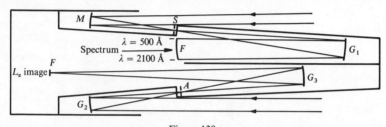

Figure 139

A combination of spectrograph with spectroheliograph.

A considerably larger normal-incidence spectrograph was used in 1956–1959 by Kachalov, Pavlenko, and Yakovleva [111] in solar spectroscopy. The resolution of this spectrograph was also substantially higher. The first spectrum was photographed during a rocket launch of May 1956. The wavelengths between 2471 and 2635 Å were recorded and measured. The results for the loner wavelengths (2636–2937 Å) recorded with the same spectrograph were published in [112].

The preliminary dispersion spectrograph described in [113] is intended for the 500–1500 Å region. The diagram of this instrument is shown in Figure 140. It comprises identical gratings ($R = 0.4$ m, 600 lines/mm) with crossed dispersions. The dispersion of the first grating $G_1$ is directed along the slit of the spectral instrument and the Sun is imaged in the slit plane. The second grating $G_2$ disperses light at right angles to the grating, and a slanting spectrum is thus obtained in the focal surface.

The second grating virtually eliminates the astigmatism. This is accomplished by a suitable deformation of the grating, which appropriately displaces the foci of the meridional and the sagittal rays (see p. 97). This approach, however, does not eliminate the astigmatism in a wide spectral region, as the astigmatism is a function of wavelength. For all practical purposes, if the astigmatism is corrected at 1500 Å, the Sun's image between 1200 and 1900 Å is adequately stigmatic in the sense that the overlapping portions of the solar disk are not larger than 1′ (about 1/30 of the solar diameter).

This spectrograph was later built in two additional modifications: one with a 1200 lines/mm grating and 20 Å/mm dispersion for the 1200–2000 Å region (resolution 0.2 Å) and the other with 2400 lines/mm, double the previous dispersion and a higher resolution.

Spectrographs of this type give very little scattered light, so that weak continua in the short-wave region of the spectrum could be observed [103].

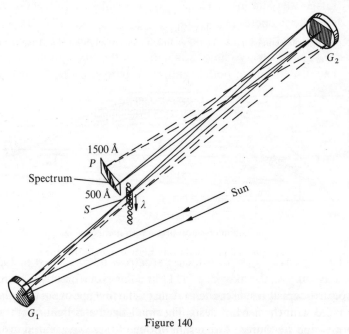

Figure 140

A solar spectrograph with crossed-dispersion gratings.
$G_1$, $G_2$ gratings, $S$ slit and primary spectrum, $P$ plate and spectrum.

A similar astigmatism-correcting device was used by Rense and Violet [114, 115] in their grazing-incidence spectrograph, diagramed in Figure 141.

A toroidal mirror $M$ illuminated by the Sun at an angle $\alpha'$ equal to the angle of incidence on the grating $\alpha$ (85°) is mounted in front of the slit $S$. The mirror corrects the astigmatism of the grating $G$ and improves its effective width. As a result, the instrumental efficiency is increased eightfold, despite the additional 50% losses in the mirror.

A grazing-incidence solar spectrograph was also designed by Austin, Purcell, and Tousey [116, 117]. The long-wave radiation in this instrument is suppressed by a 1000 Å aluminum film mounted in front of the slit. The effective width of the grating ($R$ = 0.4 m, 600 lines/mm) is improved by using a slit with silvered sides, making an angle of 30′ with each other. This approximately tripled the effective light flux.

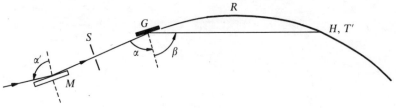

Figure 141

A toroidal-mirror spectrograph.

*R* photographic emulsion, *H, T'* the common focus of meridional and sagittal rays.

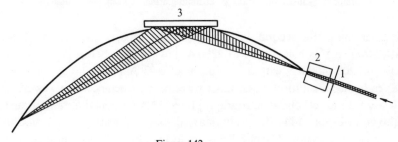

Figure 142

A short-wave solar spectrograph:

1) aluminum film,   2) slit with silvered sides,   3) grating.

As the spectroscopists began concentrating on narrow regions of the solar spectrum, they were faced with the need of designing small-sized and light-weight instruments of sufficiently high resolution. A diagram of one of these specialized instruments for observing the $L_\alpha$ line shape is shown in Figure 143 [103]. It comprises two gratings of equal radius of curvature (0.5 m, 1200 lines/mm), which are however ruled differently. The preliminary dispersion grating works in the first order; at a certain incidence angle, it gives a reflection maximum for the $L_\alpha$ line. The light hits the second grating almost parallel to its surface, but the grooves are ruled in such a way that the incident light is almost normal to the reflecting sides of the grooves. The grating is so designed that under these conditions a reflection maximum in $L_\alpha$ is obtained in the thirteenth order. The angle of incidence on the first grating is chosen so that the astigmatism of the second grating automatically corrects the astigmatism of the first grating. The gratings are aluminized and coated with an $MgF_2$ layer (see §11). This instrument produced excellent stigmatic images of the $L_\alpha$ line with resolution of 0.03 Å (see Figure 243).

The attempts to reach even higher resolutions lead to the development of echelle spectrographs [118]. One of these instruments was described by Purcell et al. [119, 120]. It comprises an echelle working in orders 60 through 120 and a crossed $CaF_2$

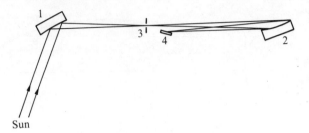

Figure 143

High-resolution spectrograph:

1) preliminary dispersion grating   2) main grating,   3) slit,   4) astigmatic spectrum.

prism serving as the second dispersing element. Quartz and lithium fluoride achromats confined this instrument to 2200 Å, but it nevertheless gave a solar spectrum between 2200–4000 Å with a resolution of 0.03 Å [103].

Even higher resolution in the short-wave part of the spectrum was achieved with a reflection-optics echelle spectrograph [120a]. The optical diagram of the instrument is shown in Figure 144. The preliminary dispersion grating 1 and the slit 2 define a narrow spectral region. The parallel beam formed by the parabolic mirror 3 falls on the echelle 4. The diffracted light is reflected by the plane mirror 6 to be focused on film 5 by mirror 3. Resolutions of 0.007 Å were attained in laboratory, but no results of actual performance have been published so far.

The two last instruments use plane gratings with focusing optics. A plane grating is also used in Fastie's solar monochromator [121]. The astigmatism in this instrument is corrected by using curved slits; the entrance and the exit slits are arranged as arcs of one circle whose center lies on the axis of the focusing mirror. The geometry of the components and their relative size are shown in Figure 145a. Figure 145b shows the position of the monochromator in the rocket.

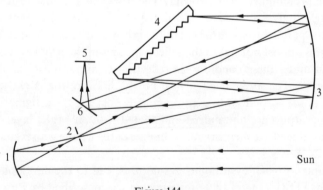

Figure 144

An echelle solar spectrograph.

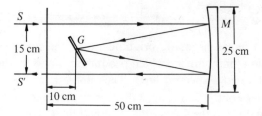

Figure 145*a*

The optical system of a solar monochromator.

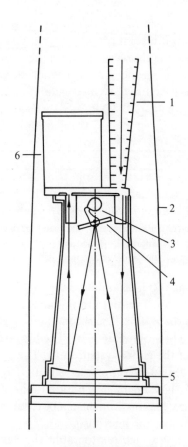

Figure 145*b*

The position of the solar monochromator in a rocket:

1) aperture,   2) rocket hull,   3) grating transmission,   4) grating,   5) mirror,   6) electronics.

## Spectroheliographs

The distribution of monochromatic brightness over the surface of the solar disk is studied with the aid of instruments which produce an image of the Sun in the mono-chromatic light of various spectral lines. The simplest of these spectroheliographs give a stigmatic image of the Sun using a dispersing system of sufficient dispersion, so that the images obtained in the light of the strongest lines do not overlap and the com-bined image produced by the continuum is relatively weak.

Spectroheliographs for the vacuum ultraviolet were developed almost simulta-neously with rocket-borne spectrographs. Purcell described an instrument for photo-graphing the Sun in $L_\alpha$ light [122, 122a]. A diagram of this instrument is shown in Figure 146 (it is similar to the instrument described on p. 133).

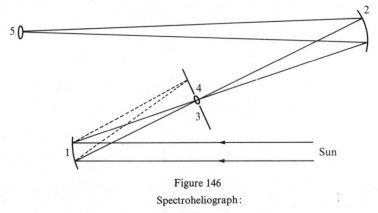

Figure 146

Spectroheliograph:

1) first grating deformed to correct the astigmatism,    2) second grating suppressing the scattered light and forming a magnified image,    3) diaphragm,    4) first image of the Sun on $L_x$ light,    5) final stigmatic image of the Sun in $L_\alpha$ light.

Both gratings ($R = 0.4$ m, 600 lines/mm) are used in first order; they are mounted so that the dispersions add up. The first grating images the Sun in the plane of the diaphragm which isolates the $L_\alpha$ line. The second grating gives a magnified image of the Sun in the plane of the photographic plate. The first grating is deformed so as to correct the astigmatism of the entire system in $L_\alpha$. The application of two gratings mounted in succession adequately suppresses all interference from scattered light. Exposures of 0.02 sec. with this camera gave photographs of the Sun with a resolution of about 0.5–1 minute of arc. This instrument can be recommended to photograph the Sun in the light of other spectral lines also.

A simple spectroheliograph which photographs the Sun in the light of the He II 303.8 Å line comprises an imaging grating and a thin aluminum foil mounted on a shallow grating at a distance of 1 cm from the focal plane; the aluminum foil acts as a filter cutting off the long-wave radiation [103].

A photoelectric spectroheliograph is shown in Figure 147 [103]. A stigmatic image of the Sun is formed by a grating in which three quarters of the surface are ruled with 600 lines/mm and the other quarter is ruled with 500 lines/mm, as shown in the Figure ($R = 1$ m). Three stigmatic images of the Sun, 4.5 mm in diameter, are formed in different orders near the normal to the grating; the corresponding wavelengths are indicated in the figure. These images are scanned by three miniaturized Bendix photo-multipliers with an internal diameter of 20 micron and 1 cm long [123]. The end surface of this photomultiplier covers 1 minute of arc of the solar disk image. For scanning, the entire instrument is moved back and forth over 40′, and in each cycle it is tilted by 1′ until an area of 40′ × 40′ has been covered (this is the size of the entire image of the Sun). The measurement results are telemetered to the Earth.

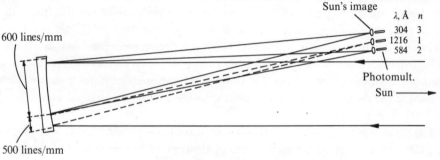

Figure 147

A photoelectric spectroheliograph.

Solar images at shorter wavelengths have been obtained with a pinhole camera (Figure 148). The image is formed by light passing through a filter covering the pinhole. The first photograph of the Sun at 60–20 Å was obtained with a 15 cm camera with a pinhole 0.12 mm in diameter. A Parlodion film* coated with a thin aluminum layer served as filter [124].

## 19. INTERFERENCE INSTRUMENTS

### Interferometers

The first interferometer for the vacuum ultraviolet was built by Filippov [125]. This is a modification of the Rozhdestvenskii interferometer [126] shown in Figure 149. Plates $F$ are fluorite, plates $S$ glass. The fluorite plates are coated with a thin layer of platinum with about 50% transmittance. The glass plates are coated with an opaque specular layer. The path of the light in the interferometer is clear from the figure.

---

* Parlodion is the trade name of a nitrocellulose film $C_{12}H_{16}(NO_3)_4$.

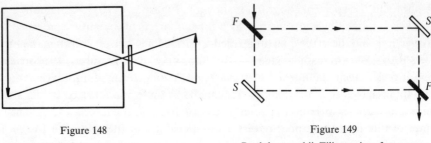

Figure 148                                    Figure 149

Pinhole camera.            Rozhdestvenskii–Filippov interferometer.

Somewhat later a similar interferometer was built by Ladenburg [127]. Recently Perry-Thorne described a new vacuum interferometer, shown in Figure 150 [128]. The light from a hydrogen tube $H$ passes through a collimating fluorite lens $L$ to hit at 15° the beam-splitting fluorite plate $B$. After passing through the absorption cell and the compensating plate $C$, the first beam is reflected from the surfaces $M_1$ and $B$ to interfere with the beam reflected from mirror $M_2$. The concave mirror $N$ focuses the horizontal interference fringes in the plane $P$, whose horizontal lines are sharply imaged in the focal plane of the spectrograph. The interference fringes were observed to 1500 Å (the short-wave limit).

The plane $P$ in this instrument was distant 1 cm from the slit $S$. Note that the interference fringes in the spectrum are almost always inclined, so that in case of a large astigmatism, i.e, a large distance between the planes $P$ and $S$, the fringe edges are diffuse. A stigmatic spectrograph should therefore be preferred.

The interferometer is intended for measuring the refractive indices of gases and, in the author's opinion, it requires further improvement before it can be used for systematic research work.

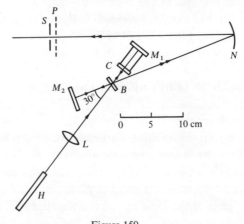

Figure 150

A vacuum interferometer.

**Interference filters**

Schroeder [129] described an interference filter made up of reflecting aluminum layers with a layer of lead fluoride sandwiched in between. The filter is transparent at wavelengths longer than 1500 Å; its passband is 200–300 Å. A multilayer filter was used to improve the contrast. Its transmittance is fairly low, 0.7% at 1900 Å. Bradley et al. [130] described filters for wavelengths above 1800 Å. These filters comprise aluminum mirrors applied onto a quartz substrate with an $MgF_2$ layer as a dielectric. The passband is 225 Å. Three filters were made for wavelengths between 1800 and 1900 Å with transmittances of 15, 16, and 19% (much higher than the transmittance of $PbF_2$ filter).

# 20. POLARIZATION INSTRUMENTS

Reflection always alters the state of polarization of light, except in the case of normal incidence. The degree of polarization for a transparent dielectric is calculated from the Fresnel formula. For absorbing media the calculations are much more difficult, and the state of polarization of the reflected light is not always readily determined. Moreover, the state of polarization depends on surface conditions, in particular on the presence of surface films with properties which are markedly different from the properties of the bulk material. The degree of polarization of reflected light therefore has to be found experimentally.

So far, polarization by reflection is the only means of polarizing light at wavelengths shorter than 1200 Å. A number of reflecting layers have been studied as potential polarizers and it has been established that reflection from $MgF_2$, LiF, and gold does indeed produce partial polarization around 1200 Å.

Polarization is often observed in diffracted light because of the reflection from the grooves of the diffraction grating. Since gratings polarize light, the energy of the diffracted beam may depend on the state of polarization of the incident beam. Effects of this type were investigated by a number of authors [131–133]. So far no theory has been developed to account for the various experimental findings, whose interpretation is a very complex undertaking. For example, a rectangular groove produces maximum polarization, whereas grooves of other shape (with dihedral angles of 110–120°) cause virtually no polarization. The polarization of light reflected by a grating can be reduced by making the light fall at right angles to the groove sides and using the grating at blaze angle. No polarization of diffracted light between 1200 and 1600 Å was observed in case of normal incidence on the grating [134, 135]. Between 580 and 1900 Å the degree of polarization depends on wavelength: it moreover differs for gratings made of different materials, and for aluminum gratings it varies with time, apparently due to the formation of oxide films.

Rabinowitch et al. [136] measured the polarization of light transmitted by a Seya–Namioka monochromator. The light flux emerging from the monochromator slit 2 was measured for different orientations of the mirror 2 directing the radiation to the detector 3 (Figure 151). Figure 152 plots the reflection coefficient of gold and silicon mirrors for the case when the plane of incidence was perpendicular to the exit slit of the monochromator $(r_1)$ and for the case when the plane of incidence was parallel to the slit $(r_2)$. The effect of polarization on the reflection coefficient of an aluminized grating was also studied by Arakawa et al. [137, 137a].

Polarization effect may introduce considerable distortion into the spectral distribution of intensity. The experimental results therefore must never be accepted at their face value.

At wavelengths longer than 1100–1200 Å, lithium fluorite [135, 138] or magnesium fluoride [139] polarization optics can be used. A stack polarizer was made of lithium

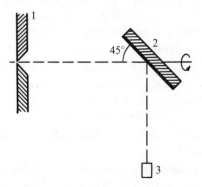

Figure 151

Experimental setup for measuring polarization by reflection.

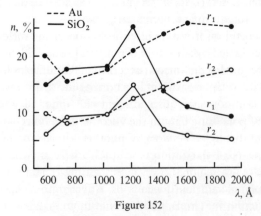

Figure 152

The effect of polarization on reflection.

fluoride. The plates were 13 mm in diameter, 0.3–0.8 mm thick. The polarizer and the analyzer could be rotated without breaking the vacuum. The light fell on the stack at 60° (Brewster's angle at 1200 Å is 58°40′). Polarizers made up of four or six plates were used [135]. Figure 153 plots the degree of polarization vs. wavelength for these two polarizers.

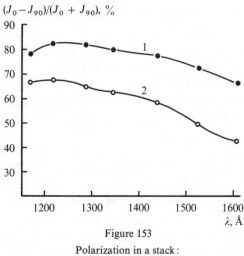

Figure 153

Polarization in a stack:

1) six plates,   2) four plates.

Although the six-plate stack gives a higher degree of polarization, its transmittance is substantially lower. Thus, at 1400 Å, the transmittance of the four-plate stack is about 20%, whereas that of the six-plate polarizer is 10%. At 1200 Å, the six-plate stack transmits about 4%, and the four-plate stack transmits about 12% of the incident radiation. These polarizers were applied to solid-state spectroscopy [140].

Johnson [139] described a magnesium fluoride Wollastone prism. It measured 6 × 20 mm and was 3 mm thick; it was made up of two prisms with mutually perpendicular optical axes, set at a distance of 1 mm from each other. The prisms were mounted between the grating and the slit at a distance of 12.5 cm from the slit. When the spectrum was photographed with a 1-m normal-incidence instrument, the plate showed two spectra with a relative displacement of 2.5 mm.

Another method of polarizing light in the vacuum ultraviolet—namely by passing an unpolarized beam through a network of parallel wires—has not been applied so far. These grid polarizers are in common use in the visible and the infrared. The main problem in the short-wave region, however, is the development of adequate technology for the production of sufficiently fine grids. Another possible approach is polarization by Tyndall scattering. This method, however, will never give sufficient energy intensity in the scattered beam.

## 21. SOME ASPECTS OF EXPERIMENTAL TECHNIQUE

**Instrument adjustment**

In the far ultraviolet, the experimental physicist often has to assemble his entire equipment from scratch, but even if he is lucky enough to have a commercially manufactured instrument at his disposal, the system should be carefully adjusted and focused. Unfortunately, no general prescription can be given for the various operations needed to ensure correct alignment of the instrument component, since the focusing and adjustment techniques differ for instruments of different design. The manual of any commercially manufactured instrument generally contains the pertinent instructions. Since concave-grating spectrographs and spectrometers, with the principal optical components mounted on the Rowland circle, are in common use, we will consider here only the adjustment and focusing of these instruments.

The relative position of the slit, the grating, and the photographic emulsion (or the exit slit in case of photoelectric recording) should be carefully fixed. We are thus dealing with the arrangement in space of three rigid bodies, each with six degrees of freedom. Precise alignment in all the 18 degrees of freedom is a fairly complex undertaking, but in practice the optical system is indifferent to certain displacements. For example, the grating, the slit, and the film holder can be centered with sufficient accuracy on one horizontal plane by using a gauge or even a simple ruler to measure the distance of the center point of each component from the principal plateau of the instrument.

The alignment of the optical components of a concave-grating instrument has been discussed in detail in [10, 141–143], and also in Sawyer's book [42]. The adjustment of vacuum monochromators using the Seya–Namioka and the Eagle mounting is treated in [144, 145]. These references provide excellent practical information for the construction of large spectral instruments.

Here we will briefly consider only the principal adjustment techniques; they can be effected using the achromatic image of the slit in zero order. The zero-order spectrum is primarily used to position the slit parallel to the grating grooves. This alignment is particularly significant for instruments with pronounced astigmatism. If the astigmatic images of the different parts of the grating overlap, the spectral lines are broadened, and the degree of broadening increases with the increase in the angle between the groove and the slit.

The slit should be rotated about the incident beam until the sharpest image of the slit in zero order is obtained. The final adjustment can be done photographically, using close doublets: the resolution of the doublet components provides an indication of parallel alignment. In highly astigmatic instruments, the zero order spectrum can be viewed or even photographed by covering the central part of the slit. If the slit and the grooves are not parallel, the slit image is split (low densities of about 0.3–0.5

should be maintained, to avoid line blending due to halation). A similar technique can be applied to adjust a monochromator. Note that to ensure parallel alignment of the grooves and the slit, the grating should not be moved in its setting.

When the grating is turned about an axis which lies in its plane at right angles to the grooves, the center of the entrance slit image is displaced from the center of the film holder aperture or from the center of the exit slit (in monochromators). To align these centers, the zero-order image should be projected onto a screen coinciding with the focal surface and the grating should then be tilted until the image is centered on an appropriate marking on the screen, which identifies the position of the film slit.

The slit and the grating should be mounted on the Rowland circle at certain points, so as to maintain a fixed incidence angle. The final adjustment is accomplished by a small rotation of the grating about an axis through its center, parallel to the grooves.

In certain instruments, rotation of the grating and displacement of the focal surface can be carried out independently. When the zero-order spectrum is accurately focused on the focal surface, the higher orders may nevertheless prove to be unfocused. This is an indication that the focal surface does not coincide with the Rowland circle. This deficiency can be rectified by turning the grating, and sometimes by moving or turning the film holder or adjusting the position of the exit slit.

Grazing-incidence instruments are particularly sensitive to displacements of the focal plane. This is clear from Figure 154. When the focal plane is displaced a distance $c$ along the normal, the spectral line is shifted a distance $c'$ and is broadened by an amount $b'$, as compared to the broadening $b$ which would have obtained in the case of a focal plane perpendicular to the incident beam. These magnitudes and the angle between the incident beam and the focal ray are related by the approximate equality

$$b' = b/\phi = c'/f\phi = c/\phi^2 f. \tag{15}$$

Taking a relative aperture $1/f = 0.01$ (which is practicable for grazing-incidence instruments) and a photographic resolution $b = 0.01$ mm, we obtain for $\phi = 10°$, $c \leq 0.03$ mm, whereas for $\phi = 3°$ the displacement of the focal surface must not exceed

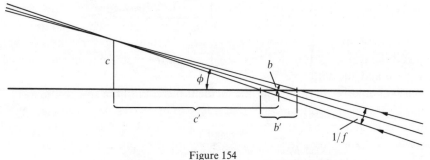

Figure 154

The effect of focal plane displacement on focusing.

0.01 mm. All this requires extreme accuracy in the relative positioning of the components and in focusing, so that the adjustment screws should be fabricated with very high precision.

### Source mounting

The radiant energy source should be set on the straight line joining the center points of the grating and the slit. Source position is generally chosen by viewing the illuminated area of the slit through a wide open exit slit on which the zero-order spectrum is focused. If the slit cannot be opened for these observations, the source position can be properly fixed by examining the position of the diffraction maxima. The source should be mounted so that the central maximum symmetrically covers the grating. The adjustment is easily done by moving the source and following the position of the diffraction pattern.

The entire effective area of the grating should be illuminated. At other wavelengths, this is easily accomplished by using special illuminating optics. In the short-wave region, there are obvious restrictions on the use of optics, and the source must be set sufficiently near the slit to provide adequate coverage of the grating.

The angular dimensions of the source should thus be sufficient to illuminate all the parts of the grating from all the points of the slit. Most sources used in vacuum spectroscopy are small, and to ensure adequate angular size they must be placed quite near the slit. The source diameter $AA'$ or $BB'$ needed to fill the collimator or the grating can be readily calculated from the drawing in Figure 155.

Most sources, however, cannot be placed too near the slit, as it may be damaged by the discharge or contaminated by particles of sputtered electrode material. The source is therefore generally mounted at a greater distance than that required to ensure full

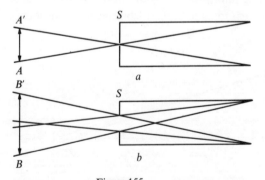

Figure 155

Collimator illumination through a rectangular slit:

*a* horizontal aperture,   *b* vertical aperture.

illumination of the grating. To protect the slit against possible damage (at wavelengths longer than 1200 Å), it is generally covered with a $CaF_2$ or LiF plate.

Grating illumination is often improved by means of condensers, e.g., lenses above 1200 Å and mirrors at shorter wavelengths (in rockets, in particular; see §18).

There is another possibility of using focusing optics down to very short wavelengths. Baez [146] was the first to apply a transparent Fresnel zone plate as optics in the vacuum ultraviolet. The Fresnel zone plate was originally used in the visible spectrum. This plate is made up of 19 gold rings, with widths and radii varying according to a certain relation. The diameter of the central zone was 0.0426 mm, the diameter of the largest ring was 0.26 mm, and the last zone was 20 micron wide; the thickness of the gold foil was 10 micron. All the rings were fixed to a thin gold cross, which supported the entire construction. At 100 Å, the focal distance of the plate was 400 cm, and at 1000 Å, only 40 cm. We see from the above that the zone plate (manufactured in cooperation by two firms) is still a fairly expensive jeweller's toy, without much practical use. There is, however, always a possibility that an ingenious technological approach will adapt this technique to practical application.

## Photographing the spectra

The short-wave region is photographed using a special photographic emulsion sensitized at the relevant wavelengths. However, experience with SWR film, specially intended for the vacuum ultraviolet, and with photographic material of other brands has shown that the film is often displaced during exposure and the emulsion layer develops cracks [34]. This is so because the emulsion rapidly loses moisture in vacuum, the gelatin layer contracts, and significant stresses develop in the film. The film should therefore be vacuum-dried before charging in a simple desiccator with a suitable hygroscopic material ($H_2SO_4$, $P_2O_5$, etc.).

## Vacuum

The vacuum required inside the spectral instrument largely depends on the particular wavelengths involved and the path length of the light beam in the instrument. This problem was studied in some detail by Ditchburn [147].

The strong light absorption at short wavelengths (300—900 Å) is primarily associated with photoionization of the main air gases and impurities. To restrict the absorption to at most 30% for a path length of 2 m ($R = 1$ m) the pressure in the instrument should be less than $3 \cdot 10^{-3}$ T. For a path length of 12 m ($R = 6$ m) the pressure should not exceed $5 \cdot 10^{-4}$ T. In individual narrow lines, however, the absorption coefficient is much higher, and the absorbance becomes negligible only at pressures below $10^{-6}$ T. This presents serious requirements concerning vacuum seals, degassing of the inner walls, and pump speed.

Systems with differential pressure are often used: a fairly high pressure is permissible in the source chamber, whereas a much lower pressure is maintained in the spectral instrument. If the two parts of the system cannot be partitioned off by a window, gas will inevitably leak through the spectral slit from the source chamber into the spectral instrument. The pump should therefore have a sufficient speed ensuring the desired pressure in the instrument.

The corresponding pumping speeds can be estimated without much difficulty. The transmission capacity of the slit can be determined for air or for some gas of a close molecular weight, using the approximate relation $Q = 10A$ liter/sec, where $A$ is the slit area in square centimeters [148]. For a slit 0.01 mm wide and 1 cm high, we find $Q = 10^{-2}$ liter/sec. If the source pressure is 10 T, and the permissible pressure in the spectral instrument is $10^{-4}$ T, equilibrium between the leaking gas and the pumped-out gas requires a pumping speed of 1000 liter/sec.

These speeds are not readily attainable, and a better policy is therefore to set a diaphragm after the slit, providing an additional pumping outlet for the small volume between the slit and the diaphragm. Since this is indeed a small volume, it can be maintained at a substantially higher pressure than the rest of the instrument and lower pumping speeds will thus be sufficient. Two or more intermediate buffer spaces are sometimes introduced [149]. A diagram of a differential pumpout system with an approximate distribution of pressures and indication of the required pumping speeds is shown in Figure 156. We see that relatively low pumping speeds are needed in this system.

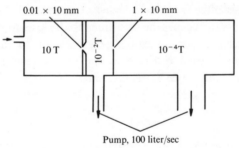

Figure 156

Differential pumpout system.

Evacuation of large instruments naturally requires high-power pumps: they should ensure fast pumpout of gases leaking through the faulty seals and, during the preliminary stages, they should be able to effectively degas the walls. The degassing is a very slow process, especially if the parts cannot be heated. Conversely, gases are readily absorbed on the inner walls of the instrument as soon as there is any leakage of air into the system. Therefore (especially in large instruments), the film holder part should be separated by vacuum-tight seals from the main part of the instrument, as, e.g., in the Douglas and Porter instrument or in the SP-99 spectrograph (see §17), where the film holder chamber has its own vacuum pump.

We have noted above that oil vapor pumps may lead to the deposition of a low-reflectance oil film on the surface of the grating, and these pumps are preferably replaced by mercury vapor pumps. It should be remembered, however, that mercury vapor readily amalgamates with gold, platinum, aluminum, and other common coatings of gratings, thus damaging the grating irretrievably. Mercury vapor pumps can therefore be recommended without reservation for instruments with glass gratings only, and in all other cases special tests should be made.

## Window bonding

An important aspect of the experimental technique is concerned with the bonding of windows to cuvettes, lamps, and discharge tubes. If the window does not heat during system operation, it is bonded with Picein, apiezon grease, or epoxy resin. Heat-resistant bonding is more difficult to accomplish because of the considerable difference in the expansion coefficients of glass and fluorite or lithium fluoride (the window material).* Various techniques can be used to offset the effect of the difference in the expansion coefficients [150–154]. For example, the fluorite window is bonded with epoxy to the flat side of a copper cylinder. The other end of the cylinder is welded to glass. Copper and fluorite have done expansion coefficients, and this bonding withstands heating up to 130°C [151].

Bonding can be achieved by means of a flat Teflon washer [155] which is cemented between the window and the vacuum envelope of the instrument. This requires preliminary chemical treatment in a solution of the sodium–naphthalene complex in tetraturafurane. The epoxy is applied on degreased and thoroughly dried surfaces of the components, which are then pressed to expel the extra adhesive. This bonding withstands a change in temperature from −190 to 100°C.

A silver chloride bonding is described in [154]. A small cup is attached to a tube whose diameter is slightly less than the diameter of the window (Figure 157). The cup is filled with silver chloride, and the tube with the cup is placed in the furnace at 470°C (sufficient to melt the silver chloride); silver chloride is added into the cup until the melt overflows. The furnace is then cooled and the window is inserted, so that it is in contact with the melt, but not with the ends of the tube. After that the temperature is again raised to 450°C and the furnace is slowly cooled. The resulting bonding withstands temepratures above 430°C.

Bonding of a lithium fluoride window to a glass tube by means of a silver junction is described in [150]. The glass tube is bonded to the silver rod by means of silver

* The linear expansion coefficient of silver is $20 \cdot 10^{-6}$ deg$^{-1}$. The expansion coefficients of fluorite, lithium fluoride, and glass are, respectively, $20 \cdot 10^{-6}$ deg$^{-1}$, $40 \cdot 10^{-6}$ deg$^{-1}$, and $10^{-6}$ deg$^{-1}$.

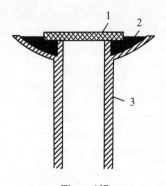

Figure 157
Window bonding:

1) LiF window,    2) AgCl layer,    3) glass.

chloride, and the silver rod in its turn is bonded to the window with silver chloride. A thin silver tube 10 mm long with 0.1 mm thick walls is used. It is washed with nitric acid and then rinsed with distilled water. Two rings 3 mm thick are cut from fused silver chloride and flattened under a press. These rings, the window, and the intermediate rings and tubes are assembled and placed in a furnace which is gradually heated to 500°C. This temperature is maintained for 5 min. and the furnace is then allowed to cool slowly (over a few hours). Deviation from these heating and cooling conditions may lead to breakage of windows.

### Cleaning of gratings

The grating surface collects dust and dirt in routine use. It therefore has to be cleaned occasionally, but the time to cleaning should not be less than a few years. The adhering dust particles are best swept off by a mild jet of air. If this is not enough, the grating should be washed. Gratings are also to be washed before the reflecting coating is applied.

In the procedure described in [155] for washing the grating preparatory to the application of the reflecting layer, ethanol (about 1 liter) is slowly poured onto the grating. This rinsing will prove sufficient for most new gratings. Otherwise, the grating is additionally washed in a solution of collodion in ether. When the solution has dried, the grating is covered with a film which is then carefully stripped off (the film should not be allowed to remain too long on the grating surface). Aluminum-coated gratings are washed with petroleum ether, since aluminum film is washed off with alcohol. Replica gratings made of resins and plastics should not be washed in acetone and other solvents, which may damage the surface of the replica. In general, the grating is to be washed only in cases of extreme need.

## BIBLIOGRAPHY

1. LYMAN, TH. *The Spectroscopy of the Extreme Ultra-Violet,* 2nd ed., London–New York, Longmans, Green and Co. 1928.
2. HOAG, J.B. *Astrophys. J., 66,* 225 (1927).
3. ROWLAND, H.A. *Philos. Mag., 13,* 469 (1882); **16,** 197 (1883).
4. GLASEBROOK, R.T. *Philos. Mag., 15,* 414 (1883).
5. MASCART, E. *J. d. Phys., 2,* 5 (1883).
6. BAILY, W. *Philos. Mag., 22,* 47 (1886).
7. RUNGE, C. and R. W. MEISSNER. *Handbuch der Astrophysik,* G. Eberhard, Editor, **I,** p. 235, Berlin, Springer-Verlag. 1933.
8. KAYSER, H. *Handbuch der Spektroskopie,* **1,** p. 397. Leipzig, 1900.
9. BEUTLER, H.G. *J. Opt. Soc. America,* **35,** 311 (1945).
10. MACK, J.E., J.R. STEHN, and B. EDLEN. *J. Opt. Soc. America,* **22,** 245 (1932).
11. NAMIOKA, T. *J. Opt. Soc. America,* **49,** 446, 460, 951 (1959).
12. NAMIOKA, T. In: *Kosmicheskaya astrofizika,* W. Liller, Editor, p. 285. IL. 1962.
13. KASTNER, S.O. and W.M. NEUPERT. *J. Opt. Soc. America,* **53,** 1180 (1963).
14. WOOD, R.W. *Physical Optics.* New York, Macmillan Co. 1934.
15. SHUSTER, A. *Vvedenie v teoreticheskuyu optiku (Introduction to Theoretical Optics).* Gostekhizdat. 1935.
16. SHENSTONE, A.G. *J. Opt. Soc. America,* **53,** 1253 (1963).
17. FASTIE, W.G. *J. Opt. Soc. America,* **52,** 1313 (1962).
18. TOUSEY, R. *Appl. Optics,* **1,** 679 (1962).
18a. LANDON, D.O. *Appl. Optics,* **2,** 450 (1963).
19. EDLÉN, B. *Repts. Progr. Phys.,* **26,** 181 (1963).
19a. WOOD, R.W. *Philos. Mag.,* **20,** 770 (1910).
20. JARELL, R.F. and G.W. STROKE. *Appl. Optics,* **3,** 1251 (1964).
21. SAYCE, L.A. and A. FRANKS. *Proc. Roy. Soc.,* **A282,** 353 (1964).
22. GERASIMOV, F.M., S.S. NAUMOV, and L.M. DESINOV. *Optika i Spektroskopiya,* **16,** 133 (1964).
23. SPRAGUE, G., D.H. TOMBOULIAN, and D.E. BEDO. *J. Opt. Soc. America,* **45,** 756 (1955).
24. LUKIRSKII, A.P. and E.P. SAVINOV. *Optika i Spektroskopiya,* **14,** 285, 295 (1963).
25. CRIPS, R.S. *Optica acta,* **8,** 137 (1961).
26. GERASIMOV, F.M. *Optiko-mekhanicheskaya Promyshlennost',* No.11, 33 (1965).
27. WADSWORTH, F.L.O. *Astrophys. J., 3,* 47 (1896).
28. HABER, H. *J. Opt. Soc. America,* **40,** 153 (1950).
29. GREINER, H and E. SCHÄFFER. *Optik,* **16,** 288 (1959).
30. NAMIOKA, T. *J. Opt. Soc. America,* **51,** 4 (1961).
31. NAMIOKA, T. *J. Opt. Soc. America,* **51,** 13 (1961).
32. SHCHEPETKIN, YU.P. *Optika i Spektroskopiya,* **4,** 383, 513 (1958).
33. SHCHEPETKIN, YU.P. *Optika i Spektroskopiya,* **6,** 822 (1959).
34. RENSE, W.A. In: *Kosmicheskaya astrofizika,* W. Liller, Editor, p. 26. IL 1962.
34a. SCHÖNHEIT, E. *Optik,* **23,** 305 (1965).
35. BRIX, P. and G. HERZBERG. *Canad. J. Phys.,* **32,** 110 (1954).

36. ASTOIN, N., J. ROMAND, and B. VODAR. *J. phys. et radium*, **16**, 491 (1955).

37. VODAR, B. *J. Quant. Spectr. Rad. Trans.*, **2**, 393 (1962).

38. CUREY, J. and G. HERZBERG. *Ann. Physik,* **19**, 800 (1934).

39. DOUGLAS, A.E. and G. HERZBERG. *J. Opt. Soc. America,* **47**, 625 (1957).

40. NAMIOKA, T. *J. Quant. Spectr. Rad. Trans.*, **2**, 697 (1962).

41. FRISH, S.E. *Tekhnika spektroskopii (Spectroscopic Techniques).* Izdatel'stvo LGU. 1934.

42. SAWYER, R. A. *Experimental Spectroscopy,* New York, Prentice-Hall. 1951.

43. HARRISON, G.R., R.C. LORD, and J.R. LOOFBOUROW. *Practical Spectroscopy,* New York, Prentice-Hall. 1948.

43a. GERASIMOVA, N.G. *Optiko-mekhanicheskaya Promyshlennost',* No.5, 2 (1964).

44. RUNGE, C.R. and F. PASCHEN. *Abhand. Deut. Akad. Wiss., Berlin,* **1** (1902).

45. EAGLE, A. *Astrophys.,* **31**, 120 (1910).

45a. WILKINSON, P.G. *J. Mol. Spectr.,* **1**, 288 (1957).

46. SEYA, M. *Sci. of Light,* **2**, 8 (1952).

47. ONAKA, R. *Sci. of Light,* **7**, 23 (1958).

48. JOHNSON, P.D. *Rev. Scient. Instrum.,* **28**, 833 (1957).

48a. SIRKS, J.L. *Astronomy and Astrophys.,* **13**, 763 (1894).

49. SCHUMANN, V. *Sitzungsber. der Math.-Naturw. Kl. Akad. Wissensch., Wien,* **102**, 625 (1893).

50. MCLENAN, J.C., D.S. AINSLIE, and D.S. FULLER. *Proc. Roy. Soc.,* **A95**, 316 (1919).

51. HESE, H., A. ROSE, and R. GRAFIN ZU DOHNA. *Z. Phys.,* **81**, 745 (1933).

52. LEISS, L. *Z. Phys.,* **44**, 133 (1927).

53. CORDES, H. and H. SPONER. *Z. Phys.,* **63**, 334 (1930).

54. BOMKE, H. *Phys. Zs.,* **37**, 222 (1936).

55. CARIO, G. and H.D. SCHMIDT-OTT. *Z. Phys.,* **69**, 719 (1932).

56. HILSCH, R. and R.W. POHL. *Z. Phys.,* **59**, 812 (1930).

57. BOMKE, H. *Vakuumspektroskopie,* p. 31, Leipzig, Barth. 1937.

58. YAKOVLEVA, A.V., I.I. GROMOVA, and I.R. PROTAS. *Izvestiya AN SSSR,* phys. ser., **19**, 84 (1955).

59. KULIKOV, S.A. and A.V. YAKOVLEVA. *Izvestiya AN SSSR,* phys. ser., **19**, 86 (1955).

60. FISHER, F. and R. HILSCH. *Z. angew. Phys.,* **16**, 150 (1963).

61. KULIKOV, S.A. *Optiko-mekhanicheskaya Promyshlennost',* No.9, 33 (1959).

62. DOUGLAS, A.E. and J.G. POTTER. *Appl. Optics,* **1**, 727 (1962).

63. KULIKOV, S.A., S.P. ROZOV, and G.P. STARTSEV. *Optiko-mekhanicheskaya Promyshlennost',* No.5, 29 (1964).

64. CHULANOVSKII, V.M. *Trudy GOI,* **10**, No.90 (1934).

65. TSCHULANOWSKY, W.M. *Phys. Z. Sowjetunion,* **4**, 443 (1933).

66. SHENSTONE, A.G. *Proc. Roy. Soc.,* **A261**, 153 (1961).

67. POWELL, W.M. *Phys. Rev.,* **45**, 154 (1934).

68. TOUSEY, R., F.S. JOHNSON, J. RICHARDSON, and N. TORAN. *J. Opt. Soc. America,* **41**, 696 (1951).

69. PARKINSON, W.W. and F.E. WILLIAMS. *J. Opt. Soc. America,* **39**, 705 (1949).

70. VODAR, B. *Rev. optique,* **21**, 97 (1942).

71. ROBIN, S. *J. phys. et radium,* **14**, 551 (1952).

72. GERASIMOVA, N.G. and G.P. STARTSEV. *Optiko-mekhanicheskaya Promyshlennost'*, No. 1, 30 (1961).

73. AKOPYAN, M.E., I.I. BALYAKIN, and F.I. VILESOV. *Pribory i Tekhnika Eksperimenta*, No.6, 96 (1961).

74. GERASIMOVA, N.G. and S.A. KULIKOV. *Optiko-mekhanicheskaya Promyshlennost'*, No.10, 1 (1960).

75. KULIKOV, S.A., YU.A. SNIGIREV, and G.P. STARTSEV. *Optiko-mekhanicheskaya Promyshlennost'*, No. 10, 22 (1965).

76. JAMES, J.F. *J. Scient. Instrum.*, **36**, 188 (1959).

77. KULIKOV, S.A., N.A. PABLENKO, and G.P. STARTSEV. *Optiko-mekhanicheskaya Promyshlennost'*, No. 4, 24 (1965).

78. GERASIMOVA, N.G. and S.A. KULIKOV. *Optiko-mekhanicheskaya Promyshlennost'*, No.10, 1 (1960).

79. KOKIN, V.V. *Zh. Prikl. Spektr.*, **2**, 561 (1965).

80. REICH, H.J. *Z. angew. Phys.*, **16**, 299 (1963).

81. EBERT, H. *Ann. Physik*, **38**, 489 (1889).

82. ROZHDESTVENSKII, D.S. *Raboty po anomal'noi dispersii v parakh metallov (Studies of Anomalous Dispersion in Metal Vapors)*, S.E. Frish, Editor. Izdatel'stvo AN SSSR. 1951.

83. PENKIN, N.P. and A.M. SHUKHTIN. *Izvestiya AN SSSR*, phys. ser., **12**, 376 (1948).

84. FASTIE, W.G. *J. Opt. Soc. America*, **42**, 641, 647 (1952); **43**, 1174 (1953).

85. FASTIE, W.G., H.M. CROSWHITE, and T.P. MARKHAM. *Ann. geophys.*, **17**, 109 (1961).

86. GERASIMOVA, N.G. *Optiko-mekhanicheskaya Promyshlennost'*, No.6, 2 (1964).

87. STARTSEV, G.P., N.G. GERASIMOVA, S.A. KULIKOV, and S.P. ROZOV. *Optiko-mekhanicheskaya Promyshlennost'*, No.5, 15 (1965).

88. PLANTA, C. *Helv. phys. acta*, **34**, 394 (1961).

89. RIEMANN, M. *Optik aller Wellenlangen*, p. 115, Jena. 1958.

90. EDLÉN, B. *Nova acta Reg. Soc. scient. upsaliensis*, ser. IV, **9**, No.6 (1934).

91. EDLÉN, B. *Z. Phys.*, **100**, 621 (1936).

92. GABRIEL, A.H., J.R. SWAIN, and W.A. WALLER. *J. Scient. Instrum.*, **42**, 94 (1965).

93. KIRKPATRICK, H.A. *J. Quant. Spectr. Rad. Trans.*, **2**, 715 (1962).

94. GABRIEL, A.H., G.B.F. NIBLETT, and N.J. PEACOCK. *J. Quant. Spectr. Rad. Trans.*, **2**, 491 (1963).

95. FAWCETT, B.C., A.H. GABRIEL, B.B. JONES, and N.J. PEACOCK. *Proc. Phys. Soc.*, **84**, 257 (1964).

96. ALEXANDER, E., B.S. FRAENKEL, U. FELDMAN, A. JACOBS, and J. MAKOVSKY. *J. Quant. Spectr. Rad. Trans.*, **2**, 725 (1962).

97. LANDON, D.O. *Appl. Optics*, **3**, 115 (1964).

98. JEAGLE, P. *J. phys. et radium*, **24**, 179 (1963).

99. JEAGLE, P. *C.R. Acad. Sci., Paris*, **259**, 533 (1963).

100. LAQUA, K. and W.D. HAGENAH. *Proc. 10th Colloq. Spectr. Intern.*, p. 91, Washington. 1963.

101. DMITRIEVSKII, O.D., B.S. NEPORENT, and V.A. NIKITIN. *Uspekhi Fizicheskikh Nauk*, **64**, 447 (1958).

102. GABRIEL, A.H. and W.A. WALLER. *J. Scient. Instr.*, **40**, 10 (1963).

103. TOUSEY, R. *Space Sci. Rev.*, **2**, 3 (1963).

104. BRUNS, A.V. and V.K. PROKOF'EV. *Iskusstvennye Sputniki Zemli*, No.11, 15, 23 (1961).

105. HINTEREGGER, H.E. *Astrophys. J.*, **132**, 801 (1960).

106. HINTEREGGER, H.E. *J. Geophys. Res.*, **66**, 2367 (1961).

107. HINTERREGGER, H.E., L.A. HALL, and W. SCHWEIZER. *Astrophys. J.*, **140**, 319 (1964).

108. HALL, L.A., W. SCHWEIZER, and H.E. HINTEREGGER. *J. Geophys. Res.*, **70**, 105 (1965).

109. RENSE, W.A., F.E. STUART, and E.P. TODD. *Spektry zvezd v dalekom ul'trafiolete (Stellar Spectra in the Far UV)*, p. 60. Izdatel'stvo "Mir." 1964.

110. TOUSEY, R. In: *Kosmicheskaya astrofizika*, W. Liller, Editor, p. 11. IL. 1962.

111. KACHALOV, V.P., N.A. PAVLENKO, and A.V. YAKOVLEVA. *Izvestiya AN SSSR*, geophys. ser., No.9, 1099 (1958).

112. KACHALOV, V.P., N.A. PAVLENKO, and A.V. YAKOVLEVA. *Izvestiya AN SSSR*, geophys. ser., No.8, 1177 (1959).

113. DETWILER, C.R., J.D. PURCELL, and R. TOUSEY. *The Profile of the Solar Lyman-α-line of Hydrogen*. In: *Proc. Intern. Space Sci. Symp., Nice, 1960*.

114. RENSE, W.A. and T. VIOLET. *J. Opt. Soc. America*, **49**, 139 (1959).

115. VIOLET, T. and W.A. RENSE. *Astrophys. J.*, **130**, 954 (1959).

116. AUSTIN, W.E., J.D. PURCELL, and R. TOUSEY. *J. Opt. Soc. America*, **52**, 597 (1962).

117. PURCELL, J.D. and R. TOUSEY. *Astron. J.*, **67**, 110 (1962).

118. PURCELL, J.D., A. BOGGESS, and R. TOUSEY. In: *Issledovanie verkhnei atmosfery s pomoshch'yu raket i sputnikov*, p. 73. IL. 1961.

119. PURCELL, J.D., D.L. GARRET, and R. TOUSEY. *Space Research*, W. Priester, Editor, **3**, 781, Amsterdam, North-Holland Publ. Co. 1963.

120. GARRET, D.L., J.D. PURCELL, and R. TOUSEY. *Appl. Optics*, **1**, 726 (1962).

120a. DETWILER, C.R. and J.D. PURCELL. *J. Opt. Soc. America*, **52**, 597 (1962).

121. FASTIE, W.G. *J. Quant. Spectr. Rad. Trans.*, **3**, 507 (1963).

122. PURCELL, J.D. *J. Opt. Soc. America*, **47**, 1057 (1957).

122a. PURCELL, J.D., D.M. PACKER, and R. TOUSEY. In: *Issledovanie verkhnei atmosfery s pomoshch'yu raket i sputnikov*, p. 143. IL. 1961.

123. GOODRICH, G.W. and W.C. WILLER. *Rev. Scient. Instrum.*, **32**, 846 (1961).

124. FRIEDMAN, H. In: *Kosmicheskaya astrofizika*, W. Liller, Editor, p. 136. IL. 1962.

125. FILIPPOV, A.N. *Trudy GOI*, **8**, No. 85 (1932).

126. ROZHDESTVENSKII, D.S. *Prostye sootnosheniya v spektrakh shchelonyk metallov (Simple Relations in Alkali Metal Spectra)*, p. 5. SPb. 1915.

127. LADENBURG, R. and G. WOLFSOHN. *Z. Phys.*, **79**, 42 (1932).

128. PERRY-THORNE, A. *J. Quant. Spectr. Rad. Trans.*, **2**, 427 (1962).

129. SCHROEDER, D.J. *J. Opt. Soc. America*, **52**, 1380 (1962).

130. BRADLEY, D.J., B. BATES, C.O.L. JUULMAN, and S. MAJUMDAR. *Nature*, **202**, 579 (1964).

131. STROKE, G.W. *Phys. Let.*, **5**, 45 (1963).

132. PALMER, C.H. *J. Opt. Soc. America*, **42**, 269 (1952); **46**, 50 (1956); **51**, 1438 (1961).

133. YAKOVLEV, E.A. and F.M. GERASIMOV. *Optika i Spektroskopiya*, **10**, 104 (1961).

134. TOUSEY, R. *Phys. Rev.*, **50**, 1057 (1936).

135. WALKER, W.C. *Appl. Optics*, **3**, 1457 (1964).

136. RABINOWITCH, K., L.R. CANFIELD, and R.P. MADDEN. *Appl. Optics*, **4**, 1005 (1965).

137. HAM, R.N., R.A. MACRAE, and E.T. ARAKAWA. *J. Opt. Soc. America*, **55**, 1460 (1965).

137a. HANSON, W.F. and E.T. ARAKAWA. *J. Opt. Soc. America*, **56**, 124 (1966).

138. WALKER, W.C. *J. Opt. Soc. America,* **54**, 569 (1964).
139. JOHNSON, W.C. *Rev. Scient. Instrum.,* **35**, 1375 (1964).
140. WALKER, W.C. and J. OSANTOWSKI. *Bull. Am. Phys. Soc.,* **9**, 223 (1964).
141. ANDERSON, R.O. and J.E. MACK. *J. Opt. Soc. America,* **24**, 292 (1934).
142. MACK, J.E. and J.R. STEHN. *J. Opt. Soc. America,* **23**, 184 (1933).
143. RATHENAU, G. and P.K. PEELKAMP. *Physica,* **2**, 125 (1935).
144. GERASIMOVA, N.G. *Optiko-mekhanicheskaya Promyshlennost',* No.8, 30 (1965).
145. NAGULIN, YU.S. *Optiko-mekhanicheskaya Promyshlennost',* No.6, 30 (1965).
146. BAEZ, A.V. *J. Opt. Soc. America,* **51**, 405 (1961).
147. DITCHBURN, R.W. *Optica acta,* **3**, 74 (1956).
148. GUTHRIE, A. and K. WACKERLING. *Vacuum Equipment and Techniques.* N.Y., McGraw-Hill. 1949.
149. WILKINSON, P.G. and E.T. BYRAM. *Appl. Optics,* **4**, 581 (1965).
150. FRANK, R. and R.L. STOW. *Rev. Scient. Instrum.,* **25**, 514 (1954).
151. FIVEISKAYA, A.K. and S.A. YAKOVLEV. *Optiko-mekhanicheskaya Promyshlennost',* No.2, 18 (1962).
152. LORD, R.C. and R.S. MCDONALD. *Rev. Scient. Instrum.,* **23**, 442 (1952).
153. VOGL, T.P., R.O. MCINTOSH, and M. GARBUNY. *Rev. Scient. Instrum.,* **36**, 1439 (1965).
154. PALMER, F. *Phys. Rev.,* **45**, 556 (1934).
155. CHEGODAEV, D.D., Z.K. NAUMOVA, and TS.S. DUNAEVSKAYA. *Ftoroplasty (Teflons).* Goskhimizdat. 1960.
156. MADDEN, R.P. *Physics of Thin Films. Advances in Research and Development.* G. Hass, Editor, **I**, 123. N.Y.–London, Academic Press. 1963.

# CHAPTER IV

# Detectors for the Vacuum Ultraviolet

## 22. THERMOCOUPLES

A wide range of detectors, originally developed for other spectral regions, have adequate response and sensitivity in the vacuum ultraviolet. Alongside with these, there are detectors which are used exclusively in the vacuum ultraviolet, since they are virtually insensitive to photons with energies less than 6–7 eV (ionization chambers, some photocathodes, other detectors).

The detector can be mounted at the exit of the spectral instrument, and the energy measurements are then confined to a narrow spectral interval. Another approach is to detect the undispersed radiation: in this case, a spectral region of a certain width is isolated either by the detector itself or by a special filter.

Absolute source intensities can be measured if the detector has been calibrated in absolute units. Relative measurements require the response curve of the detector on any relative scale. In either case, a nonselective detector is preferable. The detectors are generally calibrated by reference to thermocouple readings. The sensitivity of thermocouples can be determined with sufficient reliability by special measurements using blackbody radiation in the visible spectrum.

More exact measurements in the vacuum ultraviolet require calibration by means of a standard source in the appropriate spectral region, since the thermocouple response may in fact change with wavelength (although not appreciably). This wavelength dependence is unrelated to the variation of the reflection coefficient of the termocouple junction with wavelength [1]. The only reason for the wavelength dependence of the response is the loss of energy of the emitted photoelectrons. For example, at wavelengths between 400 and 1200 Å, the response of a gold thermocouple may change by a few percent owing to the variation in the photoelectric quantum yield of gold in this region [2]; at 725 Å, the error may reach 5% [1].

The main shortcoming of thermocouples is their low sensitivity, so that very wide spectrometer slits are required, and the monochromaticity of the entering beam is poor. Thermocouple measurements in the vacuum ultraviolet were mainly developed by Packer and Lock [3].

## 23. PHOTOELECTRIC DETECTORS

Photoelectric detectors are divided into closed and open types. In closed-type detectors, the photocathode is protected by a special screen which converts the short-wave ultraviolet radiation into radiation of longer wavelengths. In open-type detectors, the photocathode is directly exposed to the incident radiation.

### Closed-type detectors

Phosphors, when exposed to the extreme ultraviolet, emit light which readily passes through the glass windows of photocells or photomultipliers [4, 5]. The spectral composition of the emission of most phosphors is independent of the wavelength of the exciting radiation. The phosphor layer in detectors is applied either directly on the photomultiplier window or on a special screen mounted in front of the window. Observations can be made in transmitted and reflected radiation; the latter mode often reduces the scattering component [6, 7]. Depending on the particular phosphor used, the detectors will be selective or non-selective.

The most useful phosphor is apparently prepared by spraying with a saturated alcoholic solution of sodium salicylate [2, 8–16].* Numerous tests have established that freshly prepared layers of sodium salicylate have a constant quantum yield (to within 10%) between 400 and 3400 Å. At wavelengths shorter than 1600 Å, the quantum yield markedly drops for phosphor layers a few days old. This effect is particularly noticeable at short wavelengths [2, 11].

The quantum yield of the phosphor layer does not decrease after prolonged aging in air or in vacuum [13, 19]; the layer properties are not affected even by exposure to the 2537 Å mercury resonance line [19]. In [20], the quantum yield of sodium salicylate fell to one third of the original value at wavelengths between 500 and 3000 Å. The reasons for this change are not clear; there is a possibility that the drop in quantum yield was associated with accidental injection of impurities.

---

* The spraying techniques for screens of various thicknesses are discussed in [17, 18].

Apparently all changes of quantum yield during aging are traceable to the formation of an oil film on the screen surface: after all, oil vapor is always present in the vacuum UV monochromator. (For this reason it is better to avoid using oil vapor pumps in the vacuum system.) The quantum yield of the oil film is lower than that of sodium salicylate.

The fluorescence intensity of sodium salicylate depends on layer thickness, and one can always find the optimal thickness for a wide range of wavelengths. The existence of this optimal thickness is evident if we remember that a layer which is too thin will not absorb all the incident radiation, whereas a layer which is too thick will start absorbing its own luminescence flux. The optimal surface density of the phosphor layer (often referred to as the *layer thickness*) fluctuates according to various sources between 1 and 7 mg/cm$^2$ [17, 21, 22].

At some wavelengths, a decrease in quantum yield is observed. For example, at layer thicknesses of a few tens of a milligram per cm$^2$, the quantum yield at 2700 Å markedly decreases. This is associated with the decrease in the absorption coefficient of sodium salicylate at this wavelength, so that only part of the incident flux is absorbed inside the phosphor layer. A selective decrease of the quantum yield at layer thicknesses of 2 mg/cm$^2$ was observed at 2000 Å. This experimental fact still remains unexplained [21].*

The absolute value of the quantum yield of sodium salicylate is of considerable practical interest. This quantity has been measured by various authors [20, 23–26], but, unfortunately, the results are most contradictory. The quantum yield according to various authors varies from 25 to 100%. These fluctuations in the measured quantum yields of sodium salicylate can be attributed to incomplete absorption in thin layers [28], to presence of accidental organic impurities suppressing the quantum yield, and to dependence of the photocathode response on the angle of incidence [27]. The higher values are apparently nearest the true figure. In other words, the quantum yield of sodium salicylate is close to unity. Impure specimens or contaminated layers, however, may have a substantially lower quantum yield.

Other phosphors are sometimes used in the vacuum ultraviolet, such as terphenyl [7, 17], coronene [28, 29], anthracene [28], and lumogen (its sensitive region extends up to 4600 Å in the longwave direction) [30].

Radiations of different spectral composition can be easily compared using phosphors of constant quantum yield, since the phosphor converts the incident fluxes into light of fixed spectral composition and no correction for the detector response is required.** The common practice calls for detectors with peak response at the luminescense wavelengths of the phosphor.

---

** In [21], the absorption spectrum of sodium salicylate between 2000 and 5000 Å is given.

** However, the dependence of the instrument transmission on wavelength must nevertheless be taken into consideration.

Absolute measurements require calibration of the entire system (phosphor plus photomultiplier), which is generally done with a thermocouple [4, 9]. Photomultipliers also can be calibrated using photochemical reactions [31], e.g., the reaction of ozone formation by irradiation with the mercury resonance line (2537 Å). In these cases, the photomultiplier sensitivity is lowered by working at low voltages. If the gain is known as a function of voltage, one can then measure light fluxes substantially weaker than the fluxes needed to trigger the chemical reactions (e.g., weaker by a factor of $10^7$).

A closed-type photomultiplier will measure wavelengths which lie far beyond the transmission threshold of the glass or quartz window even without applying a special luminescent layer onto the window. This effect is associated with the phosphorescence of quartz and glass. For example a photomultiplier with a quartz window will detect radiation down to 1550 Å, and a glass-window photomultiplier responds to wavelengths down to 1750 Å [32]. However, the quantum yield of glass and quartz is much lower than the quantum yield of special phosphors. Moreover, the afterglow of glasses is fairly prolonged ($\tau = 10^{-3}$–1 sec). Thus, closed-type photomultipliers without a phosphor layer cannot be used in the vacuum ultraviolet for the detection of small and rapidly varying fluxes.

A substantial shortcoming of closed-type photomultipliers is that they respond to radiation in the visible and the near ultraviolet. To reduce the distorting influence of the scattered long-wave radiation, special filters are used transmitting only the screen luminescence wavelengths.

A system comprising a closed-type photomultiplier and a phosphor involves considerable light losses, since only part of the luminescence output reaches the photocathode. As a result, the quantum yield of the entire system seldom exceeds 1% [32a].

An ingenious method for increasing the response of closed photomultipliers to short-wave radiation was proposed by Lincke and Palumbo [32b]. The luminescing screen is coated with an aluminum layer, which is meant, on the one hand, to cut off the long-wave radiation and, on the other, to create suitable conditions for more complete utilization of the luminescence output: the metallic film reflects the visible light and directs the phosphor emission to the photomultiplier.

Closed photomultipliers can be conveniently connected to a vacuum monochromator by a fiber-optics lightpipe: one end of the lightpipe is coated with a layer of sodium salicylate and is held behind the exit slit, whereas the other end faces the photomultiplier.

## Open-type detectors

Open-type detectors, in which incident radiation falls directly on the photocathode, can be used in the vacuum ultraviolet [4, 33–38]. These detectors are highly sensitive to wavelengths below 2000 Å, and a suitable choice of the photocathode may render the device completely unresponsive to wavelengths longer than 2000 Å. As a result, errors associated with light scattering are minimized.

An important requirement to be met by detectors which work at wavelengths shorter than 1000 Å is that their response should fall off steeply between 2000 and 1000 Å. One of the methods whereby the photomultiplier or photocell response curve can be controlled calls for application of a negative voltage (relative to the cathode) to the grid. The grid will then stop the slow photoelectrons knocked out by the long-wave radiation. The peak of the response curve is thus shifted to the short-wave region. The sensitivity of a photocell with a nickel cathode at 1216 Å decreases by several orders of magnitude when a negative voltage of $-2.5$ V (relative to the cathode) is applied to the grid (Figure 158). At wavelengths longer than 1350 Å, this detector has zero response [39].

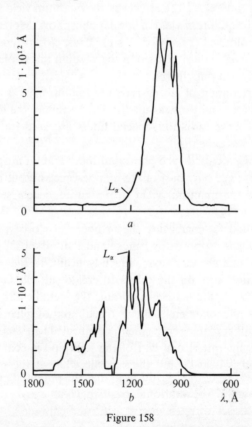

Figure 158

The shift in the peak of the spectral response curve of a detector at short wavelengths, caused by application of a negative grid potential:

*a*   negative grid potential $-2.5$ V;   *b*   positive grid potential 50 V.

The effect of long-wave radiation can be suppressed by means of filters [40]. Suitable filters are provided by thin metallic films (a few tenths of a micron thick) made of Al, Sn, In, Be, Au, Ag, Cd, and other metals [41] (see §10). The transmittance of these filters is markedly suppressed at wavelengths longer than 1200 Å. In every individual case, we can choose a filter which together with an appropriate photocathode will record radiation in a relatively narrow spectral interval. The same filter can be used to record radiation without any spectral instrument (see §27).

Open-type photomultipliers use the volume photoeffect, whose quantum yield in metals is higher than that of the surface photoeffect; more significant is the fact that the volume photoeffect does not depend on the state of the cathode surface [41a]. Pure metals can be used as the cathode (Ni, Pt, W, Cu, Ag). The quantum yield of pure metals around 1000 Å is $Y \approx 10\%$ (0.1 electron/photon) [39, 41–44], i.e., much higher than the quantum yield in the near ultraviolet, where $Y = 10^{-3}–10^{-5}$ electron/photon (see, e.g., [45]). Various photomultipliers use binary compound photocathodes with a sufficiently high quantum yield (BeCu, CuI, CsTe, CsSb, RbTe, CsI, BeO, MgO, $SrF_2$, LiF, KCl) [35–37, 46]* (Figure 159).

At wavelengths around 100 Å, CsI and $SrF_2$ photocathodes are particularly effective [48, 49]. Their quantum yield reaches several tens of percent. The radiation is detected with these photomultipliers mostly by counting the pulses of the individual photoelectrons [49]. If the operating conditions are properly chosen, the photomultiplier efficiency is determined by the photocathode quantum yield. An open-type photomultiplier functions at pressures of the order of $10^{-5}$ T. When using photomultipliers in the vacuum ultraviolet, one should take into consideration the dependence of the quantum yield on the angle of incidence on the photocathode. This dependence was originally observed for X rays ($\lambda \approx 1.3–13$ Å) [50], and later also noted for longer wavelengths ($\lambda \approx 300$ Å) [51]. The increase in the quantum yield of metals with increasing angle of incidence does not always improve the response of a grazing-incidence detector, since the reflected flux also increases with the increase in incidence angle. A cathode made up of 18 metallic layers was developed, whose geometry ensured total absorption of radiation inside the cathode; its quantum yield at 350 Å reached 28% [51a].

Short-wave ultraviolet radiation is detected with magnetic-focusing photomultipliers, in which the electrodes 1 and 2 (Figure 160) are high-resistance semiconductor slabs [41a, 52–54] (a ten-cascade photomultiplier is shown in the figure). The interelectrode spacing is a few millimeters. The same potential difference (about 1500–2000 V) is applied to both electrodes, so that the potential gradients along the two electrodes are equal. An additional positive voltage is applied to the upper electrode. The light passes through grid 5 to hit the cathode 4, which is either an extension of the dynode or is made of metal. The magnetic field (about 300 gauss)

---

* A LiF coated cathode is often used in photocells (see, e.g., [47]).

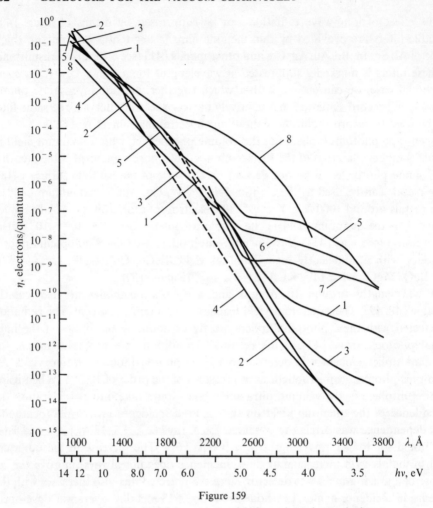

Figure 159

Spectral distribution of the quantum yield for various photocathodes:

1) BeO cathode prepared by oxidation of Cu–Be–Al alloy at $t = 840°C$,   2) BeO cathode obtained by the same method followed by oxidation at $t = 600°C$,   3) MgO cathode obtained by oxidation of Cu–Al–Mg alloy at $t = 600°C$,   4) MgO cathode obtained by the same method on the surface of Cu–Al–Mg alloy coated with a Pt layer,   5) $SrF_2$ cathode obtained by vaporization of crystal (measurements, made after exposure to short-wave light),   6) $SrF_2$ cathode obtained by vaporization of powder (measurements made before exposure to short-wave light),   7) CsI cathode obtained by vaporization of crystal,   8) Ni cathode cleaned with fine sand paper.

is perpendicular to the plane of the drawing. The electrons trace an arc until they hit the dynode 2. The electron beam is focused on the anode 3. The gain along the dynode varies depending on the voltage applied. As the voltage is raised from 1000 to 2000 V, the gain increases from $10^5$ to $10^9$ [52].

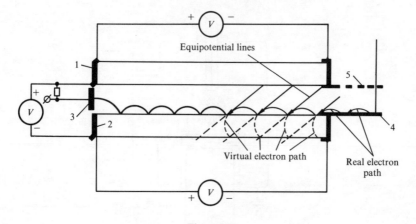

Figure 160

A diagram of a magnetic-focusing photomultiplier.

Special tests have been carried out in order to compare the response of these photomultipliers with the response of closed-type detectors at wavelengths shorter and longer than 1050 Å. It was found that for equal response at $\lambda < 1050$ Å, the response of a closed-type photomultiplier at $\lambda > 1050$ Å is 100 times higher than the response of a magnetic-focusing photomultiplier. This constitutes a tremendous advantage, as the scattered light at wavelengths longer than 1050 Å can safely be ignored in magnetic-focusing photomultipliers.

A special vacuum ultraviolet detector was proposed by Lincke and Wilkerson [55]. This detector is known as a P/S detector (photoemission/scintillation) (Figure 161). The radiation is incident at 45° onto the surface of a gold cathode, which is maintained at 15 kV relative to the earthed chamber. The photoelectrons emitted from the cathode are accelerated on their way toward the scintillator, which is a few millimeters thick. The light emitted by the scintillator passes through the photomultiplier window and is detected in the usual way. A thin aluminum film is applied on the side of the scintillator facing the cathode: this film absorbs the scattered visible radiation and also acts as a conductor for charge leakage. The energy losses of the electrons passing through the film are negligible. These detectors will effectively record radiation at wavelengths shorter than 1300 Å.

The comparison of a P/S detector with a closed-type detector with a sodium salicylate screen shows that at wavelengths shorter than 900 Å the P/S detector is more sensitive, whereas above 1000 Å it is less sensitive. The relative response of the two detectors to incident radiation is variable due to changes in the quantum yield of gold at different wavelengths.

Another vacuum ultraviolet detector was proposed by Tuzzolino [56, 57]. This detector is particularly attractive because of its small size, negligible weight, and low

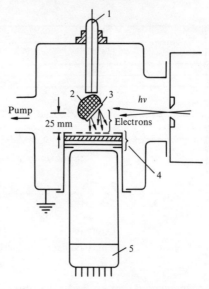

Figure 161

A diagram of a photoemission/scintillation detector:

1) electrode, 2) head, 3) cathode, 4) window and scintillator with sputtered aluminum film, 5) photomultiplier.

power consumption. A surface barrier silicon photodiode is used as the sensitive element. Photons either hit the photodiode directly, or are first absorbed in a sodium salicylate luminescent screen. A 100 Å gold film is applied to the surface of silicon. The effective area is 0.56–2.75 cm$^2$, the variation of photoresponse over the entire surface does not exceed a few percent. The quantum yield of this detector is determined by the number of electron-hole pairs produced by each photon.

Figure 162 plots the quantum yield as a function of wavelength and photon energy. The energy response of the detector is almost constant at photon energies up to 10 eV, and above 10 eV it rapidly increases. This detector is particularly effective at short wavelengths, as the quantum yield at long wavelengths is negligible. The use of a silicon photodiode in combination with a sodium salicylate layer is energetically disadvantageous: this system has a low quantum yield. Its attractive feature, however, is that it is nonselective.

Camera tubes responding in the vacuum ultraviolet may also be used for radiation detection [57a]. They record the space and time characteristics of the emitting objects. A TV tube (vidicon) with a cesium iodide cathode and a lithium fluoride window will record radiation between 1050 and 2000 Å [58].

An open-type cathodoluminescent detector was proposed by Mishchenko et al. [59]. Photoelectrons knocked out by short-wave radiation are focused on a cathodoluminescent screen, and the luminescence is then detected by a conventional photo-

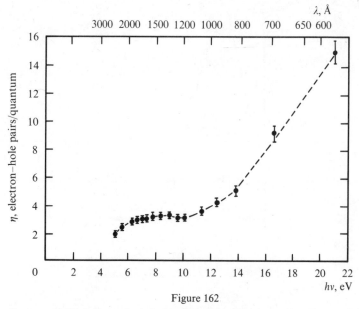

Figure 162

Quantum yield of silicon photodiode as a function of wavelength and photon energy.

multiplier. The main advantage of a cathodoluminescent detector as compared to a conventional open-type photomultiplier is that it will function with adequate stability in a poor vacuum ($p \approx 10^{-2}$ T).

## 24. THERMOPHOSPHORS

Some phosphors are capable of accumulating energy when exposed to radiation. The energy is stored for a prolonged time and it can be released abruptly in the form of radiation by heating. One of the commonest thermoluminescent materials is the $CaSO_4 \cdot Mn$ phosphor.* Radiation of wavelengths shorter than 1500 Å produces green thermoluminescence. It corresponds to the emission of the $Mn^{2+}$ ion. The emission maximum is observed at 5000 Å. Figure 163 is the spectral response curve of a thermophosphor with a peak at 1030 Å. The energy stored by the phosphor during the exposure stage is released by heating to 180°C. For constant spectral composition of the exciting radiation and under conditions of low excitation, the energy emitted by the phosphor in the form of thermoluminescence is directly proportional to the number of photons absorbed during the excitation stage. This phosphor will measure a wide scale of intensities, covering a few orders of magnitude.

* The preparation of this phosphor, as described by Watanabe [60], is attractively simple.

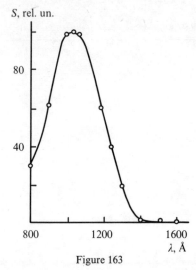

Figure 163

Spectral response curve of a thermophosphor.

The stored energy is determined by heating the phosphor and measuring the area under the thermoluminescence curve (Figure 164). This area is independent of the heating rate. The released energy can also be determined with an averaging circuit, which measures the quantity of electricity flowing through the photomultiplier during the phosphor decay time [61, 62].

If the spectral response curve of the thermophosphor is known, we can compare

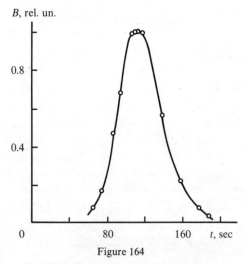

Figure 164

Thermoluminescence curve of a phosphor.

two light fluxes of different spectral composition [60, 61]. However, thermophosphors generally record a very narrow spectral interval, and their application to heterochromatic photometry is therefore severely limited. Thermophosphors are more suitable for absolute energy measurements [63, 64], and they will measure with fair accuracy the radiation energy in one particular spectral line. For example, thermophosphors have been used to measure the intensity of the He II 1215 Å line in a condensed discharge [65]; the intensity of the $L_\alpha$ line has been measured repeatedly in meteorological studies of the upper atmosphere [66, 67].

Absolute measurements require knowledge of the quantum yield of the phosphor; the quantum yield, in its turn, is highly variable depending on the method of phosphor preparation, the purity of the starting components, and a wide range of other factors, so that each individual phosphor should be calibrated. The phosphors are calibrated against a thermocouple.

The quantum yield of a phosphor near the peak energy response may reach 5–10% [60]. The phosphor described by Arkhangel'skaya et al. [65] had a quantum yield of nearly 1% at 1216 Å. The quantum yield of the thermophosphor $CaSO_4 \cdot Mn$ at 113 Å is 11% [68]. The shorter the wavelength, the higher the quantum yield, although the energy response decreases at shorter wavelengths.

The phosphor is also sensitive to gamma and beta radiations [68, 69]. As a result, the detector must be protected against hard radiations, or else a suitable correction should be introduced.

# 25. PHOTOGRAPHIC EMULSION
## AND OTHER PHOTOCHEMICAL DETECTORS

The detection of photons and the measurement of absolute and relative light intensities by means of photochemical reactions is one of the most readily accessible photometric techniques.

A number of primary photochemical reactions can be used for the detection of radiation in the vacuum ultraviolet: ozone formation [70–72], decomposition of carbon dioxide [72–74], decomposition of ammonia [72, 73, 75], decomposition of uranyl oxalate with the formation of CO and $CO_2$ [76], decomposition of nitrous oxide with the formation of $N_2O_2$ and NO [77, 78, 79], decomposition of ethylene with the formation of $H_2$ and $C_2H_2$ [80–81], and a number of other reactions. The quantum yield of all these reactions is known: it has been often measured with thermocouples or by comparison with the quantum yield of other photochemical reactions.

Numerous photochemical detectors are used in heterochromatic photometry, as they show a constant quantum yield with wavelengths varying in a wide interval. The application of photochemical detectors, except photographic emulsions, is highly involved, however, as it requires detailed chemical analyses.

Emulsions of two types are used in vacuum UV spectroscopy: 1) low-gelatin emulsions, and 2) phosphor-sensitized emulsions.

Low-gelatin emulsions were first prepared by Schumann. These emulsions show weak absorption in the vacuum ultraviolet. Ordinary photographic emulsions, on the other hand, have exceedingly high absorption, so that radiation with wavelengths shorter than 2000 Å virtually cannot be recorded. The preparation of Schumann emulsions is a fairly complex process [83, 84]. They are fragile and should be handled with great care. One of the commonest Schumann emulsions is known as SWR [84]. It has a high contrast factor and a high sensitivity; the contrast factor falls off at short wavelengths [84a]. The development time of Schumann emulsions is substantially shorter than for conventional emulsions: it is less than 1 min with a standard metol hydroquinone developer at room temperature [85].

Soviet-made emulsions are markedly sturdier than the usual Schumann emulsions, since the gelatin layer is partly replaced by surfactants; another advantage is that this combination gives a substantially lower fogging. Various Soviet-made emulsions sensitized to the vacuum ultraviolet are studied in [86–88a].

The phosphor-sensitized emulsions can be manufactured on a commercial scale: the phosphor is introduced into the emulsion layer during the manufacturing process. Plates can also be sensitized under laboratory conditions. A plate sensitive to visible light is immersed in a phosphor solution and then dried; this treatment renders it sensitive to short-wave radiation. One of the commonest phosphors—sodium salicylate—is used in nearly saturated methanolic or ethanolic solutions (5–10%).

The phosphor layer also can be applied by spraying with the appropriate solution. This gives a more homogeneous and denser layer than that obtained by immersion. A uniform layer applied by spraying has but an insignificant effect on the resolving power of the emulsion, which diminishes as thicker layers are used [89].

Absolute measurements require accurate claibration of the emulsions: the exact exposures corresponding to various photographic densities should be determined. The photographic density, however, also depends on a variety of ancillary factors, which are difficult to take into consideration. The application of these calibration methods is therefore permissible only if the standard exposures are developed simultaneously with the photographs of the source spectra whose lines are to be measured. Preliminary calibration of the emulsion generally leads to considerable errors, but it may nevertheless prove useful for tentative estimates. Data obtained for SWR emulsion show that the sensitivity is constant between 1200 and 3700 Å, reaching a few tens of ergs per square centimeter for moderate densities [84a].

Photoemulsion has a lower sensitivity than a photoelectric detector, since the photocathode quantum yield is generally much greater than the quantum yield of a photoemulsion. Moreover, photoelectric detectors are mostly linear, and therefore do not require special calibration, which is unfortunately unavoidable in the case of photoemulsions. Because of these considerations, photomultipliers are always preferred for intensity measurements in few spectral regions. If, however, a wide range of wavelengths has to be recorded simultaneously (so as to obtain an overall energy distribution of the spectrum), photographic emulsions prove most efficacious.

## 26. IONIZATION DETECTORS

Relative and absolute brightness measurements with the aid of ionization chambers are based on the photoionization of the filling gas by the incident radiation.

The general principles of the design and operation of ionization chambers are found in special books (see, e.g., [89a]). Ionization chambers (or counters*) are generally filled with an electronegative gas ($I_2$, $Cl_2$, $Br_2$, NO), which increases the work function of the cathode metal and suppresses the ionization of the gas by the photoelectrons escaping from the cathode.

Ionization chambers are thus made sensitive only to radiation which causes photoionization of the filling gas.

There are both open and closed type ionization chambers. Closed ionization chambers are used only for photons of energies at which lithium fluoride is still transparent ($\lambda > 1050$ Å). Figure 165 is a diagram of a closed ionization chamber used by Watanabe et al. [90]. The chamber is 20 mm in diameter, with a photomultiplier casing.** It was placed in a metallic chamber coupled to the monochromator entrance slit. The chamber was closed with lithium fluoride windows. The platinum electrodes did not intercept the light beam; they were 4 cm long. The electrode potential difference was a few volts, and the saturation current was reached already for 4 V. The ionic current provides a measure of the incident monochromatic radiation.

If the absorption cross section and the photoionization quantum yield are known, the incident light flux can be calculated from the ionic current. Let $l$ be the length of the ionization chamber, $\sigma_1$ the photoionization cross section, $\sigma$ the total absorption cross section, $N_0$ the total number of photons incident in 1 sec, $N$ the total number of photons absorbed in 1 sec, $N_1$ the number of ion pairs forming in 1 sec over a length $l$ in the ionization chamber (this number is determined from the saturation current of the current-voltage characteristic of the chamber), $n_0$ the number of molecules in unit volume.

From the Lambert–Beer law,

$$N_0 = \frac{N}{1 - e^{-\sigma n_0 l}}. \tag{16}$$

---

\* All that follows is equally applicable to counters, as well as to ionization chambers, since the transition from the counting mode to the ionization chamber mode is only a question of the applied potential; the optical characteristics are not affected.

\*\* The photomultiplier is not used in light flux measurements. It is only required for measuring the photoionization quantum yield.

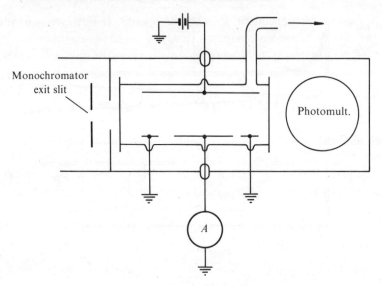

Figure 165

A diagram of a closed ionization chamber.

$N$ can be calculated from the relation

$$N = \frac{1}{\sigma_1/\sigma} N_1,$$   (17)

where $\sigma_1/\sigma$ is the photoionization quantum yield of the filling gas.

Relative measurements of flux intensities thus require knowledge of the absorption coefficient of the gas and of the photoionization quantum yield as a function of wavelength. Absolute measurements require knowledge of the absolute values of these two magnitudes.

In flux intensity measurements, the ionic current and the pressure in the ionization chamber are experimentally determined. There are measurement methods, however, which do not require knowledge of the chamber pressure. One of these is the total absorption method. Here the gas pressure and the ionization chamber length are taken so large that the exponential term in the denominator of equation (16) is ignorable, and we may take with fair accuracy $N_0 = N$. Since total absorption is attained for really large gas pressures and chamber lengths, double ion chambers are sometimes used: these chambers are suitable for flux intensity measurements at any gas pressure and do not require determination of the pressure. This arrangement is particularly important with open chambers, in which accurate pressure measurement is not easy.

Figure 166 is a diagram of an open double chamber [2]. The product $\sigma n_0$ entering equation (16) can be found after measuring the currents $I_1$ and $I_2$ in the

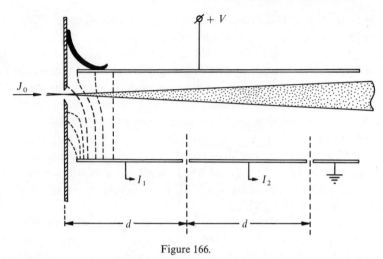

Figure 166.

A diagram of an kpen double ion chamber. Dashed curves mark the field lines; the top plate is at the potential of the entrance slit.

first and the second part of the double chamber. It is readily seen that

$$\sigma N_0 = (1/d) \ln (I_1/I_2), \tag{18}$$

where $d$ is the length of the measuring electrodes.

There should be no pressure fall inside the open double chamber. This is easily verified by comparing the experimental absorption cross sections found from equation (18) with the known cross sections for the given gas.

It is essential to make sure that all the electrons produced by the incident radiation reach the collector. In other words, the current-voltage characteristic of the chamber should be plotted and the saturation current conditions established. The current-voltage characteristic may prove to be without a plateau if the energy of the ionizing photons is more than double the ionization energy of the filling gas: in this case the free electron released by ionization still has a sufficient energy to continue ionizing the gas molecules. Hence it follows that a given ionization chamber is suitable for measurements in a fairly narrow spectral region.

The first measurements of radiation with photoionization chambers were carried out using NO as the filling gas [90].

NO is ionized at wavelengths shorter than 1350 Å. Between 1300 and 800 Å the photoionization quantum yield of NO is constant [90–92], reaching 81% [93, 94]. The determination of the photoionization quantum yield is a difficult experimental task, which requires absolute light flux measurements at the exit of the spectral instrument and after passage through the ionization chamber. These measurements are fairly complex and contain numerous sources of errors, and it is therefore advisable to make absolute energy measurements using ionization chambers filled with mon-atomic gases, whose ionization quantum yields are known.

The photoionization quantum yield of the inert gases above the ionization threshold was found to be unity [2, 95]; it was also seen to be independent of wave-length. Both these conclusions are in agreement with theoretical findings. This result is also applicable in the spectral region where autoionization is observed. For example the quantum yield of xenon at wavelengths between 920 and 1022 Å does not deviate appreciably from unity. Ionization chambers filled with inert gas will record radiation of wavelengths shorter than 1022 Å. Longer wavelengths (which are never-theless shorter than 1350 Å) use NO filled chambers, and still longer wavelengths require xylene vapor as the filling gas [96]. Other filling gases can also be used for ionization chambers [97–99].

Absolute intensity measurements in the vacuum ultraviolet are currently being made with Geiger counters [100–104]. Calibration and design features make these counters suitable for absolute intensity measurements, as described by Rumsh, Lukirskii et al. [100, 101] and also by Caruso and Neupert [104].

Geiger counters were originally used only for measurements of line intensities at wavelengths shorter than 100 Å. They are now applied on a wider scale, and are used in measurements of longer-wave radiations. The upper limit of measurable wave-lengths is at around 300 Å: there is an acute shortage of materials which are sufficiently transparent and durable at longer wavelengths [103].

Ionization chambers and counters are currently the most suitable detectors for absolute energy measurements in the vacuum ultraviolet.


## 27. FILTERING DETECTORS

Undispersed radiation is often measured in rocket-borne instruments with coun-ters and ionization chambers, which are used together with filters to isolate a rela-tively narrow spectral region [105]. The long-wave limit of the detected radiation is determined by the ionization potential of the filling gas, and the short-wave limit is fixed by the transmission threshold of the window material. Table 4 lists the charac-teristics of some typical chambers which are used for detection of undispersed radia-tion.

Given the ionization potentials of atoms and molecules [97, 99] and the trans-parency thresholds of various materials, one can select ionization chambers for other spectral regions, too. No material is sufficiently transparent between 1000 and 100 Å if used in thick layers, but thin films of aluminum oxide, nitrocelluloid films, and SiO films a few hundreds and thousands of angstroms thick are transparent (see §10). Ionization chambers are very common and widespread radiation detectors.

We see from the table that the sensitive regions of most counters are sufficiently

Table 4 [38, 94, 96, 106]*

| Filling gas | Window material | Sensitive range, Å | Quantum yield, rel. units |
|---|---|---|---|
| Ethyl chloride** | LiF | 1050–1130 | — |
| Ethyl bromide** | LiF | 1050–1200 | — |
| Hydrogen sulfide** | LiF | 1050–1240 | 0.50–0.60 |
| Acetone** | LiF | 1050–1290 | — |
| Nitrogen oxide**, † | LiF | 1050–1350 | 0.30–0.40 |
| Ethylene oxide | LiF | 1050–1180 | 0.10–0.20 |
| Iodine†† | LiF | 1050–1260 | — |
| Acetone** | $CaF_2$ | 1230–1290 | 0.08–0.10 |
| Nitrogen oxide** | $CaF_2$ | 1230–1350 | 0.20–0.30 |
| Ethyl iodide** | $CaF_2$ | 1230–1330 | — |
| Benzene** | $CaF_2$ | 1230–1340 | — |
| Toluene** | $BaF_2$ | 1350–1410 | — |
| p-Xylene** | $BaF_2$ | 1350–1470 | — |
| Diethyl sulfide | $BaF_2$ | 1350–1480 | 0.10–0.20 |
| p-Xylene** | $\alpha Al_2O_3$ (sapphire) | 1420–1470 | — |
| Mesithylene** | $\alpha Al_2O_3$ (sapphire) | 1420–1480 | — |

\* In quantum yield calculations, the quantim yield of NO at $\lambda = 1216$ Å was taken as 81%; quantum yield data are borrowed from [106]. The quantum yields are given for the transmittance of a 1 mm thick window.

\*\* Curves of quantum yield vs. wavelength for these chambers can be found in [94].

† An ionization chamber of useful design is described in [106a].

†† Iodine vapor counters are described in [107]; the photoionization quantum yield for these counters is about 40%.

narrow, but to record isolated lines, even higher monochromaticity is required. This can be accomplished with the aid of gas filters (see §9).

Counters will also detect longer wavelengths than those listed in the table. As far as we know, the action of existing counters in the long-wave region of the spectrum is based on the photoeffect of the cathode material, and not on photoionization. In particular, radiation with wavelengths between 1725 and 2100 Å was recorded using a chamber filled with a mixture of ethylene and argon (each gas with a partial pressure of 10 T). A chromium–iron alloy cathode was used [108].

Radiation with wavelengths shorter than 1050 Å can be measured with open photon counters [96, 109]. The light in these counters passes through a pinhole ($\approx 0.1$ mm). To offset the effects of gas leakage through this pinhole, a continuous stream of gas is pumped into the counter. Inert gases are used as filling. Helium-filled chambers will detect radiation with wavelengths shorter than 504 Å, neon-filled chambers wavelengths shorter than 575 Å, and argon, krypton, and xenon, wavelengths shorter than 787 Å, 886 Å, and 1022 Å, respectively. Successive application of counters filled with various gases makes it possible to measure light fluxes in very narrow spectral intervals.

Counters or ionization chambers will measure the energy within a certain spectral interval or even a single spectral line, if the wavelength region filtered by the counter accommodates one line only. The line intensity can be determined with sufficient accuracy if the ionization chamber is calibrated with a thermocouple or by any other method.

Absolute energy measurements within a wide spectral region are not as accurate, because the counter efficiency varies with wavelength due to variation of the window transmittance at various wavelengths.

The spectrum of undispersed radiation can also be taken with thermophosphors and photomultipliers. Thus, a thermophosphor with a red threshold at 1340 Å was used to record the short wave ultraviolet radiation of the Sun [67]. The measurements were carried out with the following filters: a $CaF_2$ filter isolated the wavelengths 1230–1340 Å; LiF filter, 1040–1340 Å; Be filter, $\lambda < 8$ Å; without filters, the device responded to all wavelengths shorter than 1340 Å. Various filter combinations permitted measuring radiation in different spectral regions. These measurements were not excessively accurate, but they provided adequate information on the distribution of solar energy in this region. The short-wave radiation of the Sun was also studied with an open-type secondary emission multiplier with a $BeO–SrF_2–MgO$ photocathode [110] with a red threshold at 1400 Å. Narrow spectral regions were defined with the following filters: Cr (2–6 Å), Be (1–8 Å), Al (8–20 Å), $(CF_2)_n$ (18–23 Å), $(CH)_n$ (44–100 Å), B (67–120 Å), Be film (110–200 Å), Sn film (500–700 Å), LiF and $CaF_2$ for $L_\alpha$.

A convenient method for recording the He 304 Å line was proposed by Samson and Cairns [111]. The $L_\alpha$ and He I 584 Å lines were excited simultaneously in the source. A carbon film attenuated the 584 Å line to 1/30 of the 304 Å line and totally absorbed all longer wavelengths. The phosphor with a response peak at 300 Å acted as an additional filter.*

Undispersed radiation can be recorded by the original method of "nonoptical spectrophotometry" [39]. As we have noted above, application of a negative potential to the grid between the cathode and the dynode substantially alters the spectral response curve of the photomultiplier. The dependence of photocurrent on the stopping potential provides an indication of the photon flux hitting the photocathode.

If a small-sized cathode is placed at the center of a spherical electrode, differentiation of the current-voltage characteristic will give the energy distribution of the photoelectrons. However, because of experimental difficulites, planar electrodes are

---

* Various filters for isolating individual bands in the vacuum ultraviolet are also discussed in §9 and §10.

generally used, and the electron energy distribution measured in this geometry corresponds to the velocity components normal to the plate electrodes. This is a so-called "normal" distribution, which depends on the composition of the incident radiation. These considerations constitute the basis for the high-response detector (Figure 167) designed by Hinteregger et al. [112–114]. The device uses an electron

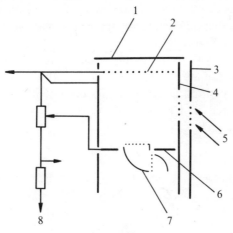

Figure 167

A diagram of a detector which combines an open photomultiplier and an analyzer with a stopping grid potential:

1) cathode,   2) grid at negative potential,   3) screen protecting from ions,   4) electrostatic protection screen,   5) radiation,   6) focusing electrode,   7) first dynode,   8) voltage divider.

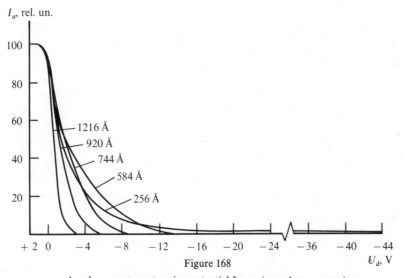

Figure 168

Anode current vs. stopping potential for various photon energies.

multiplier with a beryllium–copper cathode and an analyzer with a stopping potential between the grid and the cathode. The grid is set parallel to the cathode.

Figure 168 shows current-voltage characteristics for photons of various energies. Differentiation of these characteristics gives the electron velocity distribution at various wavelengths (Figure 169). The actual differentiation procedure is described in [113]. Even monochromatic light produces a fairly wide distribution of photoelectron energies, but qualitative information can be derived from the characteristics of the type shown in Figure 168.

The method of nonoptical spectrophotometry had been applied to measure the intensity of solar radiation before any of the other methods came into being. The applications of various detectors to measurements of relative and absolute intensities are discussed in Chapter VI.

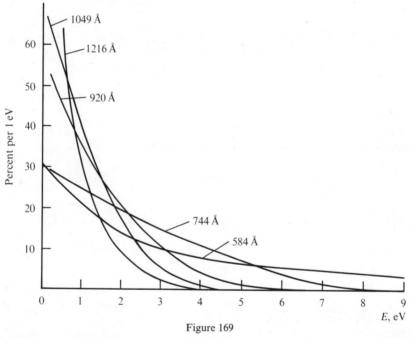

Figure 169

Relative "normal" distribution of photoelectrons from a tungsten cathode for various photon energies.

# BIBLIOGRAPHY

1. JOHNSTON, R.G. and R.P. MADDEN. *Appl. Optics*, **4**, 1574 (1965).
2. SAMSON, J.A.R. *J. Opt. Soc. America*, **54**, 6 (1964).
3. PACKER, D.M. and C. LOCK. *J. Opt. Soc. America*, **41**, 699 (1951).
4. CHECHIK, N.O., S.M. FAINSHTEIN, and T.M. LIVSHITS. *Elektronnye umnozhiteli (Electron Multipliers)*, p. 440. Gostekhizdat. 1957.
5. GYEMANT, A. *Z. Phys.*, **26**, 223 (1924).
6. BOLDT, G. and W.S. COOPER. *Z. Naturforsch.*, **19a**, 968 (1964).
7. LEMONNIER, J.C., M. PRIOL, A. QUEMERAIS, and S. ROBIN. *J. phys. et radium*, **25**, 79A (1964).
8. MASLEN, V.W., N.E. WHITE, and S.E. WILLIAMS. *Brit. J. Appl. Phys.*, **4**, 303 (1953).
9. JOHNSON, F.S., K. WATANABE, and R. TOUSEY. *J. Opt. Soc. America*, **41**, 702 (1951).
10. WATANABE, K. and E.C.Y. INN. *J. Opt. Soc. America*, **43**, 32 (1953).
11. KNAPP, R.A. and A.M. SMITH. *Appl. Optics*, **3**, 637 (1964).
12. THURNAU, D.H. *J. Opt. Soc. America*, **46**, 346 (1956).
13. HAMMANN, J.F. *Z. angew. Phys.*, **10**, 187 (1958).
14. SLAWIN, W., R.W. MOONEY, and D.T. PALUMBO. *J. Opt. Soc. America*, **51**, 93 (1961).
15. CONKLIN, R.L. *J. Opt. Soc. America*, **49**, 669 (1959).
16. EPSHTEIN, M.I. *Pribory i Tekhnika Eksperimenta*, No.3, 118 (1961).
17. BRUNET, M., M. CANTIN, C. JULLIOT, and J. VASSEUR. *J. phys. et radium*, **24**, 53A (1963).
18. KNAPP, R.A. *Appl. Optics*, **2**, 1334 (1963).
19. ALLISON, R., J. BURNS, and A.J. TUZZOLINO. *J. Opt. Soc. America*, **54**, 1381 (1964).
20. VASSEUR, J. and M. CANTIN. *Communication présentée à XIe Colloque Intern. de Spectroscopie, Belgrad*, 1963.
21. KRISTIANPOLLER, N. and R. KNAPP. *Appl. Optics*, **3**, 915 (1964).
22. SEYA, M. and F. MASUDA. *Sci. of Light*, **12**, 9 (1963).
23. NYGAARD, K.J. *Brit. J. Appl. Phys.*, **15**, 597 (1964).
24. ALLISON, R., J. BURNS, and A.J. TUZZOLINO. *J. Opt. Soc. America*, **54**, 747 (1964).
25. KRISTIANPOLLER, N. *J. Opt. Soc. America*, **54**, 1285 (1964).
26. STUDER, F.J. *J. Opt. Soc. America*, **55**, 613 (1965).
27. NYGAARD, K.J. *J. Opt. Soc. America*, **55**, 944 (1965).
28. INOKUCHI, H., Y. HARADA, and T. KONDOW. *J. Opt. Soc. America*, **54**, 842 (1964).
29. UCHIDA, Y. *Appl. Optics*, **3**, 799 (1964).
30. KRISTIANPOLLER, N. and D. DUTTON. *Appl. Optics*, **3**, 287 (1964).
31. CORRIGAN, S.J.B. and A. VON ENGEL. *Proc. Roy. Soc.*, **A245**, 335 (1958).
32. DUNKELMAN, L. and C. LOCK. *J. Opt. Soc. America*, **41**, 802 (1951).
32a. HUFFMAN, R.E., J.C. LARRABEE, and D. CHAMBERS. *Appl. Optics*, **4**, 1145 (1965).
32b. LINCKE, R. and G. PALUMBO. *Appl. Optics*, **4**, 1677 (1965).
33. ALLEN, J.S. *Rev. Scient. Instrum.*, **18**, 739 (1947).
34. DUNKELMAN, L. *J. Opt. Soc. America*, **45**, 134 (1955).
35. DUNKELMAN, L., W.B. FOWLER, and J. HENNES. *Appl. Optics*, **1**, 695 (1962).
36. TYUTIKOV, A.M. *Radiotekhnika i Elektronika*, **4**, 1884 (1959).

37. SHUBA, YU.A., A.M. TYUTIKOV, and O.M. SOROKIN. *Iskusstvennye Sputniki Zemli*, No.10, 55 (1961).

38. DUNKELMAN, L. *J. Quant. Spectr. Rad. Trans.*, **2**, 533 (1962).

39. HINTEREGGER, H.E. and K. WATANABE. *J. Opt. Soc. America*, **43**, 604 (1953).

40. SOROKIN, O.M. *Optika i Spektroskopiya*, **16**, 139 (1964).

41. WALKER, W.C., O.P. RUSTGI, and G.L. WEISSLER. *J. Opt. Soc. America*, **49**, 471 (1959).

41a. HINTEREGGER, H.E. *Space Astrophysics*, W. Liller, Editor, McGraw-Hill. N.Y. 1961.

42. WALKER, W.C., N. WAINFAN, and G.L. WEISSLER. *J. Appl. Phys.*, **26**, 1366 (1955).

43. WEISSLER, G.L. *Handbuch der Physik*, S. Flügge, Editor, **XXI**, 304. 1956.

44. WHEATON, J.E.G. *J. Opt. Soc. America*, **54**, 1287 (1964).

45. CHILDS, C.B. *J. Opt. Soc. America*, **51**, 583 (1961).

46. PATCH, R.W. *Rev. Scient. Instrum.*, **32**, 982 (1961).

47. BYRAM, E.T., T.A. CHUBB, and H. FRIEDMAN. *J. Geophys. Res.*, **66**, 2095 (1961).

48. LUKIRSKII, A.P., M.A. RUMSH, and I.A. KARPOVICH. *Optika i Spektroskopiya*, **9**, 653 (1960).

49. LUKIRSKII, A.P., M.A. RUMSH, and L.A. SMIRNOV. *Optika i Spektroskopiya*, **9**, 511 (1960).

50. RUMSH, M.A., A.P. LUKIRSKII, and V.N. SHCHEMELEV. *Doklady AN SSSR*, **135**, 55 (1960).

51. HEROUX, L., J.E. MANSON, H.E. HINTEREGGER, and W.J. MCMAHON. *J. Opt. Soc. America*, **55**, 103 (1965).

51a. SAMSON, J.A.R. and R.B. CAIRNS. *Rev. Scient. Instrum.*, **37**, 338 (1966).

52. HEROUX, L. and H.E. HINTEREGGER. *Rev. Scient. Instrum.*, **31**, 280 (1960).

53. GOODRICH, G.W. and W.C. WILEY. *Rev. Scient. Instrum.*, **32**, 846 (1961).

54. TOUSEY, R. *Appl. Optics*, **1**, 679 (1962).

55. LINCKE, R. and T.D. WILKERSON. *Rev. Scient. Instrum.*, **33**, 911 (1962).

56. TUZZOLINO, A.J. *Phys. Rev.*, **134**, 205 (1964),

57. TUZZOLINO, A.J. *Rev. Scient. Instrum.*, **35**, 1332 (1964).

57a. DAVIS, R.J. and O.P. RUSTGI. *Appl. Optics*, **1**, 131 (1962).

58. SKORINKO, G., D.D. DOUGHTY, and W.A. FEIBELMAN. *Appl. Optics*, **1**, 717 (1962).

59. MISHCHENKO, E.D., S.A. KULIKOV, and G.P. STARTSEV. *Tezisy dokladov na XVI soveshchanii po spektroskopii*, 1965 *(Summaries of Reports to the XVI Conference on Spectroscopy)*, p. 58. 1965.

60. WATANABE, K. *Phys. Rev.*, **83**, 785 (1951).

61. ARKHANGEL'SKAYA, V.A., B.I. VAINBERG, and T.K. RAZUMOVA. *Optika i Spektroskopiya*, **1**, 1018 (1956).

62. GOPSHTEIN, N.M. and F.Z. PEDOS. *Zav. Lab.*, **16**, 1264 (1950).

63. GERASIMOVA, N.G. and D.A. GUSEV. *Optiko-mekhanicheskaya Promyshlennost'*, No.30, 25 (1965).

64. YAKOVLEV, S.A. and G.A. VOLKOVA. *Zh. Prikl. Spektr.*, **2**, 363 (1965).

65. ARKHANGEL'SKAYA, V.A., N.G. GERASIMOVA, E.I. KRASNOVA, T.K. RAZUMOVA, and A.V. YAKOVLEVA. *Optiko-mekhanicheskaya Promyshlennost'*, No.12, 7 (1962).

66. KAZACHEVSKAYA, T.V., V.A. ARKHANGEL'SKAYA, G.S. IVANOV-KHOLODNYI, V.S. MEDVEDEV, T.K. RAZUMOVA, and A.V. CHUDAIKIN. *Iskusstvennye Sputniki Zemli*, No.15, 71 (1963).

67. TOUSEY, R., K. WATANABE, and J.D. PURCELL. *Phys. Rev.*, **83**, 792 (1951).

68. ARKHANGEL'SKAYA, V.A. and T.K. RAZUMOVA. *Optika i spektroskopiya (Optics and Spectroscopy)*. In: *Lyuminestsentsiya*, p. 299. 1963.
69. NOSENKO, B.M., L.S. REVZIN, and V.YA. YASKOLKO. *Optika i Spektroskopiya*, **3**, 345 (1957).
70. VAUGHAN, W.E. and W.A. NOYES. *J. Amer. Chem. Soc.*, **52**, 559 (1930).
71. WARNECK, P. *Appl. Optics*, **1**, 721 (1962).
72. GROTH, W. *Z. phys. Chem.*, **B37**, 307 (1937).
73. JUCKER, H. and E.K. RIDEAL. *J. Chem. Soc.*, 1058 (1957).
74. FEATES, F.S., B. KNIGHT, and E.W.T. RICHARDS. *Spectrochim. acta*, **18**, 485 (1962).
75. WIIG, E.O. and G.B. KISTIAKOWSKY. *J. Amer. Chem. Soc.*, **54**, 1806 (1932).
76. FORBES, G.S. and L.J. HEIDT. *J. Amer. Chem. Soc.*, **56**, 2363 (1934).
77. ZELIKOFF, M. and L.M. ASHCHENBRAND. *J. Chem. Phys.*, **22**, 1680 (1954).
78. ZELIKOFF, M. and L.M. ASCHENBRAND. *J. Chem. Phys.*, **22**, 1685 (1954).
79. NOYES, W.A. *J. Chem. Phys.*, **5**, 807 (1937).
80. SAUER, M.C. and L.M. DORFMAN. *J. Chem. Phys.*, **35**, 497 (1961).
81. OKABE, H. and J.R. McNESBY. *J. Chem. Phys.*, **36**, 601 (1962).
82. BECKEY, H.D., W. GROWTH, H. OKABE, and H.J. ROMMEL. *Z. Naturforsch.*, **19a**, 1511 (1964).
83. STRONG, J. *Procedures in Experimental Physics*. New York, Prentice-Hall. 1953.
84. SCHOEN, A.L. and E.S. HODGE. *J. Opt. Soc. America*, **40**, 23 (1950).
84a. FOWLER, W.K., W.A. RENSE, and W.R. SIMMONS. *Appl. Optics*, **4**, 1596 (1965).
85. EDLÉN, B. *Rep. Progr. Phys.*, **26**, 190 (1963).
86. UVAROVA, V.M., N.K. SUKHODREV, A.A. PANKOVA, M.R. SHPOL'SKII, and A.N. KOVANOVA. *Izvestiya AN SSSR*, phys. ser., **26**, 967 (1962).
87. MOROZOVA, N.G. and G.P. STARTSEV. *ZhNPFK*, **10**, 22 (1965).
88. KALINKINA, T.A., A.N. OSHURKOVA, A.A. PANKOVA, V.M. UVAROVA, G.I. CHISTOVA, and M.R. SHPOL'SKII. *Zh. Prikl. Spektr.*, **2**, 475 (1965).
88a. KALINKINA, T.A., A.N. KOVANOVA, A.A. PANKOVA, N.K. SUKHODREV, V.M. UVAROVA, and M.R. SHPOL'SKII. *ZhNPFK*, **9**, 286 (1964).
89. ALLISON, R. and J. BURNS. *J. Opt. Soc. America*, **55**, 574 (1965).
89a. VEKSLER, V., L. GORSHEV, and B. ISAEV. *Ionizatsionnye metody issledovaniya izluchenii (Ionization Methods in Radiation Studies)*. Gostekhizdat. 1950.
90. WATANABE, K., F.F. MARMO, and E.C.Y. INN. *Phys. Rev.*, **91**, 1155 (1953).
91. WATANABE, K. *J. Chem. Phys.*, **22**, 1564 (1954).
92. WALKER, W.C. and G.L. WEISSLER. *J. Chem. Phys.*, **23**, 1962. (1955).
93. WATANABE, K. and F.M. MATSUNAGA. Unpublished papers (cited in [94]).
94. CARVER, J.H. and P. MITCHELL. *J. Scient. Instrum.*, **41**, 555 (1964).
95. MATSUNAGA, F.M., R.S. JACKSON, and K. WATANABE. *J. Quant. Spectr. Rad. Trans.*, **5**, 329 (1965).
96. *Rriedman*, H. *Space Astrophysics*. W. Liller, Editor, McGraw-Hill. N.Y. 1961.
97. WATANABE, K., T. NAKAYAMA, and J.R. MOTTL. *J. Quant. Spectr. Rad. Trans.*, **2** 369 (1962).
98. WEISSLER, G.L., J.A.R. SAMSON, M. OGAWA, and G.R. COOK. *J. Opt. Soc. America*, **49**, 338 (1959).
99. VILESOV, F.I. *Uspekhi Fizicheskikh Nauk*, **81**, 669 (1963).

100. RUMSH, M.A., A.P. LUKIRSKII, I.A. KARPOVICH, and V.N. SHCHEMELEV. *Pribory i Tekhnika Eksperimenta,* No.5, 67 (1960).

101. LUKIRSKII, A.P., M.A. RUMSH, and L.A. SMIRNOV. *Optika i Spektroskopiya,* **9**, 505 (1960).

102. EDERER, D.L. and D.H. TOMBOULIAN. *Phys. Rev.,* **133A**, 1525 (1964).

103. EDERER, D.L. and D.H. TOMBOULIAN. *Appl. Optics,* **3**, 1073 (1964).

104. CARUSO, A.J. and W.M. NEUPERT. *Appl. Optics,* **4**, 247 (1965).

105. CHUBB, T.A. and H. FRIEDMAN. *Rev. Scient. Instrum.,* **26**, 493 (1955).

106. STOBER, A.K., R. SCOLNIK, and J.P. HENNES. *Appl. Optics,* **2**, 735 (1963).

106a. DIMITRIEV, A.B., V.V. KATYUSHINA, and L.S. SOROKIN. *Pribory i Tekhnika Eksperimenta,* No.4, 81 (1964).

107. BRACKMANN, R.T., W.L. FITE, and K.E. HAGEN. *Rev. Scient. Instrum.,* **29**, 125 (1958).

108. FRIEDMAN, H., S.W. LICHTMAN, and E.T. BYRAM. *Phys. Rev.,* **83**, 1025 (1951).

109. FRIEDMAN, H. *Physics of the Upper Atmosphere,* J.A. Ratcliffe, Editor, p. 155. New York. 1960.

110. EFREMOV, A.I., A.L. PODMOSHENSKII, I.M. PRIBYLOVSKII, and V.S. PETROV. *Optiko-mekhanicheskaya Promyshlennost',* No.3, 28 (1964).

111. SAMSON, J.A.R. and R.B. CAIRNS. *Appl. Optics,* **4**, 915 (1965).

112. HINTEREGGER, H.E., K.R. DAMON, and L.A. HALL. *J. Geophys. Res.,* **64**, 961 (1959).

113. HINTEREGGER, H.E. *Vistas in Astronautics,* M. Alperin, M. Stern, and H. Wooster, Editors, **1**, 146. Pergamon. 1958.

114. HEROUX, L. and H.E. HINTEREGGER. *Appl. Optics,* **1**, 701 (1962).

CHAPTER V

# Wavelength Measurements

## 28. LINE IDENTIFICATION

The spectral lines in the vacuum ultraviolet are identified fundamentally by the same methods as in the visible. However, even the application of the simplest line identification methods involves a number of specific difficulties in the vacuum ultraviolet.

Tentative identification can be accomplished using standard tables and atlases, but these unfortunately are in very short supply for the vacuum ultraviolet [1, 2, 2a]. They greatly facilitate the identification, especially if the atlas has been compiled for a spectrograph of the same type as the one actually used to photograph the spectrum.

If no identified spectra in the vacuum ultraviolet are available, tentative identification can be made by taking a spectrogram of Al III say,* or recording the emission of the positive column of a glow discharge in helium with inert gas impurities. Under these conditions, the only lines in the vacuum ultraviolet are the resonance lines of the inert gases.

In the absence of adequate atlases, the simplest methods of spectrum identification in the vacuum ultraviolet are the ones using wavelength standards and the overlapping of successive orders.

---

* The spectrum of Al III is readily excited in a low-voltage vacuum spark and gives characteristic doublets.

### Wavelength standards

Two spectra are photographed on the same part of the plate, the spectrum of element *B*, whose wavelengths are to be used as a standard,* and the spectrum of element *A*. The lines in the spectrum of element *A* are identified in reference to the lines of element *B*. Both sources should illuminate the same area on the grating, since otherwise ruling defects and possible misalignment of the instrument will displace the two spectra. If the spectrum lies near the normal to the grating, the instrumental dispersion can be taken as constant within narrow spectral regions and linear interpolation may be applied (see equation (5)). For large diffraction angles, the dispersion is a function of wavelength. Linear interpolation is therefore permissible only if very close spectral lines are observed. For diffraction angles close to 90°, the second derivative of wavelength with respect to arc length,

$$\frac{d^2\lambda}{ds^2} = -\frac{d \cdot \sin \beta}{kR^2} \tag{19}$$

(*d* is the grating constant, $\beta$ is the diffraction angle, *R* is the radius of curvature of the grating, *k* is the order of the spectrum), is constant and quadratic interpolation can therefore be used. For intermediate cases, i.e., for diffraction angles large enough for $d\lambda/ds$ to be variable and yet small enough for $d^2\lambda/ds^2$ not to be constant, cubic interpolation is recommended [3]. A useful equation for calculations is [4]

$$k\lambda = \lambda_0 - d \cdot \sin \frac{s_0 - s}{R}, \tag{20}$$

where $s_0$ and $s$ are measured for a line near the normal to the grating and for the unknown line; they correspond to $\lambda_0$ and $\lambda$, respectively. Three lines with known wavelengths in the spectrum make it possible to find three unknown parameters $\lambda_0$, $s_0$, and *d*. Once these parameters have been found, the wavelength of the unknown line can be determined.

The identification procedure is illustrated by the calculation of the diffraction angles for the DFS-6 instrument carried out in [5].

### Overlapping of successive orders

The wavelengths of the lines in the vacuum ultraviolet were measured by Lyman making use of the fact that the lines of short wavelengths observed in spectra of higher orders overlap with lines of longer wavelengths observed in lower orders. For example, the diffraction angle of the 4000 Å line in the spectrum of the first order is equal to the diffraction angle of the 1000 Å line in the spectrum of the fourth order (see §14).

---

* Wavelength standards are determined by calculation (see §29).

Normals accurately measured in the visible spectrum therefore can be used to measure the wavelengths of lines in the vacuum ultraviolet. Two spectra are photographed on the same plate: a comparison spectrum together with the unknown spectrum. If the comparison spectrum is produced by elements commonly present in a gas discharge, e.g., carbon or nitrogen, it is superimposed on the unknown spectrum, and the line wavelengths are found by interpolation. If, on the other hand, the comparison spectrum is photographed from a separate source and direct superposition of the two spectra may interfere with proper identification, the comparison spectrum is isolated by a special diaphragm mounted in front of the photographic plate or in front of the slit, at such a distance that its edges are sharply imaged in the focal plane (see §15).

Wavelength measurements using comparison lines in a spectrum of a different order may lead to certain errors, since spectra of different orders are sometimes focused on different surfaces, which are slightly displaced relative to each other. Moreover, asymmetry of the instrumental line contour may lead to an apparent shift of the spectral lines in spectra of different orders. The errors associated with these effects hardly exceed 0.1–0.01 Å, but in precision measurements even these small errors are inadmissible. To avoid these errors, the method of overlapping orders should be used in combination with the method of standard wavelengths. We photograph on one plate the unknown spectrum of element $A$, the spectrum of element $B$ for which the line wavelengths in the vacuum ultraviolet have been calculated, and the spectrum of element $C$ for which the line wavelengths in the visible are known and whose first-order spectrum overlaps with the lines of elements $A$ and $B$ in second, third, and higher orders. The wavelengths of the lines of element $B$ are then determined in reference to the lines of element $C$; the results of this determination are compared with the calculated wavelengths, and this procedure gives a correction curve. The lines of element $A$ are then corrected in accordance with the readings of this curve, or else it is established that the corrections are negligible.

Kelly's is the only set of tables of spectral lines in the vacuum ultraviolet [6]. Lines of numerous elements can be found in Moore's tables [7] and in the tables in [8, 9]. The wavelengths of all the lines of the isoelectronic series from H I to Ca XX, inclusive, are given in the paper by Garcia and Mack [9a]. Tables listing the wavelengths of all the light elements and their ions [3] are reproduced at the end of this chapter (see Table 7). A supplementary list of references on the spectra of elements is also given at the end of the chapter. The list includes sources published from 1940 to 1965. A similar list of references covering the period prior to 1940 will be found in Boyce's review [10].

## 29. WAVELENGTH STANDARDS

Interferometric methods are hardly used for wavelength measurements in the vacuum ultraviolet. There is only one report, published in 1936, describing the measurement of the wavelengths of the Cu II lines from 1488 to 1621 Å with a reflection echelon [11].

It is clear from the preceding discussion that the wavelength standards derived from the overlapping of successive orders are unreliable, since the spectra are invariably shifted one relative to the other and certain corrections must be introduced into the measured wavelengths if we are to obtain true standards. The corrections are based on calculated ultraviolet standards (see below).

It is therefore absolutely essential to find some independent method for the determination of wavelength standards in the vacuum ultraviolet, which does not call for measurements in that part of the spectrum. Suitable standards are provided by lines whose wavelengths can be calculated from Ritz's combination principle or from the Dirac–Sommerfeld theory of one-electron spectra.* The fundamental principles for the selection of wavelength standards in the vacuum ultraviolet are described in [3, 12, 13]. A formula for the calculation of the first seven lines in the Lyman series of H I, D I, He II, Li III, Be IV, B V, C VI, N VII, and O VIII is given in [3, 13]. Some of these lines have been adopted as wavelength standards.

This formula is written in the form

$$\lambda R \cdot 10^{-8} = \frac{1}{Z^2} \frac{n^2}{n^2 - 1} - \frac{\alpha^2}{4} \cdot \frac{n^4 - (8/3)n + 3}{(n^2 - 1)^2} + \tag{21}$$

$$+ \frac{8}{3\pi} \alpha^3 (7.489 - 2 \ln Z + 0.0526Z) \frac{n^4}{(n^2 - 1)^2}.$$

Here $\lambda$ is the wavelength in Å, $R$ is Rydberg's constant in cm$^{-1}$, corresponding to the mass of the given atom, $Z$ is the nuclear charge, $\alpha$ is the fine structure constant, $n$ is the principal quantum number.

Numerous standards have been obtained from Ritz's combination principle. Paschen was the first to suggest this idea for the selection of wavelength standards [14, 15].

Consider three energy levels $K, L, M$, with known wavenumbers for the corresponding transitions $L \rightarrow K$ and $M \rightarrow L$. The sum of the two wavenumbers gives the wavenumber of the transition $M \rightarrow K$. If this wavenumber corresponds to a line in the vacuum ultraviolet, it may be used as a standard. Spectral lines of any element that have been measured with sufficient accuracy and identified can be used as

---

* With Lamb shift correction (see §30).

wavelength standards. A factor to be remembered in wavenumber calculations is that the wavelengths of the $L \to K$ and $M \to L$ transitions are generally measured in the air, and the dispersion equation for dry standard air ($t = 155°C$, $p = 760$ T, 0.03% $CO_2$) should be used to obtain the corresponding wavelengths in vacuum:

$$(n - 1) \cdot 10^6 = 272.729 + 1.4814/\lambda^2 + 0.02039/\lambda^4, \tag{22}$$

where $\lambda$ is the wavelength in air, in microns; $n$ is the refractive index of dry air. For special tables for converting the wavelengths in air to wavenumbers, see [17].

As an example of the application of wavelength standards, let us consider Herzberg's standards used in the measurement of the wavelength of the deutrium $L_\alpha$ line (see §30) [18]. Herzberg's standards were provided by the lines of the principal singlet series of mercury.

The wavenumbers of the $6\ ^1S-n\ ^1P$ mercury line can be calculated from the combination principle by adding up the wavenumbers of the lines $6\ ^1S-6\ ^3P_1$, $6\ ^3P_1-7\ ^3S_1$, and $7\ ^3S_1-n\ ^1P$ or $6\ ^1S-6\ ^3P_1$, $6\ ^3P_1-7\ ^1S$, and $7\ ^1S-n\ ^1P$. The wavenumbers of the ultraviolet lines $6\ ^1S-n\ ^3P_1$ can be similarly calculated using the wavenumbers of the transitions $6\ ^1S-6\ ^3P_1$, $6\ ^3P_1-7\ ^3S$, and $7\ ^3S-n\ ^3P_1$.

The position of the $6\ ^3P_1$ level can be determined with fair accuracy from the 2537 Å mercury line, and the levels $7\ ^3S$ and $7\ ^1S$ correspond to the lines 4358 Å and 4078 Å (Figure 170). To find the energy of the level $7\ ^1P$, the wavenumber of the transition $7\ ^1P-n^1D$ should be subtracted from the sum of the wavenumbers of the transitions $6\ ^1S-6\ ^3P_1$ and $6\ ^3P_1-n\ ^1D$, i.e., the wavelengths can be calculated with great accuracy for each line of the series $6\ ^1S-n\ ^1P$ and $6\ ^1S-n\ ^3P$. Herzberg [18] gives a list of mercury lines in the visible spectrum which, if measured accurately, will provide us with appropriate wavelengths in the vacuum ultraviolet via the combination principle.

As another example, consider the standards for the measurement of the helium wavelengths [19]. The C II lines were used as standards. Thus, the following equality can be written for the 560 Å line (Figure 171):

$$\frac{1}{\lambda} = \frac{1}{2137} + \frac{1}{1760} + \frac{1}{1335};$$

and for the 595 Å line

$$\frac{1}{\lambda_1} = \frac{1}{2747} + \frac{1}{1760} + \frac{1}{1335}.$$

To determine the exact wavelengths of the two lines $\lambda = 595$ Å and $\lambda = 560$ Å we should thus measure with great precision the component wavelengths entering these two equalities. As no exact direct measurements of the 1760 Å and 1335 Å lines were available, they were determined by reference to the Mg II lines [20]. Alongside with the C II lines, the Ar II lines measured by reference to the N I lines were also used as standards.

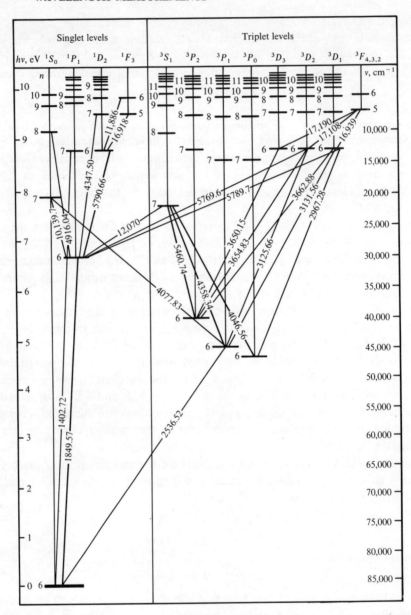

Figure 170

Energy level diagram of Hg I.

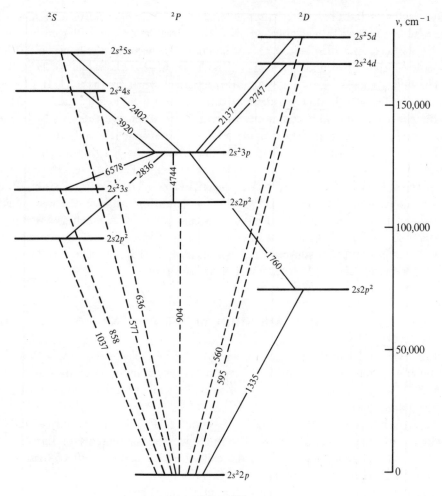

Figure 171

Level diagram of ionized carbon C II. Dashed transitions correspond to lines whose wavelengths have been determined from other standards.

Numerous examples of the application of Ritz's standards can be found in Edlén's review [13]. In particular, the wavelengths of the Ge II lines provide highly reliable standards between 1000 and 2000 Å. These standards have been repeatedly checked by experiment and theoretically [21–24].

Additional standards can be established from the calculated standards. For example, the wavelengths of Ge II, Ne II, Hg I, C I, and N I were measured in [24] using the Ge I lines between 1500 and 3060 Å as standards. Thus, 58 additional standards were introduced in the region between 1550 and 2049 Å. The measured wavelengths of the Ge II lines, supplemented by interferometric measurements in the visible region [23], established with considerable certainty the energy level profile of Ge II and thus added 23 new standards at wavelengths between 837 and 1966 Å, which show a good fit with the results of other measurements [25].

The new standards are highly useful in practical work, as these Ge II lines are readily excited in a hollow germanium cathode with a neon-filled tube. The lines of the elements which are commonly present in the discharge tube (C, N, Hg) are also readily excited, and they provide additional convenient standards.

The tables at the end of the chapter list the wavelengths of a number of elements which can be used as standards [13] (see Tables 8–19). The wavelengths are given to three, and occasionally even to four decimal places. This accuracy is not always attainable because of Stark effect broadening. Thus, for instance, the wavelengths of the Al III lines emitted by various sources may differ by as much as 1 Å [26]. It is therefore inadvisable to use the lines of multiply charged ions as standards, since they are only excited in sources with high electron and ion concentrations, where the Stark broadening and the Stark shift are substantial.

## 30. LAMB SHIFT MEASUREMENT

Unsurpassed accuracy in the measurement of line wavelengths in the vacuum ultraviolet has been attained by Herzberg in his determinations of the Lamb shift [18, 19, 27, 28]. Herzberg's classical work provided a vivid confirmation of the theory of the Lamb shift.

According to Dirac's theory, the $2\,{}^2S_{1/2}$ and $2\,{}^2P_{1/2}$ levels should coincide in hydrogen and hydrogen-like ions. The microwave measurements of Lamb et al. [29, 30] have established, however, the existence of a certain shift of these levels in both hydrogen and deuterium (Figure 172).

The shift of the S levels is given in the form [18, 31]

$$\Delta E(n,0) = \frac{8Z^4\alpha^3}{3\pi n^3}\,R\left(1 - \frac{3m}{M}\right) \times$$

$$\times \left\{ \ln\frac{mc^2}{2K_0(n,0)} + \frac{19}{30} + 3\pi Z\alpha\left[\frac{427}{384} - \frac{1}{2}\ln 2\right]\right\}, \tag{23}$$

where $n$ is the principal quantum number, $Z$ is the ion charge, $\alpha$ is the fine structure constant, $R$ is Rydberg's constant, $m$ is the electron mass, $M$ is the nuclear mass, $c$ is the velocity of light, $K_0(n,0)$ is the so-called average excitation energy. The shift is measured relative to the $P$ level.

The shift between $n\,{}^2S_{1/2}$ and $n\,{}^2P_{1/2}$ can be calculated from equation (23).

The validity of equation (23) had been borne out by numerous experiments (see

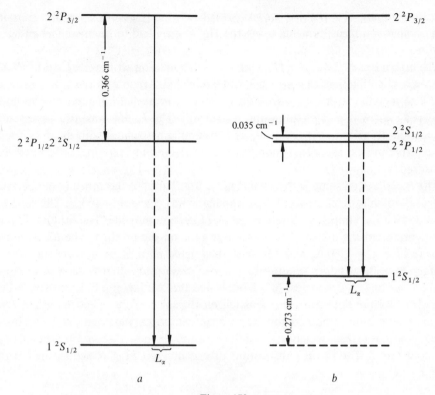

Figure 172

The lower levels of hydrogen:

*a* without Lamb shift;    *b* with Lamb shift accounted for.

[32–33], where references to earlier work are also given), but the check had been mainly made for $n \geq 2$, and Herzberg [18] was the first to determine the Lamb shift for the $1\,{}^2S$ level of atomic deuterium. The theory predicts a shift $\Delta E(1,0) = 0.272_6\,\mathrm{cm}^{-1}$. This shift could not be measured by rf spectroscopy, since the $1\,{}^2S_{1/2}$ level has no fine structure, and its position therefore is determined relative to the $2\,{}^2P_{1/2}$ level.

The verification of the theory involved measurements of the $L_\alpha$ wavelength with high accuracy. This line is made up of two components which correspond to the transitions $1\,{}^2S\text{–}2\,{}^2P_{1/2}$ and $1\,{}^2S\text{–}2\,{}^2P_{3/2}$. Herzberg succeeded in resolving these two components. The shift of the $1\,{}^2S$ level produced a shift of $0.0040\,\text{Å}$ in $L_\alpha$, and therefore the wavelength of $L_\alpha$ had to be measured to within better than $0.001\,\text{Å}$ if a reasonable estimate of the Lamb shift was to be obtained. The measurements were carried out in the fifth order of a three-meter vacuum spectrograph with $0.50\,\text{Å/mm}$ dispersion. The measurements required reliable comparison lines near $L_\alpha$.

The overlapping of successive orders was insufficiently accurate for this purpose, and comparison measurements using the $Hg^{198}$ lines had to be made (see previous section).

The high terms of the $6\,^1S-n\,^1P_1$ and $6\,^1S-n\,^3P$ emission series were hard to obtain, and the absorption lines therefore had to be recorded. Argon was added to a pressure of 7 T to mercury vapor, as without argon the mercury lines are too narrow to be observed even with a high-resolution instrument. The $L_\alpha$ line was also observed in absorption, so as to avoid the Doppler broadening associated with its emission. In these experiments, the absorption spectra of deuterium and mercury were thus measured.

The experimental setup is shown in Figure 173. Tube 8 is the continuous spectrum source (Lyman source, see §3). A 2 $\mu$F capacitor was charged to 16 kV. The tube was provided with a 3 mm bore capillary made of zirconium oxide. The lithium fluoride lens 3 projected the image of the discharge tube on the preslit 4. The focusing was adjusted for $\lambda = 1200$ Å, and the lens thus acted as a focal monochromator. A lithium fluoride window separating the two absorption chambers was mounted behind the slit 4. A cylindrical lens 5 prevented the overlapping of successive orders (see §14), and the light from this lens fell on the slit 6 of the spectrograph 7. Deuterium was produced electrolytically; atomic deuterium was then produced in the discharge tube 1, from which it was delivered into the first absorption tube through the cold trap 2. The second absorption tube contained 5 mg of the isotope $Hg^{198}$ and 7 T of argon.

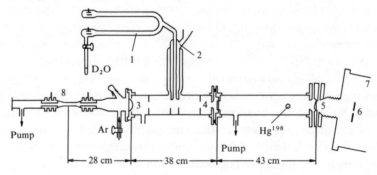

Figure 173

Experimental setup for the observation of the deuterium $L_\alpha$ and mercury standards in absorption spectrum.

The absorption spectra had to be photographed with very long exposures (of a few hours) because of the high dispersion and the low luminosity of the system; the flashes recurred every 2 sec. To ensure a higher accuracy, the spectrogram showed at the same time the second-order spectrum of iron near 3000 Å. The iron spectrum was shifted relative to the spectra of mercury and deuterium, as it was excited in a different source and photographed in a different order of the grating. The wavelengths of the mercury lines were measured in reference to the iron lines, and the measurement results were compared with the calculations based on Ritz's principle. This procedure gave a correction curve for various wavelengths, and the $L_\alpha$ wavelength could thus be determined with high precision.

The $L_\alpha$ wavelength was also measured by quadratic interpolation between the mercury lines. Both methods gave results differing by no more than 0.0002 Å. The deuterium $L_\alpha$ wavelength was found to be 1215.3378 $\pm$ 0.0003 Å, which corresponds to a Lamb shift of $0.26_2 \pm 0.03_8$ cm$^{-1}$. The theoretical value of the Lamb shift ($0.272_6$ cm$^{-1}$) coincides with the experimental figure within the margin of measuring error.

Herzberg [19] also measured the Lamb shifts for the ground level of the two helium isotopes He$^4$ and He$^3$. The problem was reduced to an exact determination of the ionization potentials of He$^4$ and He$^3$, and the wavelengths of three helium lines had to be measured with high precision: 591.4 Å (1 $^1S$–2 $^3P_1$), 584.3 Å (1 $^1S$–2 $^1P$), 537.0 Å (1 $^1S$–3 $^1P$) (Figure 174). Significant reabsorption of the last two lines was avoided by using a very low pressure discharge (about $10^{-3}$ T). An electrodeless discharge tube was used, with excitation at 2450 MHz or 10 MHz. Helium was diluted with argon (in a pressure ratio of 1:2), since in this mixture the discharge could be ignited at a lower pressure. The 591 Å line was excited at a substantially higher pressure; the exact pressure was changed from one experiment to the next and ranged from a few hundredths of a torr to several torr.

C II and Ar II lines between 610 and 520 Å were used as comparison lines. The spectra were photographed on a three-meter vacuum spectrograph with 0.25 and 0.23 Å/mm dispersion in the tenth and the eleventh orders of the diffraction grating. To prevent overlapping of lower orders, a preliminary dispersion grating was used [34a]. The wavelength measurement accuracy was improved by photographing an iron spectrum in the second order. The wavelengths of the C II and Ar II lines were determined from the iron lines and compared with the calculated wavelengths; the results were reduced to give a correction curve, which made it possible to improve on the helium lines measured by reference to the iron spectrum.

In addition to measuring the helium lines with upper levels 2 $^3P_1$, 2 $^1P_1$, and 3 $^1P_1$, it was necessary to find the ionization potentials of the corresponding excited helium atoms from the levels 2 $^3P_1$, 2 $^1P_1$, and 3 $^1P_1$. To this end, the wavelengths of a number of lines of the 3 $^3D$–$n$ $^3F$, 2 $^1P$–$n$ $^1D$, and 2 $^3P$–$n$ $^3D$ series were determined with high precision. The wavelengths of the lines in the vacuum ultraviolet were measured in the first and the second order of the six-meter diffraction spectrograph. From these measured wavelengths, the series limits could be calculated by the usual technique (see, e.g., [35]). In this way the ionization potentials of He$^4$ and He$^3$ were found. The results were compared with the ionization potentials calculated from the Dirac theory [36], and the Lamb shift of the ground level was thus determined. It was found

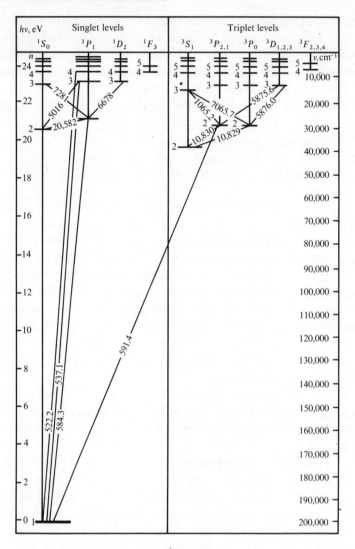

Figure 174

Level diagram of He I.

to be $(1.1_9 \pm 0.15)\,\mathrm{cm}^{-1}$ for $\mathrm{He}^4$ and $(1.2_3 \pm 0.15)\,\mathrm{cm}^{-1}$ for $\mathrm{He}^3$, whereas the calculated figure is $(1.3_3 \pm 0.2)\,\mathrm{cm}^{-1}$ for both isotopes (36, 37).

The Lamb shift of the ground level of the lithium ion was determined by Herzberg and Moore [27], who measured the ionization potential of the lithium ion from the ground level and compared it with the calculated value [32]. The measured Lamb shift was found to be $(8.0 \pm 3)\,\mathrm{cm}^{-1}$, whereas the theoretical shift is $7.8\,\mathrm{cm}^{-1}$ [36].

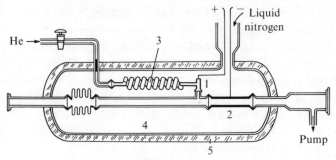

Figure 175

A discharge tube for the excitation of He II lines:

1) anode,  2) cathode,  3) cold trap,  4) liquid nitrogen,  5) glass wool.

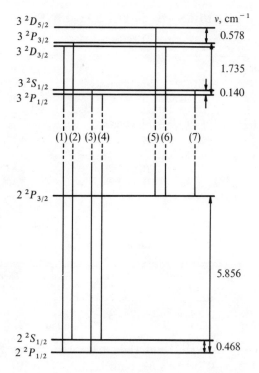

Figure 176

Transitions for the He II 1640 Å line.

Herzberg [28] also measured the Lamb shift of the $2\,^2S_{1/2}$ level of He II. To this end, he studied the fine structure of the 1640 Å He II line.* The scheme of transitions for this line is shown in Figure 176. The He II lines were excited in a hollow cathode with liquid nitrogen cooling. The tube is schematically shown in Figure 175.

The pressure in the discharge tube varied from 0.1 to 6 T. The entire tube was cooled by liquid nitrogen, and the outer envelope was wrapped in glass wool. The 1640 Å line was studied in fourth and fifth order, photographed on the three-meter vacuum spectrograph (dispersion 0.5–0.6 Å/mm). The exposure varied from 10 min to 4 hrs. Wavelength differences of the individual components were measured, and the results were compared with the theoretical values (see Table 5).

The fine structure of the 4686 Å He II line was also studied. Measurements of the fine structure of the two lines enabled a calculation of the Lamb shifts to be made (see Table 6). Table 6 compares Herzberg's data with the results of other authors [3].

Tables 7 through 19 list the calculated wavelengths of the spectral lines of various elements.

## TABLES OF SPECTRAL LINES

Table 5

| Components | Observed shift, cm$^{-1}$ | Term difference | Dirac theory, cm$^{-1}$ | Quantum electro-dynamics, |
|---|---|---|---|---|
| (1)–(2) | $0.47_7$ | $(2^2S_{1/2}-2^2P_{1/2})-(3^2P_{3/2}-3^2D_{3/2})$ | 0 | 0.4658 |
| (2)–(4) | $1.73_7$ | $3^2P_{3/2}-3^2P_{1/2}$ | 1.7312 | 1.7352 |
| (3)–(4) | $0.59_0$ | $(2^2S_{1/2}-2^2P_{1/2})+(3^2S_{1/2}-3^2P_{1/2})$ | 0 | 0.6082 |
| (3)–(7) | $5.85_8$ | $2^2P_{3/2}-2^2P_{1/2}$ | 5.8428 | 5.8563 |
| (5)–(7) | $2.19_6$ | $3^2D_{5/2}-3^2S_{1/2}$ | 2.3082 | 2.1711 |

Table 6

| Term difference | Herzberg [28] | Novick [32] | Series [33] | Theoretical [39] |
|---|---|---|---|---|
| $2^2S_{1/2}-2^2P_{1/2}$ | $0.48_0$ | 0.46842 | — | 0.4686 |
| $3^2S_{1/2}-3^2P_{1/2}$ | $0.14_7$ | — | 0.139 | 0.1396 |
| $4^2S_{1/2}-4^2P_{1/2}$ | $0.05_9$ | — | 0.067 | 0.0590 |

* The fine structure of this line was first studied by Chulanovskii and Mokhnatkin [38].

Table 7

SPECTRAL LINES OF THE LIGHT ELEMENTS

(in the order of decreasing wavelengths from 2000 Å)

| Wave-length | Inten-sity | Ion | Wave-length | Inten-sity | Ion | Wave-length | Inten-sity | Ion |
|---|---|---|---|---|---|---|---|---|
| 1990.530 | (5) | Al II | 1657.377 | (3) | C I | 1329.100 | (5) | C I |
| 1988.98 | (6) | Si I | 1657.007 | (15) | C I | 1329.086 | (4) | C I |
| 1935.88 | (5) | Al III | 1656.926 | (4) | C I | 1328.833 | (4) | C I |
| 1930.900 | (15) | C I | 1656.265 | (5) | C I | 1312.591 | (3) | Si III |
| 1901.34 | (10) | Si I | 1640.532 | (5) | He II | 1306.029 | (10) | O I |
| 1862.795 | (15) | Al III | 1640.332 | | | 1304.858 | (20) | O I |
| 1862.318 | (10) | Al II | 1624.37 | (5) | B II | 1303.323 | (7) | Si III |
| 1858.031 | (6) | Al II | 1624.16 | (4) | B II | 1302.168 | (30) | O I |
| 1855.928 | (2) | Al II | 1623.99 | (18) | B II | 1301.149 | (5) | Si III |
| 1854.720 | (30) | Al III | 1623.77 | (4) | B II | 1298.946 | (20) | Si III |
| 1852.47 | (5) | Si I | 1623.57 | (5) | B II | 1298.892 | (4) | Si III |
| 1850.68 | (10) | Si I | 1611.85 | (15) | Al III | 1296.726 | (5) | Si III |
| 1847.47 | (7) | Si I | 1605.75 | (8) | Al III | 1294.545 | (7) | Si III |
| 1845.510 | (5) | Si I | 1561.437 | (20) | C I | 1264.999 | (3) | Si II |
| 1826.400 | (10) | B I | 1561.340 | (4) | C I | 1264.735 | (30) | Si II |
| 1825.899 | (5) | B I | 1560.710 | (4) | C I | 1260.418 | (15) | Si II |
| 1816.923 | (10) | Si II | 1560.682 | (10) | C I | 1251,164 | (4) | Si II |
| 1808.004 | (5) | Si II | 1560.311 | (5) | C I | 1248.426 | (3) | Si II |
| 1776.307 | (6) | Be II | 1550.77 | (15) | C IV | 1247.383 | (3) | C III |
| 1776.100 | (3) | Be II | 1548.20 | (30) | C IV | 1246.738 | (2) | Si II |
| 1769.133 | (4) | Al I | 1533.427 | (20) | Si II | 1242.79 | (15) | N V |
| 1767.735 | (3) | Al II | 1526.701 | (10) | Si II | 1238.80 | (30) | N V |
| 1766.381 | (4) | Al I | 1512.419 | (1) | Be II | 1217.643 | (4) | O I |
| 1765.811 | (2) | Al II | 1512.407 | (9) | Be II | 1215.670 | (30) | H I |
| 1765.632 | (4) | Al I | 1512.269 | (5) | Be II | 1215.185 | (3) | He II |
| 1763.947 | (6) | Al II | 1494.668 | (10) | N I | 1215.088 | | |
| 1763.874 | (1) | Al II | 1492.812 | (2) | N I | 1206.555 | (10) | Si III |
| 1762.802 | (2) | Al I | 1492.615 | (20) | N I | 1206.500 | (30) | Si III |
| 1761.979 | (2) | Al II | 1491.765 | (2) | Be I | 1200.710 | (10) | N I |
| 1760.103 | (3) | Al II | 1417.237 | (3) | Si III | 1200.224 | (20) | N I |
| 1745.249 | (8) | N I | 1402.770 | (15) | Si IV | 1199.550 | (30) | N I |
| 1742.724 | (15) | N I | 1393.755 | (30) | Si IV | 1194.498 | (3) | Si II |
| 1724.97 | (20) | Al II | 1384.14 | (6) | Al III | 1193.286 | (2) | Si II |
| 1721.26 | (12) | Al II | 1379.67 | (3) | Al III | 1176.370 | (5) | C III |
| 1719.43 | (5) | Al II | 1371.29 | (5) | O V | 1175.987 | (4) | C III |
| 1718.52 | (5) | N IV | 1362.460 | (30) | B II | 1175.711 | (15) | C III |
| 1673.405 | (5) | Ar III | 1335.708 | (20) | C II | 1175.590 | (3) | C III |
| 1670.786 | (30) | Al II | 1335.663 | (2) | C II | 1175.263 | (4) | C III |
| 1669.666 | (9) | Ar III | 1334.532 | (10) | C II | 1174.933 | (5) | C III |
| 1661.478 | (8) | Be I | 1329.600 | (5) | C I | 1152.172 | (8) | O I |
| 1658.120 | (5) | C I | 1329.577 | (15) | C I | 1134.981 | (30) | N I |
| 1657.905 | (4) | C I | 1329.123 | (3) | C I | 1134.415 | (20) | N I |

Table 7 (continued)

| Wave-length | Inten-sity | Ion | Wave-length | Inten-sity | Ion | Wave-length | Inten-sity | Ion |
|---|---|---|---|---|---|---|---|---|
| 1134.166 | (10) | N I | 919.782 | (25) | Ar II | 787.710 | (15) | O IV |
| 1128.340 | (9) | Si IV | 916.703 | (20) | N II | 780.324 | (10) | Ne VIII |
| 1128.325 | (1) | Si IV | 916.015 | (8) | N II | 775.965 | (20) | N II |
| 1122.485 | (5) | Si IV | 915.962 | (4) | N II | 772.385 | (3) | N III |
| 1113.228 | (20) | Si III | 915.612 | (4) | N II | 771.901 | (2) | N III |
| 1109.965 | (12) | Si III | 904.480 | (3) | C II | 771.544 | (1) | N II |
| 1108.368 | (4) | Si III | 904.142 | (15) | C II | 770.409 | (20) | Ne VIII |
| 1085.701 | (30) | N II | 903.962 | (6) | C II | 769.152 | (15) | Ar III |
| 1085.546 | (5) | N II | 903.624 | (3) | C II | 765.140 | (30) | N IV |
| 1084.580 | (15) | N II | 901.162 | (9) | Ar IV | 764.357 | (10) | N III |
| 1084.562 | (5) | N II | 900.362 | (5) | Ar IV | 763.340 | (5) | N III |
| 1083.990 | (7) | N II | 894.310 | (5) | Ar I | 762.001 | (5) | O V |
| 1066.659 | (20) | Ar I | 887.404 | (10) | Ar III | 761.130 | (4) | O V |
| 1066.629 | (5) | Si IV | 883.179 | (8) | Ar III | 760.445 | (15) | O V |
| 1048.219 | (25) | Ar I | 879.622 | (6) | Ar III | 760.229 | (3) | O V |
| 1037.62 | (15) | O VI | 878.728 | (20) | Ar III | 759.440 | (4) | O V |
| 1037.018 | (15) | C II | 876.057 | (4) | Ar I | 758.677 | (5) | O V |
| 1036.337 | (8) | C II | 875.534 | (8) | Ar III | 745.322 | (7) | Ar II |
| 1036.319 | (5) | Be II | 871.099 | (10) | Ar III | 744.925 | (8) | Ar II |
| 1036.299 | (10) | Be II | 866.800 | (4) | Ar I | 743.718 | (12) | Ne I |
| 1031.93 | (30) | O VI | 858.559 | (4) | C II | 740.270 | (10) | Ar II |
| 1028.157 | (2) | O I | 858.092 | (2) | C II | 735.895 | (30) | Ne I |
| 1027.431 | (4) | O I | 850.602 | (25) | Ar IV | 730.929 | (5) | Ar II |
| 1025.762 | (6) | O I | 843.772 | (20) | Ar IV | 723.361 | (5) | Ar II |
| 1025.722 | (10) | H I | 840.029 | (15) | Ar IV | 718.562 | (20) | O II |
| 1010.374 | (8) | C II | 835.292 | (20) | O III | 718.484 | (30) | O II |
| 1010.092 | (5) | C II | 835.096 | (4) | O III | 715.65 | (3) | Ar V |
| 1009.862 | (3) | C II | 834.88 | (4) | Ar V | 715.60 | (4) | Ar V |
| 997.386 | (10) | Si III | 834.467 | (20) | O II | 713.81 | (10) | Ar VIII |
| 994.790 | (6) | Si III | 833.742 | (15) | O III | 709.197 | (5) | Ar V |
| 993.519 | (2) | Si III | 833.332 | (15) | O II | 703.850 | (30) | O III |
| 991.579 | (30) | N III | 832.927 | (5) | O III | 702.899 | (15) | O III |
| 991.514 | (3) | N III | 832.762 | (8) | O II | 702.822 | (10) | O III |
| 939.790 | (15) | N III | 827.052 | (5) | Ar V | 702.332 | (10) | O III |
| 977.020 | (30) | C III | 822.161 | (4) | Ar V | 700.277 | (8) | Ar IV |
| 972.537 | (5) | H I | 818.128 | (6) | Si IV | 700.24 | (20) | Ar VIII |
| 955.335 | (3) | N IV | 815.053 | (3) | Si IV | 699.408 | (4) | Ar IV |
| 932.053 | (15) | Ar II | 801.913 | (5) | Ar IV | 696.212 | (2) | A, III |
| 924.274 | (5) | N IV | 801.409 | (15) | Ar IV | 895.817 | (4) | Al III |
| 923.669 | (4) | N IV | 801.086 | (15) | Ar IV | 693.952 | (6) | B II |
| 923.211 | (15) | N IV | 800.573 | (5) | Ar IV | 689.007 | (12) | Ar IV |
| 923.045 | (3) | N IV | 796.661 | (2) | O II | 687.345 | (10) | C II |
| 922.507 | (4) | N IV | 790.203 | (30) | O IV | 687.053 | (5) | C II |
| 921.982 | (5) | N IV | 790.103 | (3) | O IV | 686.335 | (6) | N III |

Table 7 (continued)

| Wavelength | Intensity | Ion | Wavelength | Intensity | Ion | Wavelength | Intensity | Ion |
|---|---|---|---|---|---|---|---|---|
| 685.816 | (30) | N III | 566.613 | (2) | Si III | 489.501 | (15) | Ne III |
| 685.513 | (12) | N III | 564.529 | (5) | Ne VII | 488.868 | (7) | Ne III |
| 684.996 | (6) | N III | 562.992 | (4) | Ne VII | 488.103 | (8) | Ne III |
| 683.278 | (8) | Ar IV | 562.805 | (20) | Ne VI | 486.740 | (10) | Na VII |
| 679.400 | (6) | Ar II | 562.735 | (2) | Ne VII | 482.987 | (20) | Ne V |
| 677.951 | (5) | Ar II | 561.728 | (15) | Ne VII | 481.361 | (10) | Ne V |
| 677.147 | (20) | B III | 561.378 | (3) | Ne VII | 481.281 | (6) | Ne V |
| 677.004 | (10) | B III | 559.947 | (4) | Ne VII | 480.406 | (10) | Ne V |
| 676.241 | (6) | Ar II | 558.61 | (5) | Ne VII | 479.379 | (12) | Ar VII |
| 671.852 | (6) | Ar II | 558.595 | (10) | Ne VI | 475.656 | (8) | Ar VII |
| 670.948 | (5) | Ar II | 558.481 | (5) | Ar V | 473.938 | (4) | Ar VII |
| 666.010 | (6) | Ar II | 555.639 | (4) | Ar VI | 469.865 | (15) | Ne IV |
| 661.869 | (5) | Ar II | 555.262 | (6) | O IV | 469.817 | (15) | Ne IV |
| 660.286 | (5) | N II | 554.514 | (30) | O IV | 465.221 | (30) | Ne VII |
| 645.178 | (5) | N II | 554.074 | (12) | O IV | 463.938 | (7) | Ar V |
| 644.837 | (3) | N II | 553.328 | (6) | O IV | 463.263 | (15) | Na V |
| 644.634 | (1) | N II | 551.371 | (8) | Ar VI | 462.388 | (20) | Ne II |
| 644.148 | (5) | O II | 548.905 | (5) | Ar VI | 462.007 | (25) | Ar VI |
| 643.256 | (5) | Ar III | 544.731 | (4) | Ar VI | 461.051 | (10) | Na V |
| 641.808 | (12) | Ar III | 543.891 | (20) | Ne IV | 460.725 | (30) | Ne II |
| 637.282 | (20) | Ar III | 542.073 | (15) | Ne IV | 459.897 | (5) | Na V |
| 629.732 | (30) | O V | 541.127 | (8) | Ne IV | 450.633 | (10) | C III |
| 629.738 | (6) | Ne I | 538.312 | (5) | C III | 459.521 | (6) | C III |
| 626.822 | (7) | Ne I | 538.149 | (3) | C III | 459.462 | (2) | C III |
| 625.852 | (6) | O IV | 538.080 | (1) | C III | 458.155 | (2) | Si IV |
| 625.130 | (4) | O IV | 537.030 | (12) | He I | 457.815 | (4) | Si IV |
| 624.617 | (2) | O IV | 527.693 | (6) | Ar V | 457.475 | (20) | Ar VI |
| 619.101 | (4) | Ne I | 525.795 | (30) | O III | 455.270 | (5) | Ne II |
| 618.671 | (5) | Ne I | 524.189 | (5) | Ar V | 454.072 | (6) | Ne VI |
| 619.627 | (5) | Ne I | 522.213 | (5) | He I | 452.745 | (4) | Ne VI |
| 609.829 | (6) | O IV | 518.271 | (5) | B III | 451.843 | (2) | Ne VI |
| 608.395 | (3) | O IV | 518.244 | (10) | B III | 449.065 | (18) | Ar V |
| 599.598 | (30) | O III | 508.182 | (30) | O III | 447.813 | (10) | Ne II |
| 597.818 | (5) | O III | 507.683 | (20) | O III | 446.949 | (8) | Ar V |
| 596.694 | (4) | Ar VI | 507.391 | (10) | O III | 446.591 | (5) | Ne II |
| 588.921 | (5) | Ar VI | 494.382 | (20) | Na VI | 446.252 | (10) | Ne II |
| 585.754 | (15) | Ar VII | 494.160 | (4) | Na VI | 445.997 | (5) | Ar V |
| 584.334 | (30) | He I | 491.950 | (20) | Na VII | 445.032 | (7) | Ne II |
| 574.281 | (5) | C III | 491.340 | (12) | Na VI | 435.649 | (10) | Ne VI |
| 572.336 | (20) | Ne V | 491.240 | (4) | Na VI | 433.176 | (5) | Ne VI |
| 572.106 | (4) | Ne V | 491.050 | (8) | Ne III | 421.669 | (15) | Ne IV |
| 569.830 | (12) | Ne V | 490.310 | (7) | Ne III | 419.714 | (6) | C IV |
| 569.759 | (4) | Ne V | 489.641 | (4) | Ne III | 419.525 | (3) | C IV |
| 568.418 | (5) | Ne V | 489.580 | (6) | Na VI | 416.198 | (20) | Ne V |

Table 7 (continued)

| Wave-length | Inten-sity | Ion | Wave-length | Inten-sity | Ion | Wave-length | Inten-sity | Ion |
|---|---|---|---|---|---|---|---|---|
| 412.240 | (8) | Na IV | 335.050 | (6) | N IV | 238.361 | (3) | O IV |
| 411.333 | (7) | Na IV | 320.979 | (5) | O III | 220.352 | (6) | O V |
| 410.540 | (6) | Na IV | 319.638 | (20) | Na IV | 217.826 | (20) | Si VII |
| 410.371 | (15) | Na IV | 317.641 | (15) | Na VI | 209.303 | (5) | N V |
| 409.615 | (7) | Na IV | 312.453 | (5) | C IV | 209.270 | (10) | N V |
| 408.682 | (8) | Na IV | 312.422 | (10) | C IV | 192.906 | (10) | O V |
| 407.136 | (10) | Ne II | 312.241 | (8) | Al VI | 192.799 | (6) | O V |
| 405.852 | (15) | Ne II | 310.908 | (7) | Al VI | 192.751 | (2) | O V |
| 403.262 | (6) | Ne IV | 309.852 | (6) | Al VI | 184.117 | (10) | O VI |
| 401.939 | (30) | Ne VI | 309.596 | (15) | Al VI | 183.937 | (5) | O VI |
| 401.138 | (12) | Ne VI | 308.560 | (7) | Al VI | 173.082 | (20) | O VI |
| 400.722 | (10) | Na V | 308.264 | (12) | Na V | 172.935 | (10) | O VI |
| 399.820 | (6) | Ne VI | 307.248 | (8) | Al VI | 172.169 | (5) | O V |
| 395.558 | (5) | O III | 307.152 | (6) | Na V | 161.686 | (15) | Al IV |
| 388.218 | (15) | Ne IV | 303.782 | (30) | He II | 160.073 | (25) | Al IV |
| 387.141 | (10) | Ne IV | 283.579 | (10) | N IV | 150.124 | (5) | O VI |
| 386.203 | (8) | C III | 283.470 | (6) | N IV | 150.089 | (10) | O VI |
| 384.178 | (20) | C IV | 283.420 | (2) | N IV | 118.968 | (15) | Si V |
| 384.032 | (10) | C IV | 281.397 | (15) | Al V | 117.860 | (20) | Si V |
| 380.107 | (15) | Na III | 278.699 | (30) | Al V | 100.254 | (30) | Be III |
| 379.308 | (8) | Ne III | 278.445 | (8) | Si VII | 88.314 | (10) | Be III |
| 378.143 | (30) | Na III | 276.839 | (7) | Si VII | 84.758 | (3) | Be III |
| 376.375 | (10) | N II | 275.665 | (6) | Si VII | 75.928 | (30) | Be IV |
| 374.441 | (4) | N III | 275.352 | (15) | Si VII | 60.313 | (30) | B IV |
| 374.204 | (2) | N III | 274.175 | (7) | Si VII | 52.682 | (10) | B IV |
| 372.069 | (25) | Na II | 272.641 | (8) | Si VII | 50.435 | (3) | B IV |
| 365.594 | (20) | Ne V) | 266.375 | (6) | N V | 48.587 | (30) | B V |
| 361.250 | (25) | Na VI | 266.192 | (3) | N V | 40.270 | (30) | C V |
| 359.385 | (15) | Ne V | 256.317 | (10) | He II | 34.973 | (10) | C V |
| 358.72 | (20) | Ne IV | 250.940 | (7) | Ar VII | 33.736 | (30) | C VI |
| 358.472 | (10) | Ne V | 249.886 | (5) | Ar VII | 33.426 | (3) | C V |
| 357.955 | (5) | Ne V | 249.125 | (15) | Si VI | 28.787 | (30) | N VI |
| 357.831 | (15) | Ne IV | 247.710 | (20) | N V | 24.808 | (10) | N VI |
| 356.885 | (15) | Al VII | 247.563 | (10) | N V | 24.781 | (30) | N VII |
| 354.950 | (5) | Na VII | 247.205 | (5) | N IV | 23.771 | (3) | N VI |
| 353.776 | (10) | Al VII | 246.001 | (30) | Si VI | 21.602 | (30) | O VII |
| 353.204 | (25) | Na VII | 243.760 | (20) | Al VI | 18.969 | (30) | O VIII |
| 352.275 | (10) | Na VII | 243.027 | (5) | He II | 18.627 | (10) | O VII |
| 352.160 | (5) | Al VII | 238.573 | (6) | O IV | 17.768 | (3) | O VII |
| 350.645 | (5) | Na VII | | | | | | |

Table 8

CALCULATED WAVELENGTHS OF THE ATOMIC LINES OF INERT GASES

| Wavelength | Ion | Wavelength | Ion | Wavelength | Ion | Wavelength | Ion |
|---|---|---|---|---|---|---|---|
| 1469.610 | Xe I | 1066.659 | Ar I | 876.057 | Ar I | 618.671 | Ne I |
| 1295.586 | Xe I | 1048.219 | Ar I | 869.754 | Ar I | 615.627 | Ne I |
| 1250.207 | Xe I | 1030.023 | Kr I | 866.800 | Ar I | 602.725 | Ne I |
| 1235.838 | Kr I | 1003.550 | Kr I | 842.805 | Ar I | 600.036 | Ne I |
| 1192.036 | Xe I | 1001.061 | Kr I | 835.002 | Ar I | 598.890 | Ne I |
| 1170.410 | Xe I | 963.374 | Kr I | 834.392 | Ar I | 598.705 | Ne I |
| 1164.867 | Kr I | 953.404 | Kr I | 826.364 | Ar I | 595.919 | Ne I |
| 1129.307 | Xe I | 951.056 | Kr I | 825.346 | Ar I | 584.3340 | He I |
| 1110.713 | Xe I | 946.535 | Kr I | 743.718 | Ne I | 537.0296 | He I |
| 1099.716 | Xe I | 945.441 | Kr I | 735.895 | Ne I | 522.2128 | He I |
| 1085.442 | Xe I | 928.711 | Kr I | 629.738 | Ne I | 515.6165 | He I |
| 1078.584 | Xe I | 923.713 | Kr I | 626.822 | Ne I | 512.0982 | He I |
| 1070.409 | Xe I | 894.310 | Ar I | 619.101 | Ne I | 509.9979 | He I |
| 1068.167 | Xe I | 879.946 | Ar I | | | | |

Table 9

CALCULATED WAVELENGTHS OF THE LINES OF Be I, B I, Mg II, Al I, Al II, Ca II

| Wavelength | Intensity | Ion | Wavelength | Intensity | Ion | Wavelength | Intensity | Ion |
|---|---|---|---|---|---|---|---|---|
| 1850.691 | (10) | Ca II | 1691.779 | (2) | Ca II | 1369.4231 | (3) | Mg II |
| 1843.088 | (5) | Ca II | 1680.129 | (0.5) | Ca II | 1367.7082 | (2) | Mg II |
| 1840.061 | (15) | Ca II | 1680.051 | (5) | Ca II | 1367.2568 | (4) | Mg II |
| 1838.008 | (10) | Ca II | 1673.860 | (3) | Ca II | 1367.2537 | (0.4) | Mg II |
| 1826.400 | (10) | B I | 1670.786 | (30) | Al II | 1365.5442 | (2) | Mg II |
| 1825.899 | (5) | B I | 1661.478 | (8) | Be I | 1342.5351 | (3) | Ca II |
| 1818.349 | (6) | B I | 1651.9909 | (8) | Ca II | 1341.8892 | (6) | Ca II |
| 1817.849 | (3) | B I | 1649.8579 | (15) | Ca II | 1309.4434 | (2) | Mg II |
| 1814.647 | (1) | Ca II | 1644.4415 | (9) | Ca II | 1308.2809 | (3) | Mg II |
| 1814.495 | (10) | Ca II | 1643.7700 | (5) | Ca II | 1308.2792 | (0.3) | Mg II |
| 1807.337 | (5) | Ca II | 1642.8020 | (1) | Ca II | 1307.8754 | (1) | Mg II |
| 1769.133 | (4) | Al I | 1554.6415 | (8) | Ca II | 1306.7139 | (2) | Mg II |
| 1766.381 | (4) | Al I | 1553.1761 | (5) | Ca II | 1240.3947 | (5) | Mg II |
| 1765.632 | (4) | Al I | 1491.765 | (2) | Be I | 1239.9252 | (10) | Mg II |
| 1762.892 | (2) | Al I | 1482.8903 | (5) | Mg II | 1026.1133 | (3) | Mg II |
| 1753.4744 | (10) | Mg II | 1480.8797 | (3) | Mg II | 1025.9681 | (6) | Mg II |
| 1750.6637 | (5) | Mg II | 1478.0037 | (6) | Mg II | 946.7694 | (2) | Mg II |
| 1737.6283 | (9) | Mg II | 1477.9972 | (0.6) | Mg II | 946.7032 | (4) | Mg II |
| 1737.6124 | (1) | Mg II | 1475.9998 | (4) | Mg II | 907.4115 | (1) | Mg II |
| 1734.8523 | (5) | Mg II | 1433.7493 | (5) | Ca II | 907.3752 | (2) | Mg II |
| 1698.183 | (4) | Ca II | 1432.5028 | (3) | Ca II | | | |

Table 10

CALCULATED WAVELENGTHS OF THE LINES OF CI, CII, AND CIII

| Wave-length | Inten-sity | Ion | Wave-length | Inten-sity | Ion | Wave-length | Inten-sity | Ion |
|---|---|---|---|---|---|---|---|---|
| 1760.819 | (3) | C II | 1323.9059 | (6) | C II | 687.3521 | (6) | C II |
| 1760.473 | (1) | C II | 1323.8617 | (1) | C II | 687.3453 | (50) | C II |
| 1760.395 | (6) | C II | 1280.846 | (4) | C I | 687.0526 | (30) | C II |
| 1751.825 | (10) | C I | 1280.597 | (3) | C I | 636.2511 | (2) | C II |
| 1658.120 | (50) | C I | 1280.403 | (2) | C I | 635.9945 | (1) | C II |
| 1657.905 | (40) | C I | 1280.334 | (10) | C I | 595.0245 | (1) | C II |
| 1657.377 | (30) | C I | 1280.134 | (3) | C I | 595.0219 | (9) | C II |
| 1657.007 | (150) | C I | 1279.891 | (4) | C I | 594.8000 | (5) | C II |
| 1656.926 | (40) | C I | 1279.229 | (3) | C I | 574.2809 | (60) | C III |
| 1656.265 | (50) | C I | 1261.552 | (15) | C I | 565.5280 | (5) | C III |
| 1602.970 | (5) | C I | 1261.425 | (5) | C I | 560.4367 | (4) | C II |
| 1561.437 | (200) | C I | 1261.122 | (5) | C I | 560.2394 | (2) | C II |
| 1561.369 | (3) | C I | 1260.996 | (3) | C I | 549.5700 | (1) | C II |
| 1561.340 | (40) | C I | 1260.929 | (4) | C I | 549.5110 | (5) | C II |
| 1560.710 | (40) | C I | 1260.735 | (4) | C I | 549.3785 | (2) | C II |
| 1560.682 | (100) | C I | 1189.630 | (5) | C I | 549.3195 | (1) | C II |
| 1560.311 | (50) | C I | 1189.447 | (3) | C I | 538.3120 | (100) | C III |
| 1481.760 | (20) | C I | 1189.247 | (2) | C I | 538.1487 | (60) | C III |
| 1467.400 | (5) | C I | 1189.065 | (1) | C I | 538.0801 | (20) | C III |
| 1459.028 | (3) | C I | 1188.991 | (2) | C I | 535.2885 | (20) | C III |
| 1364.164 | (10) | C I | 1188.833 | (2) | C I | 511.5225 | (20) | C III |
| 1357.133 | (3) | C I | 1066.1332 | (5) | C II | 492.6500 | (5) | C III |
| 1335.7077 | (300) | C II | 1065.9199 | (1) | C II | 460.0487 | (8) | C III |
| 1335.6627 | (30) | C II | 1065.8913 | (7) | C II | 450.7338 | (12) | C III |
| 1334.5323 | (150) | C II | 1037.0182 | (150) | C II | 433.3391 | (8) | C III |
| 1329.6005 | (50) | C I | 1036.3367 | (80) | C II | 389.0898 | (5) | C III |
| 1329.5775 | (150) | C I | 904.4801 | (30) | C II | 389.0045 | (3) | C III |
| 1329.1230 | (30) | C I | 904.1416 | (150) | C II | 388.9687 | (1) | C III |
| 1329.1001 | (50) | C I | 903.9616 | (60) | C II | 386.2028 | (150) | C III |
| 1329.0863 | (40) | C I | 903.6235 | (30) | C II | 322.5741 | (8) | C III |
| 1328.8332 | (40) | C I | 858.5590 | (20) | C II | 310.1697 | (5) | C III |
| 1323.9955 | (1) | C II | 858.0918 | (10) | C II | 291.3261 | (2) | C III |
| 1323.9513 | (9) | C II | | | | | | |

Table 11

CALCULATED WAVELENGTHS OF THE NI AND NII LINES

| Wave-length | Inten-sity | Ion | Wave-length | Inten-sity | Ion | Wave-length | Inten-sity | Ion |
|---|---|---|---|---|---|---|---|---|
| 1200.7102 | (30) | N I | 953.9702 | (15) | N I | 671.773 | (5) | N II |
| 1200.2237 | (60) | N I | 953.6552 | (10) | N I | 671.630 | (3) | N II |
| 1199.5501 | (90) | N I | 953.4155 | (10) | N I | 671.411 | (4) | N II |
| 1160.9370 | — | N I | 952.5230 | (3) | N I | 671.386 | (15) | N II |
| 1159.8172 | — | N I | 952.4151 | (3) | N I | 671.016 | (5) | N II |
| 1134.9806 | (150) | N I | 952.3037 | (3) | N I | 660.286 | (25) | N II |
| 1134.4153 | (100) | N I | 951.2951 | (1) | N I | 645.178 | (30) | N II |
| 1134.1657 | (50) | N I | 951.0795 | (3) | N I | 644.837 | (20) | N II |
| 1085.701 | (150) | N II | 916.710 | (40) | N II | 644.634 | (10) | N II |
| 1085.546 | (30) | N II | 916.701 | (100) | N II | 635.197 | (3) | N II |
| 1085.529 | (2) | N II | 916.020 | (20) | N II | 582.156 | (3) | N II |
| 1084.580 | (80) | N II | 916.012 | (40) | N II | 574.650 | (5) | N II |
| 1084.562 | (30) | N II | 915.962 | (30) | N II | 533.815 | (3) | N II |
| 1083.990 | (40) | N II | 915.612 | (30) | N II | 533.729 | (8) | N II |
| 965.0415 | (10) | N I | 910.6456 | (5) | N I | 533.650 | (3) | N II |
| 964.6259 | (20) | N I | 910.2785 | (10) | N I | 533.581 | (5) | N II |
| 963.9906 | (30) | N I | 909.6977 | (15) | N I | 533.511 | (3) | N II |
| 960.2017 | — | N I | 908.7962 | (2) | N I | 529.867 | (5) | N II |
| 959.4940 | (3) | N I | 908.2336 | (3) | N I | 529.722 | (2) | N II |
| 955.8818 | (3) | N I | 775.965 | (100) | N II | 529.637 | (2) | N II |
| 955.5297 | (2) | N I | 748.369 | (10) | N II | 529.491 | (1) | N II |
| 955.4374 | — | N I | 746.984 | (15) | N II | 529.413 | (2) | N II |
| 955.2647 | (2) | N I | 745.841 | (5) | N II | 529.355 | (2) | N II |
| 954.1044 | (3) | N I | 672.001 | (5) | N II | | | |

Table 12

CALCULATED WAVELENGTHS OF THE O I LINES

| Wavelength | Intensity | Wavelength | Intensity | Wavelength | Intensity |
|---|---|---|---|---|---|
| 1358.5125 | (3) | 990.1270 | (4) | 948.6867 | (10) |
| 1355.5975 | (5) | 988.7733 | (20) | 879.554 | (3) |
| 1306.0286 | (10) | 988.6548 | (4) | 879.104 | (4) |
| 1304.8579 | (30) | 978.6170 | (2) | 879.023 | (2) |
| 1302.1683 | (50) | 977.9595 | (6) | 878.976 | (3) |
| 1152.152 | (10) | 976.4480 | (10) | 877.882 | (10) |
| 1041.6876 | (4) | 973.8857 | (3) | 877.802 | (4) |
| 1040.9427 | (12) | 973.2346 | (9) | 792.968 | (4) |
| 1039.2303 | (20) | 971.7376 | (15) | 792.938 | (3) |
| 1028.1571 | (5) | 952.9414 | (1) | 792.507 | (2) |
| 1027.4309 | (15) | 952.3179 | (3) | 792.233 | (3) |
| 1025.7616 | (25) | 950.8845 | (5) | 791.974 | (10) |
| 990.8010 | (5) | 950.7340 | (2) | 791.514 | (4) |
| 990.2044 | (10) | 950.1134 | (6) | | |

Table 13

CALCULATED WAVELENGTHS OF THE LINES OF Si I, Si II, Si III AND Si IV

| Wave-length | Inten-sity | Ion | Wave-length | Inten-sity | Ion | Wave-length | Inten-sity | Ion |
|---|---|---|---|---|---|---|---|---|
| 1986.374 | (20) | Si I | 1501.150 | (5) | Si III | 939.097 | (5) | Si III |
| 1980.629 | (10) | Si I | 1500.241 | (50) | Si III | 901.734 | (2) | Si II |
| 1977.608 | (15) | Si I | 1436.160 | (5) | Si III | 899.404 | (1) | Si II |
| 1904.650 | (12) | Si I | 1435.772 | (10) | Si III | 892.000 | (10) | Si II |
| 1880.966 | (5) | Si I | 1367.047 | (5) | Si III | 889.721 | (5) | Si II |
| 1875.814 | (10) | Si I | 1361.596 | (8) | Si III | 823.409 | (15) | Si III |
| 1873.104 | (8) | Si I | 1309.273 | (20) | Si II | 818.128 | (30) | Si IV |
| 1853.142 | (10) | Si I | 1304.366 | (10) | Si II | 815.053 | (15) | Si IV |
| 1848.745 | (18) | Si I | 1264.999 | (10) | Si II | 749.939 | (5) | Si IV |
| 1848.141 | (20) | Si I | 1264.735 | (100) | Si II | 653.334 | (10) | Si III |
| 1845.510 | (25) | Si I | 1260.418 | (50) | Si II | 652.219 | (6) | Si III |
| 1843.767 | (15) | Si I | 1197.391 | (10) | Si II | 651.672 | (2) | Si III |
| 1841.149 | (10) | Si I | 1194.498 | (25) | Si II | 566.613 | (15) | Si III |
| 1829.898 | (7) | Si I | 1193.286 | (20) | Si II | 560.980 | (5) | Si IV |
| 1822.456 | (10) | Si I | 1190.412 | (10) | Si II | 559.533 | (3) | Si IV |
| 1817.445 | (1) | Si II | 1023.698 | (5) | Si II | 516.344 | (10) | Si IV |
| 1816.923 | (20) | Si II | 1020.696 | (3) | Si II | 515.118 | (5) | Si IV |
| 1808.004 | (15) | Si II | 997.386 | (100) | Si III | 466.131 | (5) | Si III |
| 1702.855 | (5) | Si I | 994.790 | (60) | Si III | 458.155 | (10) | Si IV |
| 1700.622 | (4) | Si I | 993.519 | (20) | Si III | 457.815 | (20) | Si IV |
| 1533.427 | (100) | Si II | 992.694 | (2) | Si II | 455.065 | — | Si IV |
| 1526.701 | (50) | Si II | 992.681 | (20) | Si II | 454.112 | — | Si IV |
| 1501.881 | (25) | Si III | 989.871 | (10) | Si II | 361.659 | — | Si IV |
| 1501.827 | (5) | Si III | 967.944 | (15) | Si III | 361.560 | — | Si IV |
| 1501.197 | (40) | Si III | | | | | | |

Table 14

RITZ'S ArII STANDARDS

| Wave-length | Inten-sity | Wave-length | Inten-sity | Wave-length | Inten-sity | Wave-length | Inten-sity |
|---|---|---|---|---|---|---|---|
| 1976.765 | (3) | 1919.199 | (3) | 1834.038 | (2) | 1603.075 | (4) |
| 1974.462 | (3) | 1907.988 | (4) | 1831.527 | (5) | 1600.694 | (6) |
| 1973.483 | (2) | 1900.638 | (4) | 1830.770 | (5) | 1600.133 | (4) |
| 1972.274 | (2) | 1889.029 | (6) | 1788.104 | (3) | 1598.722 | (2) |
| 1962.161 | (3) | 1888.782 | (4) | 1771.829 | (2) | 1593.587 | (2) |
| 1961.361 | (4) | 1886.386 | (4) | 1713.218 | (2) | 1590.233 | (2) |
| 1946.795 | (2) | 1879.790 | (2) | 1606.926 | (4) | 1589.465 | (5) |
| 1941.074 | (3) | 1877.523 | (4) | 1606.197 | (3) | 1586.261 | (2) |
| 1933.694 | (2) | 1873.140 | (6) | 1604.082 | (5) | 1580.770 | (2) |
| 1932.230 | (2) | 1868.660 | (3) | 1603.442 | (4) | 1578.812 | (3) |

Table 14 (continued)

| Wave-length | Inten-sity | Wave-length | Inten-sity | Wave-length | Inten-sity | Wave-length | Inten-sity |
|---|---|---|---|---|---|---|---|
| 1576.898 | (3) | 754.8243 | (3) | 679.4001 | (6) | 578.6046 | (2) |
| 1575.815 | (3) | 748.1977 | (4) | 679.2187 | (3) | 578.1068 | (2) |
| 1574.993 | (6) | 745.3217 | (7) | 677.9521 | (5) | 576.7361 | (2) |
| 1567.987 | (4) | 744.9252 | (8) | 676.2428 | (6) | 573.3622 | (2) |
| 1562.442 | (2) | 740.2695 | (10) | 672.8565 | (2) | 572.0139 | (2) |
| 1560.191 | (4) | 730.9293 | (5) | 671.8516 | (6) | 560.2229 | (2) |
| 1559.072 | (3) | 725.5481 | (4) | 670.9450 | (5) | 556.8172 | (2) |
| 1382.228 | (2) | 723.3611 | (5) | 666.0112 | (6) | 548.7810 | (2) |
| 1377.211 | (4) | 718.0903 | (4) | 664.5626 | (4) | 547.4602 | (2) |
| 1363.032 | (2) | 704.5233 | (4) | 661.8692 | (5) | 547.1647 | (2) |
| 1354.915 | (2) | 698.7748 | (4) | 612.3719 | (5) | 546.1770 | (2) |
| — | — | 697.9414 | (2) | 602.8581 | (2) | 543.7307 | (2) |
| 932.0528 | (10) | 697.4893 | (2) | 597.7003 | (2) | 543.2035 | (2) |
| 919.7815 | (10) | 693.3015 | (2) | 583.4368 | (2) | 542.9125 | (2) |
| 762.1995 | (3) | 686.4888 | (2) | 580.2634 | (3) | | |

Table 15

RITZ'S CuII STANDARDS

| Wave-length | Inten-sity | Wave-length | Inten-sity | Wave-length | Inten-sity | Wave-length | Inten-sity |
|---|---|---|---|---|---|---|---|
| 1663.0020 | (30) | 1569.2128 | (10) | — | — | 1019.6546 | (15) |
| 1660.0015 | (20) | 1566.4151 | (40) | 1065.7823 | (20) | 1018.7078 | (50) |
| 1656.3218 | (20) | 1565.9242 | (40) | 1059.0961 | (60) | 1018.0644 | (15) |
| 1649.4576 | (25) | 1558.3446 | (30) | 1056.9546 | (60) | 1017.9982 | (15) |
| 1621.4262 | (60) | 1541.7036 | (75) | 1054.6902 | (60) | 1012.6831 | (3) |
| 1617.9154 | (20) | 1540.3889 | (30) | 1049.7552 | (50) | 1012.5974 | (25) |
| 1611.1180 | (10) | 1535.0028 | (25) | 1044.7434 | (80) | 1011.4360 | (2) |
| 1610.2969 | (15) | 1519.4917 | (50) | 1036.4693 | (60) | 1010.6397 | (3) |
| 1608.6396 | (25) | 1517.6312 | (20) | 1035.1629 | (8) | 1008.5692 | (30) |
| 1606.8341 | (40) | 1488.6375 | (75) | 1033.5677 | (10) | 1004.0555 | (30) |
| 1604.8474 | (20) | 1485.6777 | (40) | 1031.7662 | (8) | 1001.0128 | (8) |
| 1602.3882 | (40) | 1485.6104 | (40) | 1028.3282 | (25) | 999.7942 | (5) |
| 1598.4024 | (40) | 1473.9786 | (25) | 1027.8310 | (50) | 998.3061 | (8) |
| 1593.5562 | (60) | 1444.1303 | (2) | 1022.1022 | (5) | 992.9531 | (25) |
| 1590.1649 | (40) | 1442.1387 | (15) | 1020.1076 | (15) | 989.2367 | (8) |

Table 16

TENTATIVE MEASUREMENTS OF Fe II LINES

(E—Edlén, W—Wilkinson)

| E | W | E | W | E | W |
|---|---|---|---|---|---|
| 1964 | 1964.342 (12) | 1674.254 (4) | 1674.251 (2) | 1570.242 (20) | 1570.244 (20) |
| 1936.799 (1) | — | 1673.462 (2) | 1673.460 (15) | 1569.674 (12) | 1569.674 (12) |
| 1925 | 1925.983 (20) | 1670 | 1670.742 (25) | 1568.016 (4) | 1568.026 (8) |
| 1904 | 1904.784 (15) | 1663.221 (7) | 1663.217 (15) | 1566.819 (20) | 1566.821 (20) |
| 1888.733 (7) | 1888.731 (20) | 1659.483 (12) | 1659.479 (20) | 1563 | 1563.788 (25) |
| 1877.467 (7) | 1877.460 (20) | 1658.771 (7) | 1658.773 (15) | 1559 | 1559.084 (20) |
| 1876.838 (4) | 1876.839 (15) | 1654.476 (4) | 1654.474 (5) | 1558.690 (7) | — |
| 1876 | 1876.181 (8) | 1654 | 1654.111 (5) | 1558.542 (7) | — |
| 1860.055 (4) | 1860.049 (20) | 1650 | 1650.704 (20) | 1551.933 (2) | — |
| 1859 | 1859.741 (15) | 1649 | 1649.572 (20) | 1548.692 (1) | — |
| 1848.771 (2) | 1848.768 (12) | 1649.423 (7) | — | 1512.053 (2) | — |
| 1846.573 (2) | — | 1647 | 1647.159 (25) | 1506.898 (4) | — |
| 1841 | 1841.701 (10) | 1646 | 1646.182 (20) | 1496.523 (4) | — |
| 1835.874 (2) | 1835.868 (15) | 1643.576 (12) | 1643.574 (15) | 1463.198 (4) | — |
| 1793.367 (4) | 1793.360 (10) | 1641 | 1641.759 (25) | 1454.308 (7) | — |
| 1788 | 1788.072 (35) | 1640.150 (12) | 1640.152 (12) | 1448.393 (7) | — |
| 1785 | 1785.161 (40) | 1637.397 (12) | 1637.396 (15) | 1442.746 (2) | — |
| 1772.509 (7) | 1772.505 (15) | 1636 | 1636.321 (30) | 1434.994 (4) | — |
| 1764.117 (1) | — | 1635 | 1635.398 (35) | 1430.895 (12) | — |
| 1731 | 1731.373 (1) | 1634 | 1634.345 (20) | 1430.780 (20) | — |
| 1726.391 (7) | 1726.393 (12) | 1633.908 (12) | 1633.904 (15) | 1424.716 (7) | — |
| 1724.966 (2) | 1724.967 (8) | 1632.668 (4) | — | 1420.911 (7) | — |
| 1724.854 (4) | 1724.856 (8) | 1631 | 1631.120 (30) | 1418.855 (1) | — |
| 1720 | 1720.616 (20) | 1629 | 1629.154 (30) | 1417.727 (7) | — |
| 1716.577 (2) | — | 1625 | 1625.909 (15) | 1413.699 (12) | — |
| 1712.997 (20) | 1712.995 (20) | 1625.520 (12) | 1625.520 (20) | 1408.478 (30) | — |
| 1708.621 (7) | 1708.627 (8) | 1623.091 (4) | 1623.090 (8) | 1405.797 (2) | — |
| 1706.142 (2) | — | 1621 | 1621.685 (30) | 1405.604 (2) | — |
| 1702 | 1702.043 (25) | 1618 | 1618.470 (25) | 1401.772 (4) | — |
| 1699.193 (2) | — | 1612.802 (20) | 1612.809 (20) | 1397.572 (4) | — |
| 1696.794 (7) | 1696.794 (8) | 1610.921 (7) | 1610.924 (15) | 1383.578 (7) | — |
| 1693.936 (2) | — | 1608 | 1608.456 (35) | 1379.466 (12) | — |
| 1691.271 (2) | 1691.271 (8) | 1588.286 (7) | 1588.295 (10) | 1376.672 (1) | — |
| 1690.759 (2) | 1690.757 (8) | 1584.949 (12) | 1584.954 (15) | 1375.172 (20) | — |
| 1689.828 (2) | 1689.830 (10) | 1581 | 1581.274 (8) | 1373.717 (12) | — |
| 1686.692 (2) | — | 1580 | 1580.625 (25) | 1371.024 (50) | — |
| 1686.455 (4) | 1686.450 (8) | 1577.166 (2) | — | 1368.098 (4) | — |
| 1685.954 (4) | 1685.960 (5) | 1574.923 (7) | 1574.925 (20) | 1366.720 (7) | — |
| 1679.381 (7) | 1679.380 (15) | 1574.768 (2) | — | 1364.575 (20) | — |
| 1676.853 (2) | — | 1573.825 (4) | — | 1361.372 (7) | — |
| 1674.716 (4) | — | 1572 | 1572.750 (1) | — | — |

Table 17

RITZ'S Ge I AND Ge II STANDARDS

| Wave-length | Inten-sity | Wave-length | Inten-sity | Wave-length | Inten-sity | Wave-length | Inten-sity |
|---|---|---|---|---|---|---|---|
| Ge I | | 1876.0103 | (3) | 1750.0432 | (5) | 1675.5605 | (2) |
| 1998.8869 | (10) | 1874.2565 | (8) | 1748.8572 | (2) | 1674.2703 | (2) |
| 1997.8064 | (1) | 1865.0525 | (6) | 1744.2546 | (1) | 1671.0096 | (2) |
| 1989.1174 | (4) | 1861.0945 | (2) | 1744.0537 | (1) | 1670.6085 | (3) |
| 1988.2668 | (9) | 1860.0865 | (8) | 1742.1951 | (4) | 1667.8015 | (4) |
| 1987.8492 | (7) | 1853.1336 | (7) | 1739.1024 | (4) | 1665.2751 | (3) |
| 1970.8796 | (9) | 1849.6354 | (2) | 1738.4791 | (3) | 1661.3453 | (3) |
| 1965.3830 | (7) | 1846.9578 | (2) | 1738.1185 | (3) | 1658.3752 | (2) |
| 1963.3728 | (5) | 1845.8723 | (7) | 1724.3082 | (1) | 1651.9547 | (4) |
| 1962.0133 | (10) | 1844.4102 | (6) | 1720.7464 | (1) | 1651.5288 | (2) |
| 1955.1150 | (8) | 1842.4098 | (6) | 1718.6883 | (1) | 1647.5310 | (2) |
| 1953.8018 | (2) | 1841.3275 | (7) | 1718.4933 | (1) | 1643.1931 | (1) |
| 1944.1163 | (6) | 1824.3023 | (4) | 1716.7844 | (5) | 1630.1733 | (2) |
| 1938.3003 | (5) | 1813.9087 | (2) | 1715.8355 | (3) | — | — |
| 1937.4823 | (6) | 1804.4523 | (4) | 1713.0806 | (3) | | |
| 1934.0482 | (6) | 1802.6246 | (4) | 1702.3873 | (2) | Ge II | |
| 1929.8262 | (10) | 1801.4323 | (5) | 1696.7160 | (2) | 1581.0678 | (8) |
| 1923.4674 | (6) | 1793.0711 | (5) | 1695.8597 | (2) | 1576.8528 | (50) |
| 1917.5924 | (8) | 1786.0686 | (3) | 1694.3424 | (3) | 1538.0887 | (20) |
| 1912.4087 | (5) | 1785.0460 | (5) | 1691.8657 | (2) | 1264.7087 | (10) |
| 1908.4342 | (5) | 1774.1755 | (5) | 1691.6254 | (2) | 1261.9041 | (50) |
| 1904.7015 | (9) | 1766.0648 | (4) | 1691.0897 | (6) | 1237.0580 | (50) |
| 1903.5620 | (3) | 1765.2843 | (5) | 1690.9030 | (2) | 1075.0711 | (20) |
| 1901.0607 | (1) | 1764.1852 | (5) | 1690.0349 | (4) | 1055.0252 | (10) |
| 1895.1968 | (6) | 1759.2712 | (2) | 1685.2221 | (1) | 1017.0592 | (2) |
| | | 1758.2792 | (6) | 1681.3426 | (1) | 1016.6369 | (10) |
| | | | | | | 999.1003 | (5) |

Table 18

CALCULATED WAVELENGTHS OF Hg I LINES

| Isotope Hg[198] | Natural isotope mixture | Isotope Hg[198] | Natural isotope mixture |
|---|---|---|---|
| 1849.4918 | 1849.496 | 1235.8371 | 1235.839 |
| 1435.5031 | 1435.505 | 1232.2293 | 1232.231 |
| 1402.6190 | 1402.620 | 1222.3711 | 1222.373 |
| 1307.7509 | 1307.752 | 1220.3672 | 1220.369 |
| 1301.0103 | 1301.012 | 1213.9035 | — |
| 1268.8247 | — | 1212.6478 | 1212.650 |
| 1259.2418 | 1259.244 | 1208.2242 | — |
| 1250.5637 | 1250.565 | 1207.3784 | 1207.380 |

Table 19

CALCULATED WAVELENGTHS OF THE RESONANCE LINES IN THE
ONE-ELECTRON SPECTRA FROM H I TO O VIII

|        | $1s-2p$ | $1s-3p$ | $1s-4p$ | $1s-5p$ | $1s-6p$ | $1s-7p$ |
|--------|---------|---------|---------|---------|---------|---------|
| H I    | 1215.6701 | 1025.7223 | 972.5368 | 949.7431 | 937.8035 | 930.7483 |
| D I    | 1215.3394 | 1025.4433 | 972.2723 | 949.4847 | 937.5484 | 930.4951 |
| He II  | 303.7822 | 256.3170 | 243.0266 | 237.3308 | 234.3472 | 232.5842 |
| Li III | 134.9977 | 113.9051 | 107.9990 | 105.4679 | 104.1421 | 103.3586 |
| Be IV  | 75.9277 | 64.0648 | 60.7431 | 59.3196 | 58.5739 | 58.1333 |
| B V    | 48.5874 | 40.9964 | 38.8709 | 37.9599 | 37.4828 | 37.2008 |
| C VI   | 33.7360 | 28.4656 | 26.9898 | 26.3573 | 26.0260 | 25.8303 |
| N VII  | 24.7810 | 20.9099 | 19.8259 | 19.3613 | 19.1179 | 18.9742 |
| O VIII | 18.9689 | 16.0059 | 15.1762 | 14.8206 | 14.6343 | 14.5243 |

## BIBLIOGRAPHY

1. KALININ, S.K., V.L. MARZUVANOV, and T.B. BEKBAULOVA. *Atlas spektral'nykh linii v oblasti* 2095–1840 Å *(Atlas of Spectral Lines for* 2095–1840 Å*)*. Alma-Ata. 1960.

2. KAPORSKII, L.N., F.Z. PEDOS, N.S. SVENTITSKII, and Z.I. SHLEPKOVA. *Izvestiya AN SSSR,* phys. ser., **26**, 968 (1962).

2a. KALININ, S.K., S.M. MUKHTAROV, and V.M. PEREVERTUN. *Atlas spektra ugleroda (vakuumnaya oblast') (Atlas of the Carbon Spectrum in the Vacuum Ultraviolet)*. 1966.

3. EDLÉN, B. *Rep. Progr. Phys.,* **XXVI**, 181. 1963.

4. WILKINSON, P.G. and K.L. ANDREW. *J. Opt. Soc. America,* **53**, 710 (1963).

5. PEDOS, F.Z. and V.K. PROKOF'EV. *Optiko-mekhanicheskaya Promyshlennost',* No.3, 14 (1959).

6. KELLY, R.L. *U.S. At. Energy Comm.,* UCRL–5612. 1959; *Vacuum Ultraviolet Emission Lines.* 1960.

7. MOORE, C.E. *An Ultraviolet Multiplet Table. Nat. Bur. Stand.,* No.488, Section 5, 1–5, 1950, 1952, 1961, 1962. Washington.

8. ZAIDEL', A.N., V.K. PROKOF'EV, S.M. RAISKII, and E.YA. SHREIDER. *Tablitsy spektral'-nykh linii (Tables of Spectral Lines)*. Fizmatgiz. 1962.

9. STRIGANOV, A.R. and N.S. SVENTITSKII. *Tablitsy spektral'nykh linii neitral'nykh i ionizo-vannykh atomov (Tables of Spectral Lines of Neutral and Ionized Atoms)*. Atomizdat. 1966.

9a. GARCIA, J.D. and J.E. MACK. *J. Opt. Soc. America,* **55**, 654 (1965).

10. BOYCE, J.C. *Rev. Mod. Phys.,* **13**, 1 (1941).

11. MCADAM, D.L. *Phys. Rev.,* **50**, 185 (1936).

12. HERZBERG, G. *Trans. Intern. Astron. Union,* **XIA**, 97 (1961).

13. EDLÉN, B. *Trans. Intern. Astron. Union,* **X**, 211 (1960).

14. PASCHEN, F. *Ann. Phys.,* **35**, 860 (1911).

15. PASCHEN, F. *Ann. Phys.,* **40**, 602 (1913).

16. BARREL, H. *J. Opt. Soc. America,* **41**, 295 (1951).

17. COLEMAN, C.D., W.R. BOZMAN, and W.F. MEGGERS. *Table of Wavenumbers,* I (2000–7000 Å); II (7000–10,000 Å).
18. HERZBERG, G. *Proc. Roy. Soc.,* **A234**, 516 (1956).
19. HERZBERG, G. *Proc. Roy. Soc.,* **A248**, 309 (1958).
20. RISBERG, P. *Arkiv. fys.,* **9**, 483 (1955).
21. ANDREW, K.L. and K.W. MEISSNER. *J. Opt. Soc. America,* **48**, 31 (1958).
22. MEISSNER, K.W. et al. *J. Opt. Soc. America,* **48**, 1001 (1958).
23. KAUFMAN, V. and K.L. ANDREW. *J. Opt. Soc. America,* **52**, 1223 (1962).
24. WILKINSON, P.G. and K.L. ANDREW. *J. Opt. Soc. America,* **53**, 710 (1963).
25. SHENSTONE, A.G. *Proc. Roy. Soc.,* **A276**, 293 (1963).
26. MAZING, M.A. and N.A. VRUBLEVSKAYA. *Optika i Spektroskopiya,* **16**, 11 (1964).
27. HERZBERG, G. and H. MOORE. *Canad. J. Phys.,* **37**, 1293 (1959).
28. HERZBERG, G. *Z. Phys.,* **146**, 269 (1956).
29. LAMB, W.E. and R.C. RETHERFORD. *Phys. Rev.,* **79**, 549 (1950).
30. TRIEBWASSER, S., E.S. DAYHOFF, and W.E. LAMB. *Phys. Rev.,* **89**, 98 (1953).
31. SALPETER, E.E. *Phys. Rev.,* **89**, 92 (1953).
32. NOVICK, R., E. LIPWORTH, and P.F. YERGIN. *Phys. Rev.,* **100**, 1153 (1955).
33. SERIES, G.W. *Proc. Roy. Soc.,* **A226**, 377 (1954).
34. BRIX, P. and G. HERZBERG. *Canad. J. Phys.,* **32**, 110 (1954).
34a. DOUGLAS, A.E. and G. HERZBERG. *J. Opt. Soc. America,* **47**, 625 (1957).
35. FRISH, S.E. *Opticheskie spektry (Optical. Spectra).* Fizmatgiz. 1963.
36. PEKERIS, C.L. *Phys. Rev.,* **112**, 1649 (1958).
37. KABIR, P.K. and E.E. SALPETER. *Phys. Rev.,* **108**, 1256 (1957).
38. CHULANOVSKII, V.M. and M.P. MOKHNATKIN. *Doklady AN SSSR,* **7**, 1 (1934).
39. KOPFERMANN, H., H. KRÜGER, and H. ÖHLMANN. *Z. Phys.,* **126**, 760 (1949).

# BIBLIOGRAPHY ON THE SPECTRA OF ELEMENTS IN THE VACUUM ULTRAVIOLET*

## Ag

SHENSTONE, A.G. *Phys. Rev.,* **57**, 897 (1940) (Ag I).

## Al

ERIKSSON, K.B.S. and H.B.S. ISBERG. *Arkiv fys.,* **23**, 527 (1963) (Al I).
FERNER, E. *Arkiv mat., astron., fys.,* **36A**, No.1 (1948) (Al V, Al VI, Al VII, Al VIII, Al IX, Al X, Al XI).
FLEMBERG, H. *Arkiv mat., astron., fys.,* **28A**, No.18 (1942) (Al XII).

## Ar

PETERSSON, B. *Arkiv fys.,* **27**, 317 (1964) (Ar I).
HERZBERG, G. *Proc. Roy. Soc.,* **248A**, 309 (1958) (Ar II).

---

* The autoionization lines of the inert gases are not included (see §38).

MINNHAGEN, L. *Arkiv fys.,* **14**, 123, 483 (1959) (Ar II).

MINNHAGEN, L. *Arkiv fys.,* **18**, 97 (1960) (Ar II).

SCHÖNHEIT, E. *Optik,* **23**, 305 (1965/66) (Ar II, Ar III, Ar IV, Ar V, Ar VI, Ar VII, Ar VIII).

EDLÉN, B. *Phys. Rev.,* **62**, 434 (1942) (Ar III).

PHILIPPS, L.W. and W.L. PARKER. *Phys. Rev.,* **60**, 301 (1941) (Ar V, Ar VI, Ar VII, Ar VIII, Ar IX).

FAWCETT, B.C., B.B. JONES, and R. WILSON. *Proc. Phys. Soc.,* **78**, 1223 (1961) (Ar VI, Ar VIII).

FAWCETT, B.C. *Proc. Phys. Soc.,* **86**, 1087 (1965) (Ar IX, Ar X).

FAWCETT, B.C., A.H. GABRIEL, B.B. JONES, and N.J. PEACOCK. *Proc. Phys. Soc.,* **84**, 257 (1964) (Ar IX, Ar X, Ar XI, Ar XII).

FAWCETT, B.C. and A.H. GABRIEL. *Proc. Phys. Soc.,* **84**, 1038 (1964) (Ar XI, Ar XII).


## As

MEGGERS, W.F., A.G. SHENSTONE, and C.E. MOORE. *J. Res., Nat. Bur. Standards,* **45**, 346 (1950) (As I).


## Au

PLATT, J.R. and R.A. SAWYER. *Phys. Rev.,* **60**, 866 (1941) (Au I, Au II).

IGLESIAS, L. *J. Res., Nat. Bur. Standards,* **64A**, 481 (1960) (Au III).


## B

CLEARMAN, H.E. *J. Opt. Soc. America,* **42**, 373 (1952) (B I).

MAL'TSEV, A.A., D.I. KATAEV, and V.M. TATEVSKII. *Optika i Spektroskopiya,* **9**, 713 (1960) (B I, B II, B III).

TYRÉN, F. *Nova acta Reg. Soc. scient. upsaliensis,* **12**, No.1, 7 (1940) (B IV).


## Be

JOHANSSON, L. *Arkiv fys.,* **23**, 119 (1962) (Be I).

JOHANSSON, L. *Arkiv fys.,* **20**, 489 (1961) (Be II).


## Bi

CLEARMAN, H.E. *J. Opt. Soc. America,* **42**, 373 (1952) (Bi I).


## Br

TECH, J.L. *J. Res., Nat. Bur. Standards,* **67A**, 505 (1963) (Br I).

RAMANADHAN, R. and K.R. RAO. *Indian J. Phys.,* **18**, 319 (1944) (Br II).

RAO, R.B. *Indian J. Phys.,* **32**, 497 (1958) (Br II).

RAO, Y.B. *Indian J. Phys.,* **32**, 497 (1958) (BR II).

MARTIN, W.C. and J.L. TECH. *J. Opt. Soc. America,* **51**, 591 (1961) (Br II).

RAO, Y.B. *Indian J. Phys.,* **30**, 371 (1956) (Br III).

RAO, Y.B. *Indian J. Phys.,* **35**, 386 (1961) (Br III).


## C

SHENSTONE, A.G. *Phys. Rev.,* **72**, 411 (1947) (C I).

WILKINSON, P.G. *J. Opt. Soc. America,* **45**, 862 (1955) (C I, C II).

HERZBERG, G. *Proc. Roy. Soc.*, **248A**, 309 (1958) (C I, C II).
WILKINSON, P.G. and K.L. ANDREW. *J. Opt. Soc. America*, **53**, 711 (1963) (C I).
GLAD, S. *Arkiv fys.*, **7**, 7 (1953) (C II).
BOCKASTEN, K. *Arkiv fys.*, **9**, 457 (1955) (C III, C IV).
BOCKASTEN, K. *Arkiv fys.*, **10**, 567 (1956) (C IV).
BOCKASTEN, K., R. HALLIN, and T.P. HUGHES. *Proc. Phys. Soc.*, **81**, 522 (1963) (C IV).
TYRÉN, F. *Nova acta Reg. Soc. scient. upsaliensis*, **12**, No.1, 7 (1940) (C V).

## Ca

KAISER, T.R. *Proc. Phys. Soc.*, **75**, 152 (1960) (Ca I).
GARTON, W.R.S. and K. CODLING. *Proc. Phys. Soc.*, **86**, 1067 (1965) (Ca I).
EDLÉN, B. and P. RISBERG. *Arkiv fys.*, **10**, 553 (1956) (Ca II).
EDLÉN, B. *Phys. Rev.*, **62**, 434 (1942) (Ca V).
PARKER, W.L. and L.W. PHILLIPS. *Phys. Rev.*, **57**, 140 (1940) (Ca IX).

## Cd

SHENSTONE, A.G. and J.T. PITTENGER. *J. Opt. Soc. America*, **39**, 219 (1949) (Cd II, Cd III).
MAZUMDER, K.C. *Indian J. Phys.*, **17**, 229 (1943) (Cd III).
GREEN, M. *Phys. Rev.*, **60**, 117 (1941) (Cd IV).

## Ce

SUGAR, J. *J. Opt. Soc. America*, **55**, 33 (1965) (Ce III).

## Cl

AVELLEN, S. *Arkiv fys.*, **8**, 211 (1954) (Cl I).
EDLÉN, B. *Phys. Rev.*, **62**, 434 (1942) (Cl II).
PARKER, W.L. and L.W. PHILLIPS. *Phys. Rev.*, **57**, 140 (1940) (Cl VI).

## Co

RUSSELL, H.N., R.B. KING, and C.E. MOORE. *Phys. Rev.*, **58**, 407 (1940) (Co I).
SHENSTONE, A.G. *Canad. J. Phys.*, **38**, 677 (1960) (Co III).
ANDERSON, E.E. and J.E. MACK. *Phys. Rev.*, **59**, 717 (1941) (Co VII).
ALEXANDER, E., U. FELDMAN, and B.S. FRAENKEL. *J. Opt. Soc. America*, **55**, 650 (1965) (Co IX, Co X).

## Cr

KIESS, C.C. *J. Res., Nat. Bur. Standards*, **51**, 247 (1953) (Cr I).
KIESS, C.C. *J. Res., Nat. Bur. Standards*, **47**, 385 (1951) (Cr II).
ALEXANDER, E., U. FELDMAN, and B.S. FRAENKEL. *J. Opt. Soc. America*, **55**, 650 (1965) (Cr VI, Cr VII).

## Cu

SHENSTONE, A.G. *Philos. Trans. Roy. Soc.*, **A241**, 297 (1948) (Cu I).
WILKINSON, P.G. *J. Opt. Soc. America*, **47**, 182 (1957) (Cu II).
READER, J., K.W. MEISSNER, and K.L. ANDREW. *J. Opt. Soc. America*, **50**, 221 (1960) (Cu II).

SHENSTONE, A.G. and L. WILETS. *Phys. Rev.,* **83**, 104 (1951) (Cu III).
ALEXANDER, E., U. FELDMAN, and B.S. FRAENKEL. *J. Opt. Soc. America,* **55**, 650 (1965) (Cu XI).

**F**

LIDEN, K. *Arkiv fys.,* **1**, 229 (1949) (F I).
BOCKASTEN, K., R. HALLIN, and T.P. HUGHES. *Proc. Phys. Soc.,* **81**, 522 (1963).
TYRÉN, F. *Nova acta Reg. Soc. scient. upsaliensis,* **12**, No.1, 7 (1940) (F VIII).
FLEMBERG, H. *Arkiv mat., astron., fys.,* **28A**, No.18 (1942) (F VIII).
EDLÉN, B. *Arkiv fys.,* **4**, 441 (1952).

**Fe**

RUSSELL, H.N. and C.E. MOORE. *Trans. Amer. Philos. Soc.,* **34**, 113 (1944) (Fe I).
WILKINSON, P.G. *J. Opt. Soc. America,* **47**, 182 (1957) (Fe I, Fe II).
EDLÉN, B. and P. SWINGS. *Astrophys. J.,* **95**, 532 (1942) (Fe III).
GLAD, S. *Arkiv fys.,* **10**, 291 (1956) (Fe III).
ALEXANDER, E., U. FELDMAN, and B.S. FRAENKEL. *J. Opt. Soc. America,* **55**, 650 (1965)
  (Fe VIII, Fe IX).

**Ge**

VELD, R.D. VAN and K.W. MEISSNER. *J. Opt. Soc. America,* **46**, 598 (1956) (Ge I).
ANDREW, K.L. and K.W. MEISSNER. *J. Opt. Soc. America,* **48**, 31 (1958) (Ge I).
MEISSNER, K.W., R.D. VAN VELD, and P.G. WILKINSON. *J. Opt. Soc. America,* **48**, 1001
  (1958) (Ge I, Ge II).
ANDREW, K.L. and K.W. MEISSNER. *J. Opt. Soc. America,* **49**, 146 (1959) (Ge I).
KAUFMAN, V. and K.L. ANDREW. *J. Opt. Soc. America,* **52**, 1223 (1962) (Ge I, Ge II).
WILKINSON, P.G. and K.L. ANDREW. *J. Opt. Soc. America,* **53**, 710 (1963) (Ge II).
SHENSTONE, A.G. *Proc. Roy. Soc.,* **A276**, 293 (1963) (Ge II).

**He**

HERZBERG, G. *Proc. Roy. Soc.,* **A248**, 309 (1958) (He I).
MARTIN, W.C. *J. Res., Nat. Bur. Standards,* **64A**, 19 (1960) (He I).

**Hg**

WILKINSON, P.G. *J. Opt. Soc. America,* **45**, 862 (1955) (Hg II).
WILKINSON, P.G. *J. Opt. Soc. America,* **53**, 710 (1963) (Hg I, Hg II).

**Hf**

CORLISS, C.H. and W.F. MEGGERS. *J. Res., Nat. Bur. Standards,* **61**, 269 (1958) (Hf I, Hf II,
  Hf III, Hf IV).
KLINKENBERG, P.F.A., TH. A.M. VAN KLEEF, and P.E. NOORMAN. *Physica,* **27**, 1177 (1961)
  (Hf III, Hf IV).

**I**

ONAKA, R. *Phys. Rev.,* **106**, 1178 (1957) (I I).
KIESS, C.C. and C.H. CORLISS. *J. Res. Nat., Bur. Standards,* **63A**, 1 (1959) (I I).

MINNHAGEN, L. *Arkiv fys.*, **21**, 415 (1962) (I I).
MARTIN, W.C. and C.H. CORLISS. *J. Res., Nat. Bur. Standards*, **64A**, 443 (1960) (I II).
FERNANDO, I. *Current Sci.*, **17**, 362 (1948) (I VII).

## In

CLEARMAN, H.E. *J. Opt. Soc. America*, **42**, 373 (1952) (In I).
FERNANDO, I. *Current Sci.*, **17**, 362 (1948) (In III).
GREEN, M. *Phys. Rev.*, **60**, 117 (1941) (In V).

## K

EDLÉN, B. *Phys. Rev.*, **62**, 434 (1942) (K IV).
PARKER, W.L. and L.W. PHILLIPS. *Phys. Rev.*, **57**, 140 (1940) (K VIII).

## Kr

PETERSSON, B. *Arkiv fys.*, **27**, 317 (1964) (Kr I).
SCHÖNHEIT, E. *Optik*, **23**, 305 (1965/1966) (Kr II, Kr III, Kr IV, Kr V, Kr VI, Kr VII,
    Kr VIII).
FAWCETT, B.C., B.B. JONES, and R. WILSON. *Proc. Phys. Soc.*, **78**, 1223 (1961) (Kr V, Kr VI,
    Kr VII, Kr VIII).
FAWCETT, B.C. and A.H. GABRIELL. *Proc. Phys. Soc.*, **84**, 1038 (1964) (Kr IX, Kr X).
KONONOV, E.YA. and S.L. MANDEL'SHTAM. *Optika i Spektroskopiya*, **19**, 145 (1965) (Kr X,
    Kr XI, Kr XII, Kr XIII).

## Li

HERZBERG, G. and H.R. MOORE. *Canad. J. Phys.*, **37**, 1293 (1959) (Li II).
FREYTAG, E. *Naturwissenschaften*, **46**, 314 (1959) (Li II, Li III).
BOGEN, P. and H. CONRADS. *C.R. VI Conf. Internat. Phénomènes d'Ionisation dans les Gaz*,
    *Paris*, 1963, **3**, 337 (Li III).

## Mg

RISBERG, P. *Arkiv fys.*, **9**, 483 (1955) (Mg II).
SODERQVIST, J. *Arkiv mat., astron. fys.*, **32A**, No.19, 1946 (Mg IV, Mg V, Mg VI, Mg VII,
    Mg VIII, Mg IX, Mg X).
SODERQVIST, J. *Arkiv mat., astron., fys.*, **30A**, No.11 (1944) (Mg VIII, Mg IX, Mg X)..
FLEMBERG, H. *Arkiv mat., astron., fys.*, **28A**, No.18 (1942) (Mg XI).

## Mn

GARCIA–RIQUELME, O. *An. Real. soc. esp. fis. y quim.*, **45A**, 435, 547 (1949) (Mn I).
CATALAN, M.A., W.F. MEGGERS, and O. GARCIA–RIQUELME. *J. Res., Nat. Bur. Standards*,
    **68A**, 9 (1964) (Mn I).
CURTIS, C.W. *J. Opt. Soc. America*, **42**, 300 (1952) (Mn II).
IGLESIAS, L. *J. Opt. Soc. America*, **46**, 449 (1956) (Mn II).
IGLESIAS, L. *J. Opt. Soc. America*, **47**, 852 (1957) (Mn II).
GARCIA–RIQUELME, O., L. IGLESIAS, and R. VELASCO. *An. Real. soc. esp. fis. y quim.*, **53A**, 77
    (1957) (Mn II).

IGLESIAS, L. and R. VELASCO. *An. Real. soc. esp. fis. y quim.*, **59A**, 227 (1963) (Mn II).

IGLESIAS, L. *An. Real. soc. esp. fis. y quim.*, **60A**, 147 (1964) (Mn II).

CATALAN, M.A. *An. Real. soc. esp. fis. y quim.*, **53A**, 179 (1957) (Mn III).

ALEXANDER, E., U. FELDMAN, and B.S. FRAENKEL. *J. Opt. Soc. America*, **55**, 650 (1965) (Mn VIII).

## Mo

RICO, F.R. *An. Real. soc. esp. fis. y quim.*, **53A**, 185 (1957) (Mo II, Mo III, Mo IV, Mo V).

KIESS, C.C. *J. Res. Nat. Bur. Standards*, **60**, 375 (1958) (Mo II).

RICO, F.R. *An. Real. soc. esp. fis. y quim.*, **50A**, 185 (1954) (Mo III).

RICO, F.R. *An. Real. soc. esp. fis. y quim.*, **61A**, 103 (1965) (Mo III).

CHARLES, G.W. *Phys. Rev.*, **77**, 120 (1950) (Mo VI, Mo VII, Mo VIII).

## N

WILKINSON, P.G. *J. Opt. Soc. America*, **45**, 862 (1955) (N I).

ERIKSSON, K.B.S. *Arkiv fys.*, **13**, 429 (1958) (N I).

HERZBERG, G. *Proc. Roy. Soc.*, **248A**, 309 (1958) (N I).

ERIKSSON, K.B.S. *Arkiv fys.*, **13**, 303 (1958) (N II).

TILFORD, S.G. *J. Opt. Soc. America*, **53**, 1051 (1963) (N V).

HALLIN, R. *Arkiv fys.*, **30**, 539 (1965) (N IV, N V).

BOCKASTEN, K., R. HALLIN, K.B. JOHANSSON, and P. TSUI. *Phys. Lett.*, **8**, 181 (1964) (N V, (N VI).

TYRÉN, F. *Nova acta Reg. Soc. scient. upsaliensis*, **12**, No.1, 7 (1940) (N VI).

## Na

WILKINSON, P.G. *J. Opt. Soc. America*, **45**, 862 (1955) (Na III).

SODERQVIST, J. *Arkiv mat., astron., fys.*, **32A**, No.19 (1946) (Na V, Na VI, Na VII, Na VIII, Na IX).

SODERQVIST, J. *Arkiv mat., astron., fys.*, **30A**, No.11 (1944) (Na VII, Na VIII, Na IX).

## Nb

IGLESIAS, L. *An Real. soc. esp. fis. y quim.*, **50A**, 135 (1954) (Nb II).

IGLESIAS, L. *An Real. soc. esp. fis. y quim.*, **53A**, 249 (1957) (Nb II).

IGLESIAS, L. *J. Opt. Soc. America*, **45**, 856 (1955) (Nb III).

CHARLES, G.W. *Phys. Rev.*, **77**,120 (1950) (Nb V, Nb VI, Nb VII),

## Ne

PETERSSON, B. *Arkiv fys.*, **27**, 317 (1964) (Ne I).

MEISSNER, K.W., R.D. VAN VELD, and P.G. WILKINSON. *J. Opt. Soc. America*, **48**, 1001 (1958) (Ne II).

WILKINSON, P.G. and K.L. ANDREW. *J. Opt. Soc. America*, **53**, 710 (1963) (Ne II).

BASHKIN, S., L. HEROUX, and J. SHAW. *Phys. Lett.*, **13**, 229 (1964) (Ne II, Ne III, Ne IV, Ne V, Ne VI, Ne VII).

TILFORD, S.G. and L.E. GIDDINGS. *Astrophys. J.*, **141**, 1222 (1965) (Ne IV).

PAUL, F.W. and H.D. POLSTER. *Phys. Rev.*, **59**, 424 (1941) (Ne IV, Ne V, Ne VI).

FAWCETT, B.C., B.B. JONES, and R. WILSON. *Proc. Phys. Soc.,* **78**, 1223 (1961) (Ne VI, Ne VII, Ne VIII).

BOCKASTEN, K., R. HALLIN, and T.P. HUGHES. *Proc. Phys. Soc.,* **81**, 522 (1963) (Ne VI, Ne VII, Ne VIII).

FAWCETT, B.C., A.H. GABRIEL, B.B. JONES, and N.J. PEACOCK. *Proc. Phys. Soc.,* **84**, 257 (1964) (Ne VII, Ne VIII, Ne IX).

HOUSE, L.L. and G.A. SAWYER. *Astrophys. J.,* **139**, 775 (1964) (Ne VII, Ne VIII).

## Ni

WILKINSON, P.G. *J. Opt. Soc. America,* **45**, 862 (1955) (Ni I, Ni II).

SHENSTONE, A.G. *J. Opt. Soc. America,* **44**, 749 (1954) (Ni III).

ANDERSON, E.E. and J.E. MACK. *Phys. Rev.,* **59**, 717 (1941) (Ni VIII).

ALEXANDER, E., U. FELDMAN, and B.S. FRAENKEL. *J. Opt. Soc. America,* **55**, 650 (1965) (Ni X, Ni XI).

## O

WILKINSON, P.G. *J. Opt. Soc. America,* **45**, 862 (1955) (O I).

HERZBERG, G. *Proc. Roy. Soc.,* **248A**, 309 (1958) (O I).

TILFORD, S.G. and P.G. WILKINSON. *J. Opt. Soc. America,* **54**, 322 (1964) (O III).

BOCKASTEN, K., R. HALLIN, K.B. JOHANSSON, and P. TSUI. *Phys. Lett.,* **8**, 181 (1964) (O III, O V).

BOCKASTEN, K., R. HALLIN, and T.P. HUGHES. *Proc. Phys. Soc.,* **81**, 522 (1963) (O VI).

PEACOCK, N.J. *Proc. Phys. Soc.,* **84**, 803 (1964) (O VI, O VII).

TYRÉN, F. *Nova acta Reg. Soc. scient. upsaliensis,* **12**, No.1, 7 (1940) (O VII).

EDLÉN, B. *Arkiv fys.,* **4**, 441 (1952) (O VII).

JAHODA, F.C., F.L. RIBE, G.A. SAWYER, and R.W.P. McWHIRTER. *C.R. VI Conf. Internat. Phénomènes d'Ionisation dans les Gaz., Paris,* 1963, **3**, 347 (O VIII).

## Os

GLUCK, G.G., Y. BORDARIER, J. BAUCHE, and TH.A.M. VAN KLEFF. *Physica,* **30**, 2068 (1964).

## P

MARTIN, W.C. *J. Opt. Soc. America,* **49**, 1071 (1959) (P I, P II).

## Pb

GLEARMAN, H.E. *J. Opt. Soc. America,* **42**, 373 (1952) (Pb I).

## Pd

SHENSTONE, A.G. *Proc. Roy. Soc.,* **A219**, 419 (1953) (Pd I).

## Po

CHARLES, G.W., D.J. HUNT, G. PISH, and D.L. TIMMA. *J. Opt. Soc. America,* **45**, 869 (1955) (Po I).

## Pr

ZALUBAS, R. and M. WILSON. *J. Res. Nat. Bur. Standards,* **69A**, 59 (1965).

GROSSWHITE, H.M., G.H. DIEKE, and W.J. CARTER. *J. Chem. Phys.*, **43**, 2047 (1965) (Pr IV).
SUGAR, J. *J. Opt. Soc. America*, **55**, 1058 (1965) (Pr IV).

## Re

KLINKENBERG, P.F., W.F. MEGGERS, R. VELASCO, and M.A. CATALAN. *J. Res., Nat. Bur. Standards*, **59**, 319 (1957) (Re I).
MEGGERS, W.F., M.A. CATALAN, and M. SALES. *J. Res., Nat. Bur. Standards*, **61**, 441 (1958).

## Rh

MOLNAR, J.P. and W.J. HITCHCOCK. *J. Opt. Soc. America*, **30**, 523 (1940) (Rh I).
SANCHO, F.J. *An. Real. soc. esp. fis. y quim.*, **54A**, 41, 65 (1958) (Rh II).

## Ru

SHENSTONE, A.G. and W.F. MEGGERS. *J. Res., Nat. Bur. Standards*, **61**, 373 (1958).

## S

TORESSON, Y.G. *Arkiv fys.*, **18**, 417 (1960) (S I).
FERNER, E. *Arkiv mat., astron., fys.*, **36A**, No. 1 (1948) (S VII, S VIII, S IX, S X).

## Sb

MEGGERS, W.F. and C.J. HUMPHREYS. *J. Res., Nat. Bur. Standards*, **28**, 463 (1942).
FERNANDO, I. *Current. Sci.*, **17**, 362 (1948) (Sb V).

## Sc

EDLÉN, B. *Phys. Rev.*, **62**, 434 (1942) (Sc VI).
PARKER, W.L. and L.W. PHILIPS. *Phys. Rev.*, **57**, 140 (1940) (Sc X).
FAWCETT, B.C. *Proc. Phys. Soc.*, **86**, 1087 (1965) (Sc XII, Sc XIII).

## Si

RADZIEMSKI, L.J. and K.L. ANDREW. *J. Opt. Soc. America*, **55**, 474 (1965) (Si I).
WILKINSON, P.G. *J. Opt. Soc. America*, **45**, 862 (1955) (Si I, Si II).
MAL'TSEV, A.A., D.I. KATAEV, and V.M. TATEVSKII. *Optika i Spektroskopiya*, **9**, 713 (1960) (Si I, Si II).
SHENSTONE, A.G. *Proc. Roy. Soc.*, **A261**, 153 (1961) (Si II).
TORESSON, Y.G. *Arkiv fys.*, **18**, 389 (1960) (Si III).
TORESSON, Y.G. *Arkiv fys.*, **17**, 179 (1960) (Si IV).
FERNER, E. *Arkiv mat. astron. fys.*, **28A**, No.4 (1942) (Si V, Si VI, Si VII, Si VIII, Si IX, Si X, Si XI, Si XII).

## Sn

MEGGERS, W.F. *J. Res. Nat. Bur. Standards*, **24**, 153 (1940) (Sn I).
GREEN, M. *Phys. Rev.*, **60**, 117 (1941) (Sn VI).

## Te

HANDRUP, M.B. and J.E. MACK. *Physica*, **30**, 1245 (1964) (Te II).

CROOKER, A.M. and Y.N. JOSHI. *J. Opt. Soc. America,* **54**, 553 (1964) (Te III, Te IV, Te V, Te VI).

## Th

KLINKENBERG, P.F.A. *Physica,* **16**, 618 (1950) (Th III).
KLINKENBERG, P.F.A. and R.J. LANG. *Physica,* **15**, 774 (1949) (Th IV).

## Ti

FAWCETT, B.C. *Proc. Phys. Soc.,* **86**, 1087 (1965) (Ti XIII, Ti XIV).

## Tl

CLEARMAN, H.E. *J. Opt. Soc. America,* **42**, 373 (1952) (Tl I).
REEVES, E.M., W.R.S. GARTON, and A. BASS. *Proc. Phys. Soc.,* **86**, 1077 (1965) (Tl I).

## V

MEGGERS, W.F. and C.E. MOORE. *J. Res., Nat. Bur. Standards,* **25**, 83 (1940) (V II).
IGLESIAS, L. *An. Real. soc. esp. fis. y quim.,* **58**, 191 (1962) (V III).
ALEXANDER, E., U. FELDMAN, and B.S. FRAENKEL. *J. Opt. Soc. America,* **55**, 650 (1965) (V VI).
FAWCETT, B.C. *Proc. Phys. Soc.,* **86**, 1087 (1965) (V XV, V XVI).

## W

LAUN, D.D. *J. Res., Nat. Bur. Standards,* **68**, 207 (1964).

## Xe

PETERSSON, B. *Arkiv fys.,* **27**, 317 (1964) (XE I).
HERMAN, L. and K.C. CLARK. *J. Quant. Spectr. Rad. Trans.,* **5**, 765 (1965).
MINNHAGEN, L., B. PETERSSON, and L. STIGMARK. *Arkiv. fys.,* **16**, 541 (1960) (Xe I, Xe II, Xe III).
FAWCETT, B.C., B.B. JONES, and R. WILSON. *Proc. Phys. Soc.,* **78**, 1223 (1961) (Xe, V, Xe VI, Xe VII, Xe VIII, Xe IX).
SCHÖNHEIT, E. *Optik,* **23**, 305 (1965/1966) (Xe VI, Xe VII, Xe VIII, Xe IX).
FAWCETT, B.C., A.H. GABRIELL, B.B. JONES, and N.J. PEACOCK. *Proc. Phys. Soc.,* **84**, 257 (1964) (Xe IX).

## Yb

BRYANT, B.W. *J. Opt. Soc. America,* **55**, 771 (1965) (Yb III, Yb IV).

## Zn

CROOKER, A.M. and K.A. DICK. *Cand. J. Phys.,* **42**, 766 (1964) (Zn IV).
ALEXANDER, E., B.S. FRAENKEL, U. FELDMAN, and A. JACOBS. *J. Quant. Spectr. Rad. Trans.,* **2**, 725 (1962) (Zn VIII).

## Zr

KIESS, C.C. *J. Res., Nat. Bur. Standards,* **56**, 167 (1956) (Zr III, Zr IV).

# CHAPTER VI

# Energy Measurements
# in the Vacuum Ultraviolet

## 31. METHODS OF MEASUREMENT OF ABSOLUTE AND
## RELATIVE INTENSITIES

The main tasks of energy measurements in spectroscopy are to determine the intensity distribution in continuous spectra, to compare the integrated intensities of individual spectral lines, and finally to measure the absolute spectral or integrated source intensity.

If the geometrical parameters of the source and the conditions of light propagation are known, the measured intensity or brightness can be converted to other energy characteristics, such as the power radiated by unit source volume for the entire line width (this power is often defined as the spectral line intensity). The total power radiated by the source in any given wavelength interval, the luminous flux transmitted through the spectrometer slit, and other parameters can also be calculated from these data [1].

We will consider both homochromatic and heterochromatic photometry.

Homochromatic photometry is fairly simple, and it does not require preliminary calibration of the entire recording system (the spectral instrument and the radiation detector). Absolute measurements and heterochromatic photometry are much more complicated.

Absolute measurements can be carried out by two fundamentally different techniques. The first method makes use of standard light sources with a known energy distribution in the spectrum. The second method calls for a preliminary determination of the instrument transmission and the detector sensitivity.

We can write a general functional relation

$$i = K_1(\lambda)K_2(\lambda)\Phi(\lambda), \tag{24}$$

where $i$ is the instrument reading (e.g., the reading of the ammeter which measures the current in the photomultiplier amplifier circuit, the count rate of ions in the ionization chamber, etc.), $\Phi(\lambda)$ is the luminous flux incident on the slit, $K_1(\lambda)$ is the transmission of the spectral instrument, $K_2(\lambda)$ is a coefficient which represents the detector sensitivity: this is the signal produced in the detector by one photon of incident radiation (for ionization chambers, this coefficient depends on the photoionization quantum yield of the filling gas, on the absorption cross section in the gas, and on a number of other factors).

## First method

A standard source of known spectral brightness is used. The incoming luminous flux $\Phi(\lambda)$ can then be calculated from the known geometry of the spectral instrument. The output signal $i$ then gives the product $K_1(\lambda)K_2(\lambda)$ (the effective quantum yield of the entire system) at various wavelength. The entire recording system (the spectral instrument plus the detector) is thus calibrated as a whole.

In what follows we will consider some methods for setting up standard sources in the vacuum ultraviolet (see §33).

## Second method

The two coefficients entering equation (24) are determined independently. If the transmission $K_1(\lambda)$ is known (see §34), the incoming luminous flux can be determined simply by measuring the outgoing flux. The coefficient $K_2(\lambda)$ is determined by comparison with a standard detector. Absolute measurements require knowledge of the product $K_1(\lambda)K_2(\lambda)$. For relative measurements, on the other hand, it suffices to know how the product of these coefficients varies with wavelength. The second method is particularly suitable for measurement of relative intensities with a nonselective detector.

The method using a source of known spectral brightness has a number of advantages compared to the method which involves separate measurements of the instrument transmission and the detector response. Here the instrument is calibrated under the actual working conditions, and we do not require the detector response: the entire setup is calibrated as a whole.

## 32. HOMOCHROMATIC PHOTOMETRY

Comparison of two fluxes of identical spectral composition in the vacuum ultraviolet in principle does not differ from a similar comparison in the near ultraviolet. Photoelectric recording can be done with any detector which responds to the relevant wavelengths. Photographic recording, however, is not so easy in the vacuum ultraviolet, since the usual methods of plate calibration do not apply: it is impossible to make a stepped wedge attenuator which will be transparent in the vacuum ultraviolet. Moreover, most of the instruments used in the vacuum ultraviolet are astigmatic, and the application of stepped wedges is not an easy undertaking.

The characteristic curves are generally constructed by the method of grids [2,3]. The transmission of two grids is not additive, and they should not be placed one behind the other because of moiré effects. Grids can be placed either in front of the slit or in front of the grating. Before a grid can be used, however, one has to establish that the diffraction effects do not cause a noticeable dependence of grid transmission on wavelength. If the transmission is distorted to such an extent that this dependence is felt, grids calibrated in the visible spectrum are inapplicable to the vacuum ultraviolet. The grids are therefore best calibrated photoelectrically after having been mounted in the spectrometer.

Simple and convenient methods have been developed for producing a whole range of grids [3]. The main shortcoming of the grid method is that each point on the characteristic curve is obtained by taking a separate exposure, and the requirements of source stability are thus exceptionally exacting. The characteristic curves can be plotted from the known multiplet intensity ratios. For example, the lines of the light elements with few outer electrons closely follow the *LS* coupling intensity rule, and the intensity ratio of the multiplet components can be calculated theoretically.

Before this method can be applied, one has to establish that there is no reabsorption. The results are more reliable for multiplet components with a common upper level. If the multiplet components have different upper levels, the method is applicable only in cases of known (in particular Boltzmann) distribution of atoms or ions over the levels.

The method of multiplets is an auxiliary technique. It is used after a preliminary check by other methods. The intensity ratio in some multiplets of N I, Al III, Si IV, and other ions has been checked experimentally [4–6] and found to fit the theory.

An improved version of this method calls for the measurement of the intensity ratio of the multiplet components with a linear-response detector, e.g., a photomultiplier. The slope of the characteristic curve is then found from the measured (not the theoretical!) intensity ratio [7]. Instead of measuring the intensities of the multiplet lines, one can measure the relative intensities of the rotational line structure in molecular bands [3].

Other methods are also available. For example, the dependence of line intensity on the current in the discharge tube is determined photoelectrically and the spectra are then photographed at various currents. The characteristic curve of the emulsion is then plotted from the known intensity ratios of the various photographs [8]. This method is clearly valid if the dependence of source intensity on all the other parameters of the electrical circuit (e.g., the capacitance) is known [7]. This method is sensitive to errors associated with source instability.

One of the methods of spectrometer calibration is based on simultaneous photographs of spectra being taken in the vacuum ultraviolet and in the visible. When lines with a common upper level which lie in different spectral regions are recorded with different instruments, a change in discharge conditions will produce an equal change in the intensities of the two lines.* Measurement of the intensity ratio of two lines in the visible yields the corresponding ratio for the vacuum ultraviolet. The characteristic curve can thus be plotted.

The contrast factor of a photographic emulsion in the vacuum ultraviolet can be determined as in the visible, using stepped diaphragms or rotating disks mounted at the Sirks point (see p. 103). This method involves certain errors if the flux density at the diaphragm is nonuniform across the beam. To avoid these errors, Jones [7] used an adjustable stepped slit, calibrated with a photocell which measured the luminous fluxes from the various steps of the slit in the zero order spectrum.

The method of variable exposure is often used in the construction of the characteristic curve in the vacuum ultraviolet. This method is applicable if the deviations from the Bunsen and Roscoe law for the particular emulsion used are not large. To avoid multiple exposures, two or three photographs can be used and the entire characteristic curve is obtained by parallel translation of the sections obtained for near lines of different intensities [9,10].

In most cases, however, the characteristic curve is constructed making use of the following property of photographic emulsions: a photographic emulsion sensitized by a phosphor retains a constant contrast factor at all wavelengths [11–13]. The characteristic curve is then constructed from density markings in the part of the spectrum where normal photometry is applicable, e.g., between 2200 and 2000 Å (using grids or stepped wedge attenuators) [4,5]. A hydrogen lamp can be used as the light source. The spectrum is photographed on two films cut off the same spool; the two pieces of film are equally sensitized and are developed at the same time. This method is relatively simple and reliable.

Comparison of two radiation fluxes of approximately the same spectral composition in the vacuum ultraviolet is actually applied in all measurements involving line profiles, absorption cross sections, reflection coefficients, spectroscopic analysis, and other studies.

---

* Provided the intensity is not distorted by reabsorption.

## 33. DETERMINATION OF SYSTEM EFFICIENCY WITH STANDARD SOURCES

### The method of line pairs with a common upper level

The source used in these measurements is such that the intensity ratio of its lines can be determined in the visible spectrum.

The ratio of the intensities $B_1$ and $B_2$ of two lines in the vacuum ultraviolet is then found from the known intensity ratio $B_3/B_4$ of lines in the visible spectrum, provided that the lines $\lambda_1$ and $\lambda_3$ and also $\lambda_2$ and $\lambda_4$ have common upper levels (Figure 177) [4, 5, 14–16]. In this case we may write

$$\frac{B_1}{B_2} = \frac{B_3}{B_4} \cdot \frac{A_1}{A_2} \cdot \frac{A_4}{A_3} \cdot \frac{\lambda_2}{\lambda_1} \cdot \frac{\lambda_3}{\lambda_4}, \tag{25}$$

where $A_i$ are the transition probabilities, $\lambda_i$ are the wavelengths.

Selection of appropriate lines throughout the entire spectrum gives the dependence of the effective quantum yield of the entire system (spectral instrument + radiation detector) on wavelength. If the detector response $K_2(\lambda)$ is known, this method will give in relative units the instrument transmission at various wavelengths, $K_1(\lambda)$.

The method is applicable when the following conditions are observed:

1) No reabsorption.

2) The ratio of transition probabilities of lines with a common upper level is known.

3) The fine structure levels are resolved, and for the unresolved levels the occupancy is proportional to the statistical weight.

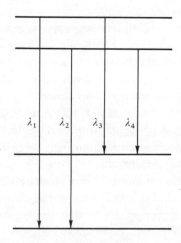

Figure 177

Energy level diagram illustrating the method of line pairs.

To determine the spectrometer efficiency, we require a selection of spectral lines covering with uniform density the entire relevant region of the spectrum. The short-wave and the long-wave parts of the spectrum are recorded simultaneously on two separate instruments, and it is absolutely essential that both instruments receive radiation from the same part of the source.

Hinnov and Hofmann used He II and H lines for calibration [15] (see Table 20). Each of these lines was paired with its counterpart in the visible spectrum, and the pairs with a common upper level were used in calibration. The 537 Å helium line, which has a common upper level with the 5015 Å helium line, could not be used, since reabsorption remained substantial at all pressures. A tube with a cooled hollow cathode was used as the light source in these measurements. The helium pressure in the light tube was chosen so that the attenuation of the He II lines by photoionization of atomic helium was negligible.

This method was applied to calibration of two spectrometers: one a grazing-incidence instrument and the other a Seya–Namioka spectrometer. The main source of errors in this calibration is the deviation from statistical distribution of atoms over the energy levels. This factor is significant, since the fine structure of H and He II remained unresolved under the experimental conditions.

An estimate of the probable deviations from equilibrium shows that significant deviations are unlikely for electron concentrations $N_e > 10^{13}$ cm$^{-3}$ in He II and $N_e > 10^{12}$ cm$^{-3}$ in H [15]. Since the electron concentrations in a hollow cathode may be substantially less, considerable errors are possible. Hot-plasma sources, such as the Stellarator [15], ZETA [16], and the creeping spark [17], are more effective in this respect.

Al III and Si IV lines can be applied to determine the spectrometer efficiency [5]. The transition probabilities for these lines are readily found from the tables of Bates and Damgaard [18]. These calculations are approximate and therefore less accurate than the calculation of the transition probabilities of the H and He II lines. The error in the determination of the transition probabilities of the Al III and Si IV lines therefore may additionally distort the spectrometer calibration. However, since the fine structure of most terms is resolved in this case, the assumption of statistical distribution is unnecessary.

It has been repeatedly established that the determination of the transition probabilities of the lines of the lithium and sodium isoelectronic series from the tables of Bates and Damgaard is sufficiently reliable [19–21]. Al III and Si IV lines were excited in a low-voltage vacuum spark [22]. Carbon, aluminum, and silumin were used as the electrode material. Lack of reabsorption was verified from line intensity ratios in doublets. The spectrum intensity and the line intensity ratio in doublets were adjusted by varying the circuit capacitance and voltage until further reduction of capacitance failed to affect the intensity in the doublet, i.e., zero reabsorption conditions were attained. A measurement of the line intensity ratio in a doublet with

Table 20

| Ion or atom | Line used in calibration $(\lambda_1, \text{Å})$ | Transition | Comparison line $(\lambda_2, \text{Å})$ | Transition | Transition probability ratio, $A_1/A_2$ |
|---|---|---|---|---|---|
| Al III | 2213 | $4^2P_{3/2}-5^2D$ | 4701 | $4^2F-5^2D$ | 1.30 |
| Si IV | 1727 | $3^2D-4^2P_{1/2}$ | 4116 | $4^2S-4^2P_{1/2}$ | 3.4 |
| He II | 1640* | 2—3 | 256* | $1s^2S-3p^2P$ | 0.80 |
| Al III | 1353 | $3^2D-5^2F$ | 4150 | $4^2D-5^2F$ | 2.1 |
| He II | 1215 | 2—4 | 4686 | 3—4 | 0.93 |
| Al III | 1162 | $3^2D-6^2F$ | 2763 | $4^2D-6^2F$ | 1.9 |
| He II | 1085 | 2—5 | 3203 | 3—5 | 1.15 |
| H | 1026 | $1s^2S-3p^2P$ | 6563 | 2—3 | 1.26 |
| H | 973 | $1s^2S-4p^2P$ | 4861 | 2—4 | 1.52 |
| H | 950 | $1s^2S-5p^2P$ | 4340 | 2—5 | 1.63 |
| H | 938 | $1s^2S-6p^2P$ | 4102 | 2—6 | 1.70 |
| Al III | 857 | $3^2P_{3/2}-5^2S$ | 3713 | $4P_{3/2}-5^2S$ | 1.39 |
| Al III | 696 | $3^2S-4^2P_{3/2}$ | 3601 | $3^2D-4^2P_{3/2}$ | 0.34 |
| Al III | 696 | $3^2S-4^2P_{3/2}$ | 5696 | $4^2S-4^2P_{3/2}$ | 0.59 |
| He I | 537 | $1s^2\ {}^1S-1s3p^1P$ | 5016 | $1s2s^1S-1s3p^1P$ | 41.4 |
| Li III | 482 | 2—5 | 4501 | 4—5 | 0.94 |
| Si IV | 455 | $3^2S-4^2P_{3/2}$ | 4089 | $4^2S-4^2P_{3/2}$ | 2.1 |
| He II | 243 | $1s^2S-4p^2P$ | 4686 | 3—4 | 1.42 |
| He II | 237 | $1s^2S-5p^2P$ | 3203 | 3—5 | 1.87 |
| He II | 234 | $1s^2S-6p^2P$ | 2733 | 3—6 | 2.12 |
| He II | 234 | $1s^2S-6p^2P$ | 6560 | 4—6 | 2.14 |
| He II | 232 | $1s^2S-7p^2P$ | 2511 | 3—7 | 2.25 |
| He II | 232 | $1s^2S-7p^2P$ | 5411 | 4—7 | 2.49 |
| He II | 231 | $1s^2S-8p^2P$ | 2385 | 3—8 | 2.34 |
| He II | 231 | $1s^2S-8p^2P$ | 4859 | 4—8 | 2.71 |
| Li III | 105 | $1s^2S-5p^2P$ | 4501 | 4—5 | 1.53 |

* The 1640 Å line can be used in calibration if the instrumental transmission at 243 Å and 256 Å is taken to be the same,

resolved upper levels provided an indication of the statistical distribution over the energy levels. The calibration was done between 450 and 2200 Å. The coefficient $K_1(\lambda_1)K_2(\lambda_1)/K_1(\lambda_2)K_2(\lambda_2)$ was determined experimentally from the relation

$$\left(\frac{B_1}{B_2}\right)' = \frac{K_1(\lambda_1)K_2(\lambda_1)}{K_1(\lambda_2)K_2(\lambda_2)}\ \frac{B_1}{B_2}\ , \qquad (26)$$

where $(B_1/B_2)'$ is the measured intensity ratio, $B_1/B_2$ is the source intensity ratio.

The spectrometer efficiency can be found also from variation in the relative intensities of the nitrogen multiplets [4]. Using the method of line pairs with a common upper level, we can even calibrate the absolute intensities of the source spectral lines.

Without reabsorption, the intensity of the short-wave component $B_1$ is related to the intensity of the long-wave component $B_3$ and the transition probabilities $A_1$ and $A_3$ by the equality

$$B_1 = B_3 \frac{A_1}{A_3} \frac{\lambda_3}{\lambda_1} . \tag{27}$$

Monochromatic radiation at wavelength $\lambda_1$ can be considered as a standard. The standard radiation flux $B_1$ and the radiation in the visible spectrum $B_3$ should be recorded simultaneously. The source intensity must be exactly the same in the direction of both instruments.

If a sufficient number of such pairs, uniformly filling the relevant region, are selected and measured in the source spectrum, we end up with a perfect standard source for the vacuum ultraviolet. Sources which can be calibrated to standards in this way were proposed in [15–17, 23, 24].

Van Eck et al. [23] measured the absolute intensity of the He I 537 Å line from the intensity of the 5015 Å line. The 537 Å line did not suffer from reabsorption, since the strong Doppler broadening reduced the absorption coefficient at the line center.

The intensities of the hydrogen Lyman lines were determined from the intensities of the Balmer series.

The light sources were hollow-cathode tubes, ZETA and Stellarator machines [15, 16]. The intensities of the He II lines ($\lambda = 231–237$ Å) were measured in the spectrum of the hollow-cathode tube, and the intensity of the Al III lines was determined in the spectrum of a low-voltage vacuum spark [24].

The intensities of the Lyman lines of doubly ionized lithium were determined from the intensity of the Paschen series. The spectrum of Li III was excited in a creeping spark [17].

The accuracy of intensity determination of a standard source depends on the errors of photometric measurements and the errors in the calculation of transition probabilities. The total error is generally not less than 40–50%. Table 20 lists the spectral lines which can be used as standards in the vacuum ultraviolet. The lines of Be II, Mg II, B III, and P V are apparently also suitable for this purpose, but their applicability has never been checked.

A significant shortcoming of standard sources whose intensity is determined by the method of line pairs is that the spectrometer is calibrated at individual wavelengths, and not for the entire spectral region. This shortcoming is particularly felt if the spectrometer transmission varies steeply (and nonmonotonically!) with wavelength.

**Blackbody emission**

A brightness standard in the vacuum ultraviolet is provided by individual spectral lines whose intensity corresponds to the emission intensity of a blackbody at the source temperature [25, 26]. Various aspects relating to such sources were discussed by Boldt [26]. He used the emission of an argon arc at atmospheric pressure. The plasma was produced in Maecker's arc [27] (see § 6). Hydrogen was pumped into the arc through the openings (see Figure 31) in amounts which did not cause a noticeable change in temperature. The concentration of hydrogen nevertheless was sufficient to emit blackbody radiation in the direction of the arc axis.

Special tests showed that the arc temperature and the hydrogen concentration remained constant in the part of the discharge where hydrogen emitted. The counter-current of gas prevented hydrogen from reaching the variable-temperature parts of the arc. The entire gas layer where hydrogen was excited thus could be regarded as homogeneous.

When a homogeneous luminous column had been created, it was necessary to ensure conditions under which the emission could be recorded with a vacuum spectrograph without the danger of absorption. To this end, a vacuum chamber with differential pumpout was used (see Figure 32, §6). For a bandwidth of about 2 Å, the emission intensity in $L_\alpha$ (1216 Å) was found to remain constant over 10 Å. Uniform radiation was thus obtained in the wavelength interval from 1211 Å to 1221 Å corresponding to blackbody radiation at 12,000°K.

If other gases are injected into Maecker's arc, radiation standards corresponding to resonance lines of other atoms are similarly obtained. For example, the C I and N I lines uniformly fill the spectral region from 1000 to 1800 Å and can be used as radiation standards [28, 29].

The emission of an optically thick helium and hydrogen layer in a shock tube also can be used as a standard source in the vacuum ultraviolet [15].

### Synchrotron radiation

As we have noted in §5, the energy distribution in the spectrum of synchrotron radiation can be accurately calculated if the electron energy is known. Experimental work has shown that the theoretical formulas adequately fit the results of measurements.

When synchrotron radiation is used as a standard source, we should remember that this radiation is polarized and we in fact measure the system efficiency for light of definite polarization. To find the spectrometer efficiency for natural unpolarized light, the degree of polarization of the synchrotron radiation and the polarization properties of the instrument should be known.

Various methods have been proposed so far for polarization measurements in the ultraviolet (see § 20), and this no longer constitutes a serious restriction.

## Radiation of highly ionized hydrogen plasma

High current densities in pulsed sources produce complete dissociation of hydrogen into atoms and a high percentage of these atoms are ionized. As a result, continuous radiation is emitted, both bremsstrahlung (free-free transitions) and recombination radiation (free-bound transitions). The spectral distribution of brightness $B(\lambda)$ can be calculated from the equation [30]

$$B(\lambda) \sim \frac{1}{\lambda^2} e^{-hc/\lambda kT}$$

where $\lambda$ is the wavelength, $h$ is Planck's constant, $c$ is the velocity of light, $k$ is Boltzmann's constant, $T$ is the temperature.

The intensity ratio of two spectral lines can be found by comparing them with the source radiation. The accuracy of these measurements is determined by the accuracy with which the temperature can be measured.* For example, if the source temperature is 20,000°C and it was measured to within 5%, the intensity ratio of the two lines at 2000 Å and 1000 Å can be determined within 20%.

## Radiation of monochromatic sources

Monochromatic sources can also be used as standard radiant sources. Their intensity is measured with detectors of known quantum yield (e.g., counters) and they are then used for spectrometer calibration.

X-ray $K$ and $L$ bands can be conveniently applied to these measurements. Each of these bands can be excited separately, and their emission is highly reproducible. $K$ and $L$ bands are excited by bombarding light elements with electrons or protons [31].

The edges of some long-wave emission bands are the following: Li $K$ 226 Å, Be $K$ 111 Å, Mg $L$ 250 Å, Al $L$ 170 Å, Si $L$ 124 Å [32].

## Other methods of efficiency measurement

The effective quantum yield of a spectrometer in $L_\alpha$ has been measured by an original method based on the selective excitation of a three-quantum level of the hydrogen atom. The number of coincidences of $H_\alpha$ and $L_\alpha$ photons was then measured with a photon counter and a coincidence circuit with a resolution of the order of $10^{-8}$ sec (Figure 178). Simultaneously measuring the number of photons corresponding to the $H_\alpha$ line, we can find the system efficiency in $L_\alpha$ [33, 34].

---

* Methods of plasma temperature determination are discussed in §44.

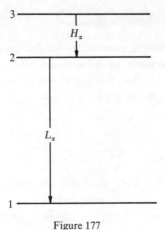

Figure 177
Energy level diagram of hydrogen.

An absolute calibration technique proposed by Garton* measures the light from a condensed helium discharge (pressure of a few torr) after it has passed through a helium-filled ionization chamber ($p \approx 0.1$ T). The intensity ratio of lines in the region of continuous absorption of helium is measured as a function of pressure in the absorption chamber. The number of absorbed photons gives the absolute response of the entire system.

Synchrotron radiation can be applied to calibrate hydrogen lamps** and condensed discharges in inert gases (see § 4). These sources may be used as secondary standards. They can be calibrated not only with synchrotron radiation but also by recording their radiation with instruments and detectors of known spectral response (nonselective detectors are the most suitable for this purpose). The technique of these measurements has been developed in considerable detail for the visible and the near ultraviolet [35].

## 34. DETERMINATION OF TRANSMISSION OF THE SPECTRAL INSTRUMENT

The transmission of a spectral instrument or its efficiency can be determined with the aid of an additional monochromator [35, 36]. In the visible and the near ultraviolet, these measurements can be carried out without any difficulty. The flux passing through the first monochromator is measured, followed by a measurement of the

---

* The method is described by Hinnov and Hofmann [15].
** Data on the energy distribution in the hydrogen spectrum are given in §2.

flux passing through both monochromators. The transmission of the second unit is determined in this way.

Absolute measurements require knowledge of the absolute transmission of the monochromator; for relative measurements, the transmission can be measured in relative units at various wavelengths. These measurements in the vacuum ultraviolet involve considerable experimental difficulties, and an additional monochromator is therefore often used to measure separately the efficiency of the diffraction grating at various incidence angles. Calibration difficulties have been successfully avoided in a number of experimental setups [37–41].

The dependence of grating efficiency on wavelength, incidence angle, coating thickness, coating material, and other factors has been studied. All these measurements show that in numerous cases the energy losses are very substantial and the grating efficiency is less than 1%. Different parts of the grating may have markedly different efficiencies [38].

We will describe one of the methods used in measuring the grating efficiency (Figure 179) [40]. The Seya–Namioka monochromator is equipped with an attachment, which comprises a square box holding an auxiliary grating $G$, a photomultiplier, and a lever arrangement which turns the photomultiplier around the axis $F$. When the photomultiplier is in position $A$, it collects the entire luminous flux $\Phi_0$ reaching the grating. If the photomultiplier is in position $B$, it picks up the luminous flux $\Phi$ attenuated by reflection from the grating being calibrated. During calibration, both gratings $G$ should be in such a position that the monochromator and the attachment transmit the same wavelength. This method will also measure the transmission of spectrographs.

When measuring the transmission of a monochromator with an additional monochromator, we should remember that the incident light is polarized by reflection from the auxiliary monochromator. The monochromator transmission $R$ for natural unpolarized light may differ from the measured transmission. Let the difference be $\Delta R$, and let us find $\Delta R/R$. The light reflected from the first grating has two com-

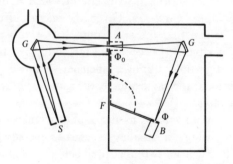

Figure 179

Setup for calibration of a diffraction grating.

ponents, $J_{\parallel}$ and $J_{\perp}$ ($J_{\parallel}$ is the energy of the radiation polarized in a plane parallel to the plane of incidence, $J_{\perp}$ is the energy of the transversely polarized radiation). The corresponding reflection coefficients are $R_{\parallel}$ and $R_{\perp}$, respectively. Let $J_{\parallel}/J_{\perp} = b$, and $R_{\parallel}/R_{\perp} = g$. Then, using simple algebraic manipulations, we find [42]

$$\frac{\Delta R}{R} = \frac{(g-1)(1-b)}{(g+1)(1+b)}. \tag{28}$$

We see that $\Delta R/R$ reaches $30\%$ when $b = g = 3$. For $g = b = \frac{1}{2}$, the error $\Delta R/R$ is of the order of $10\%$.

The coefficients $g$ and $b$ depend on wavelength, and the ratio of the monochromator transmissions for polarized and unpolarized radiation is therefore variable at different wavelengths. Hence it follows that neither the absolute nor the relative monochromator transmissions are equal for polarized and unpolarized light.

To find the monochromator transmission for polarized light, we require the degree of polarization of the incident light, or else should reduce it to a negligible level. Unfortunately, the polarization so far has always been ignored in monochromator calibration and in grating efficiency measurements (see, e.g., [38–41]). There are recent reports, however, in which the polarization of light reflected from a grating is measured (see §20).

The degree of polarization is minimized in a normal-incidence spectrometer at angles close to the blaze angle. Aluminum gratings in a Seya–Namioka monochromator give a very substantial polarization ($g = 0.2$), which is moreover highly sensitive to wavelength [43]. Intensity measurements require knowledge of the degree of polarization of the incident radiation, since otherwise considerable errors may result.

In astrophysical work, the instrument transmission is often measured with the aid of two spectrographs [44]. Thus, in UV spectroscopy of the Sun, the rocket-borne spectrograph, which had to be calibrated, recorded lines whose intensity had been measured with a laboratory spectrograph. The photographic density of the lines taken with the rocket-borne instrument provided a measure of the energy which hit the photographic emulsion. Given the energy of the incoming and the outgoing radiation, we can find the spectrograph transmission.

Tomboulian and Behring [45] proposed a method of grating efficiency measurement, using a standard grating of known efficiency. The two gratings are compared under identical conditions: the same source, the same exposure, the same slit width, the same illuminated area.

If a monochromatic light source is used, a monochromator or a spectrograph can be calibrated without using an auxiliary spectroscopic instrument [46–48]. The transmission can be found from two measurements of the luminous flux, one of the incoming and one of the outgoing light (behind the exit slit in a monochromator, or next to the emulsion in the spectrograph). This method was applied by Sprague et al. [46] to measure the grating reflection coefficients. The same method was used to determine the efficiency of a DFS-6 spectrograph [47] and a VM-70 monochromator [48, 49].

As we have noted above, spectral instruments can be calibrated by the method of line pairs with a common upper level if the detector response is known (see §33) [5, 15, 16, 49]. In [49] a monochromator was calibrated by several methods: from theoretical transitions probabilities, with the aid of a standard hydrogen source, with an auxiliary monochromator, and with a thermophosphor of known absolute sensitivity; the results were all consistent.

## BIBLIOGRAPHY

1. FRISH, S.E. *Uspekhi Fizicheskikh Nauk*, **43**, 512 (1951).
2. DITCHBURN, R.W. and D.W.O. HEDDLE. *Proc. Roy. Soc.*, **A220**, 61 (1953).
3. MOROZOVA, N.G. and G.P. STARTSEV. *ZhNPFK*, **10**, 22 (1965).
4. KRASNOVA, E.I. and A.V. YAKOVLEVA. *Optiko-mekhanicheskaya Promyshlennost'*, No.1, 21 (1963).
5. GLADUSCHAK, V.I., YU.P. KANEVSKII, and E.YA. SHREIDER. In: *Diagnostika plazmy*, B.P. Konstantinov, Editor. p. 42. Goskhimizdat. 1963.
6. BARDIN, V.K., A.N. RYABTSEV, N.K. SUKHODREV, and V.M. UVAROVA. *Tezisy k doklady na XV soveshchanii po spektroskopii (Summaries of Reports at the XVth Conference on Spectroscopy)*. Minsk. 1963.
7. JONES, B.B. *Appl. Optics*, **1**, 239 (1962).
8. PERY–THORNE, A. and W.R.S. GARTON. *Proc. Phys. Soc.*, **76**, 833 (1960).
9. PROKOF'EV, V.K. *Fotograficheskie metody kolichestvennogo spektral'nogo analiza (Photographic Methods of Quantitative Spectral Analysis)*, **2**, 58. Gostekhizdat. 1951.
10. WOODRUFF, R.W. and M.P. GIVENS. *Phys. Rev.*, **97**, 52 (1955).
11. HARRISON, G.R. and P.A. LEIGHTON. *J. Opt. Soc. America*, **20**, 313 (1930).
12. PO LEE and G.L. WEISSLER. *J. Opt. Soc. America*, **43**, 512 (1953).
13. GREINER, H. *Z. Naturforsch.*, **12a**, 735 (1957).
14. ZAIDEL', A.N., G.M. MALYSHEV, and E.YA. SHREIDER. *ZhTF*, **31**, 129 (1960).
15. HINNOV, E. and F.W. HOFMANN. *Bull. Amer. Phys. Soc.*, **7**, 150 (1962); **8**, 154 (1963); *J. Opt. Soc. America*, **53**, 1259 (1963).
16. GRIFFIN, W.G. and R.W.P. MCWHIRTER. *Proc. of the Conference on Optical Instruments and Techniques*, London, Chapman and Hall Ltd. 1962.
17. BOGEN, P.R. and H. CONRADS. *VI Conf. Internat. Phénomènes d'Ionisation dans les Gaz*, **3**, 337 (1963).
18. BATES, D.R. and A. DAMGAARD. *Phil. Trans. Roy. Soc. London*, **242**, 101 (1949).
19. BERKNER, K., W.S. COOPER III, S.N. KAPLAN, and R.V. PYLE. *Phys. Lett.*, **16**, 35 (1965).
20. DRONOV, A.P., A.G. SVIRIDOV, and N.N. SOBOLEV. *Optika i Spektroskopiya*, **5**, 490 (1958).
21. GLADUSHCHAK, V.I. and E.YA. SHREIDER. *Optika i Spektroskopiya*, **14**, 815 (1963).

22. KAPORSKII, L.N. and N.S. SVENTITSKII. *Izvestiya AN SSSR*, phys. ser., **26**, 857 (1962).
23. ECK, J. VAN, F.J. HEER, and J. KISTEMAKER. *Phys. Rev.*, **130**, 656 (1963).
24. GLADUSHCHAK, V.I. and E.YA. SHREIDER. *Optika i Spektroskopiya*, **17**, 144 (1964).
25. FÖSTER, E.W. *Proc. Phys. Soc.*, **79**, 94 (1962).
26. BOLDT, G. *Proc. of the Fifth Internat. Conf. on Ionization Phenomena in Gases, Amsterdam,* 1962, **1**, 925.
27. MAECKER, H. *Z. Naturforsch.,* **11a**, 457 (1956).
28. BOLDT, G. *Z. Naturforsch.,* **18a**, 1107 (1963).
29. LABUHN, F. *Z. Naturforsch.,* **20a**, 998 (1965).
30. GRIEM, H.R. *Plasma Spectroscopy,* p. 263. McGraw-Hill. New York. 1964.
31. CARUSO, A.J. and W.M. NEUPERT. *Appl. Optics,* **4**, 247 (1965).
32. BLOKHIN, M.A., Editor. *X-Ray Spectroscopy.* Delhi, Hindustan Publ. Corp. 1962.
33. CRISTOFORI, F., P. FENICI, G.E. FRIGERIO, N. MOLHO, and P.G. SONA. *Phys. Lett.,* **6**, 171 (1963).
34. CRISTOFORI, F., G.E. FRIGERIO, N. MOLHO, and P.G. SONA. *VI Conf. Internat. Phénomènes d'Ionisation dans les Gaz,* **1**, p. 69. 1963.
35. MAYER, H. and E.O. SEITZ. *Ultraviolette Strahlen,* Berlin, Walter de Gruyter. 1949.
36. CHRISTENSEN, R.L. and J. AMES. *J. Opt. Soc. America,* **51**, 224 (1961).
37. SMITH, A. *J. Opt. Soc. America,* **50**, 862 (1960).
38. SAMSON, J.A.R. *J. Opt. Soc. America,* **52**, 525 (1962).
39. KULIKOV, S.A. and V.G. NIKITIN. *Optiko-mekhanicheskaya Promyshlennost',* No.12, 2 (1962).
40. HAMMER, D.C., E.T. ARAKAWA, and R.D. BIRKHOFF. *Appl. Optics,* **3**, 79 (1964).
41. GLADUSHCHAK, V.I., E.P. ANDREEV, YU.F. BYDIN, and E.YA. SHREIDER. *Zh. Prikl. Spektr.,* **2**, 178 (1965).
42. MADDEN, R.P. *Physics of Thin Films. Advances in Research and Development,* G. Hass, Editor, **1**, 133. New York, London, Academic Press. 1963.
43. RABINOVITCH, K., L.R. CANFIELD, and R.P. MADDEN. *Appl. Optics,* **4**, 1005 (1965).
44. RENSE, W.A. *Space Astrophysics,* W. Liller, Editor, McGraw-Hill. N.Y. 1961.
45. TOMBOULIAN, D.H. and W.E. BEHRING. *Appl. Optics,* **3**, 501 (1964).
46. SPRAGUE, G., D.H. TOMBOULIAN, and D.E. BEDO. *J. Opt. Soc. America,* **45**, 756 (1955).
47. ARKHANGEL'SKAYA, V.A., N.G. GERASIMOVA, E.I. KRASNOVA, T.K. RAZUMOVA, and A.V. YAKOVLEVA. *Optiko-mekhanicheskaya Promyshlennost',* No.12, 7 (1962).
48. GERASIMOVA, N.G. and D.A. GUSEV. *Optiko-mekhanicheskaya Promyshlennost',* No. 3, 25 (1965).
49. GERASIMOVA, N.G., D.A. GUSEV, and G.P. STARTSEV. *Optiko-mekhanicheskaya Promyshlennost',* No.11, 24 (1965).

# CHAPTER VII

# Absorption Spectra
# in the Vacuum Ultraviolet

## 35. EXPERIMENTAL DETERMINATION OF THE ABSORPTION
## COEFFICIENT AND THE ABSORPTION CROSS SECTION
## OF A GAS

An important characteristic of absorption processes in gases is the absorption coefficient $\mu$ at normal pressure and temperature. The absorption coefficient can be found from the relation

$$\Phi = \Phi_0 \exp \left( - \frac{p}{760} \frac{273}{T} \right) \mu l. \tag{29}$$

Here $\Phi_0$ is the incident flux, $\Phi$ is the transmitted flux, $T$ is the absolute temperature, $p$ is the pressure in torr, $l$ is the length of the absorbing layer.

The absorption coefficient $\mu$ is related to the absorption cross section $\sigma_\lambda$ by the equality

$$N\sigma_\lambda = \mu, \tag{30}$$

where $N$ is the Loschmidt number (number of atoms in $1\ \text{cm}^3$ at NTP); $\sigma_\lambda$ is expressed in $\text{cm}^2$. A common unit of measurement for absorption cross sections is $1\ \text{Mbarn} = 10^{-18}\ \text{cm}^2$.

The maximum accuracy in the determination of the absorption coefficients is

**231**

attainable for $\approx 72\%$ absorbance. It is not greatly affected as the absorbance varies from 50 to 88% [1].* The absorbing cell can be placed before or after the dispersion element in the spectrometer.

For gases which at room temperature do not react with the walls of the spectrometer (and especially not with the reflecting layer of the grating), the spectrometer may act as an absorption cell [2].

Two-beam and one-beam spectrometers are used [2a] (see §17). When choosing between photoelectric and photographic recording, it should be remembered that, although the photoelectric method is more accurate, the photographic technique simultaneously records the entire spectrum and is thus entirely free from errors due to variable conditions during the measurement process.

Spectroscopy with two photomultipliers [3] or two ionization chambers [4] is now gaining acceptance in the vacuum ultraviolet. One detector records the incident flux $\Phi_0$, and the other $\Phi$. These measurements are made simultaneously, and the fluctuations in source brightness do not affect the measurement results.

Continuous spectrum sources should be preferred, as they bring out in great detail the complete structure of the absorption spectrum. Various authors have nevertheless used line spectra, provided that the total number of lines in the relevant range of wavelengths was considerable [5]. In this case, the results were not distorted by overlapping of diffraction spectra of successive orders.

In absorption spectra of metal vapors, one generally has to separate the molecular absorption spectrum from the atomic absorption spectrum. This cannot be done unless the concentration ratio of atoms to molecules is known. In a number of cases [6, 7], the concentration ratio can be calculated from the dissociation constants. From the absorption cross sections of a monatomic gas we can find the photoionization cross sections, since in a monatomic gas the two cross sections are equal in the region of continuous absorption [4, 8]. This signifies that each absorbed quantum leads to a photoionization. For molecular gases, the photoionization cross sections can be determined from the molecular absorption cross section only if the effective quantum yield is known for the photoionization of molecules: after all, the absorption of a photon by molecular gases does not necessarily lead to photoionization. It may cause excitation followed by fluorescence or photodissociation. If the photoionization cross section is not equal to the absorption cross section, the photodissociation and photoionization continua overlap.

Fluorescence following exposure to the vacuum ultraviolet has been studied in detail in [9–16]. The earlier work [9–13] dealt with the effects of unresolved short-wave radiation, and only later [14–16] was the nature of fluorescence established and the origin of fluorescence in various gases, such as nitrogen, oxygen, and carbon dioxide, studied.

---

* The relative error of measurements is assumed independent of the signal amplitude.

Fluorescence can be excited by a Lyman source [14] or the helium continuum [15]. A diagram of a fluorescence setup is shown in Figure 180.

Fluorescence in nitrogen is excited by radiation of wavelengths shorter than 661 Å, which corresponds to an energy of 18.75 eV. The following processes are therefore observed (Figure 181):

$$N_2 + h\nu \rightarrow N_2^+ \ (^2\Sigma_u^+) + e^- \ (1 \, eV)$$

followed by

$$N_2^+ \ (^2\Sigma_u^+) \rightarrow N_2^+ \ (^2\Sigma_g^+) + h\nu \ (\approx 3 \, eV).$$

Photon energies of a few electron volts correspond to emission in the visible spectrum.

The red threshold of fluorescence in carbon dioxide is 750 Å, which corresponds to the energy of the $A^2\Pi_u$ level measured from the ground state of the molecule. Fluorescence in oxygen is excited by wavelengths shorter than 722 Å (excitation of the $A^2\Pi_u$ level). The measurements in this case are less reliable, and the red threshold of oxygen fluorescence does not precisely coincide with this wavelength.

Ordinary glass is transparent to fluorescence, and this emission therefore can be recorded by a detector which responds to wavelengths between 3000 and 6500 Å.

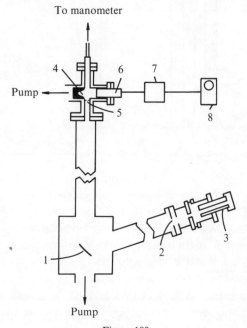

Figure 180

Experimental setup for fluorescence observations:

1) grating,   2) entrance slit,   3) source,   4) fluorescence chamber,   5) exit slit,   6) photomultiplier,
7) amplifier,   8) oscillograph.

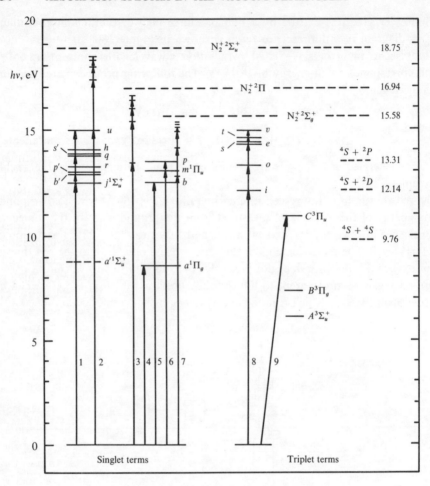

Figure 181

Energy level diagram of a nitrogen molecule.

We are still missing basic data for the determination of the fluorescence cross sections, but it is clear that fluorescence may substantially distort all absorption measurements, unless a suitable correction is introduced or a detector which is blind to the fluorescence wavelengths is employed.*

The fluorescence intensity is directly proportional to the gas pressure. To distinguish between the fluorescence and the exciting radiation, the absorption cell is

---

* It is implied that the absorption cell is placed behind the exit slit of the spectrometer: this is a common geometry, since undesirable photochemical reactions are often triggered in a cell placed before the entrance slit.

followed by a lithium fluoride filter which absorbs all wavelengths shorter than 1050 Å and freely transmits the fluorescence light. The correction for fluorescence thus can be determined.

## 36. AUTOIONIZATION AND TERM PERTURBATION

Autoionization is an inseparable aspect of any spectroscopy. It involves spontaneous transition of an atom from a discrete excited state into one of the states of a continuum [17–19]. The concept of autoionization was first introduced by Shenstone [20, 21]. Autoionization is observed if both continuous and discrete energy levels exist above the ionization limit.

Autoionization involves superposition of two systems of terms: discrete terms overlap with a continuum of terms (Figure 182). Any level lying above the ionization limit is short-lived ($10^{-13}$ sec), since its lifetime is determined primarily by ionization processes (radiationless transitions). As a result the corresponding line is highly diffuse or is absent altogether from the spectrum. The higher the probability of radiationless transition, the wider is the line. Autoionization does not necessarily occur whenever the energy level profile is suitable; its onset is determined by rigid selection rules.

### Level coupling

Autoionization can be interpreted in terms of the perturbation theory [18, 19]. If an atom has two states with different electron configurations and similar energies, a definite "coupling" or "interaction" of the energy levels occurs. As a result, the system can be described by a wave function $\psi$ which is a linear combination of the functions $\psi_1$ and $\psi_2$ corresponding to the two original states of the atom before the interaction:

$$\psi = c_1\psi_1 + c_2\psi_2, \tag{31}$$

where $c_1$ and $c_2$ are coefficients whose magnitudes squared $|c_1|^2$ and $|c_2|^2$ give the probability of finding the system described by the wave function $\psi$ in states $\psi_1$ and $\psi_2$. These coefficients are related by the equality

$$|c_1|^2 + |c_2|^2 = 1. \tag{32}$$

As we have noted before, a necessary condition of autoionization is the existence of atomic terms above the ionization limit. These terms arise following simultaneous excitation of two valent electrons or when electrons are excited from an inner shell.

Figure 183 shows the energy level diagram of an atomic system with two valent electrons (Mg I, Al II, Si III). The diagram on the left corresponds to the case when

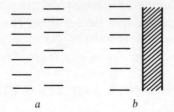

Figure 182

Two discrete series of terms (*a*). A discrete and a continuous series of terms (*b*).

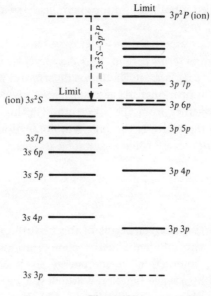

Figure 183

Term limits in the excitation of one electron and two electrons.

one electron remains fixed in the 3*s* state, and the other electron successively occupies the different states 3*p*, 4*p*, . . . , *np*, and in the limit is stripped from the atom. This state of the ion can be designated as 3*s* $^2S$. The diagram on the right corresponds to the case when one of the electrons remains in the 3*p* state, and the other electron successively occupies the states 3*p*, 4*p*, . . . , *np* and in the limit escapes from the atom. The resulting ion is designated as 3*p* $^2P$. We see from the figure that the difference in the limits of the two series corresponds to a resonance line of Mg II, Al III, Si IV (3*s* $^2S$–3*p* $^2P$).

Thus, if the two electrons are simultaneously excited, i.e., raised to the state 3*pnp* for *n* > 6, the atom may undergo spontaneous ionization, since the 3*p*7*p* level lies above the 3*s* $^2S$ level.

A similar situation is observed when one of the inner-lying electrons is excited. As an example, consider the case of the Cd atom. The ground state of the Cd atom is $(\ldots)\ 4d^{10}\ 5s^2\ {}^1S_0$. The spectrum of this atom is generally observed following excitation of one or two $5s$ electrons. If one of the inner electrons is excited, $4d$ say, the terms may fall above the ionization limit for the stripping of a $5s$ electron, and this may lead to autoionization.

The lines corresponding to the excitation of inner electrons are mainly observed in absorption spectra. In emission spectra they are not apparent, because autoionization markedly reduces the lifetime of the excited state.

These spectra were studied in detail by Beutler [22–33]. To distinguish them from the spectra of valent electrons, they were assigned the notation $I^b$.

Figure 184 is the energy level diagram of Zn $I^b$ [25]. The $I^b$ terms are produced by transitions of an electron from the $3d$ shell. Of all the terms with the configurations $3d^9 4s^2 np$ and $3d^9 4s^2 nf$, only the terms ${}^1P_1$, ${}^3P_1$, and ${}^3D_1$ are allowed; the $ns$ and $nd$ configurations violate the selection rules and are therefore forbidden. Figure 184 also shows the level diagram of Zn II. The limit of the $3d^9 4s^2$ series corresponds to the $3d^9 4s^2$ state of the ion Zn II.

Lines broadened by autoionization were observed in the emission spectra of a number of elements [34], e.g., copper [35, 36], silver [37], zinc, cadmium, mercury [38], and doubly ionized oxygen [39]. An asymmetric autoionization line of O III was discovered at 226.02 Å. At low frequencies the line is enhanced, whereas at high frequencies it is markedly suppressed, i.e., the line profile corresponds to the theoretical predictions [40]. Similar asymmetry has also been observed for other lines of the $2s^2 2p^2\ {}^3P - 2s^2 p^2 ({}^4P)np\ {}^3D$ series. The autoionization of O III is attributed to the interaction of discrete levels with the $2s^2 2p({}^2P_0)nd^3 D_0$ continuum.

Alongside with the asymmetric autoionization lines, the same spectrum also showed symmetric lines which belonged to another series of the same ion, $2s^2 2p^2\ {}^3P - 2s 2p^2({}^4P)np\ {}^3P_0$. The autoionization lines in the absorption spectra of metal vapors and gases are discussed in §37 and §38.

## Interaction of discrete levels

Another effect of energy level coupling is that the terms cannot be expressed by the conventional Ritz–Rydberg relations.

The effective quantum number in the unperturbed case can be obtained from the equality

$$n^* = n + \alpha + \frac{\beta}{n^2}, \tag{33}$$

where $n$ is the principal quantum number, $\alpha$ and B are constant coefficients, $\alpha \leq 1$, $\beta \ll \alpha$.

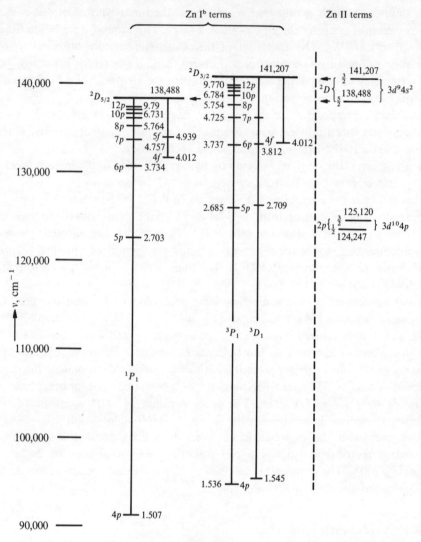

Figure 184

Energy level diagram of Zn I and Zn II.

With one perturbing level, we have the following equality for the effective quantum number:

$$n^* = n + \alpha + \beta_1 T_n + \frac{\text{const}}{T_n - T_p}, \qquad (34)$$

where $\beta_1$ is a constant coefficient, $T_n$ is the term of the series, $T_p$ is the perturbing term.*

Coupled terms are perturbed if they have equal $J$ and equal parity. In the case of $LS$ coupling, we have two additional selection rules, $\Delta L = 0$ and $\Delta S = 0$. The perturbation is generally detected by plotting the curves $n-n^* = f(n)$† or, equivalently, $n-n^* = f(T)$.

In the unperturbed case, these are clearly smooth curves. For large $n$, the curve is nearly parallel to the horizontal axis. Perturbation, however, alters the trend of this curve. For calcium (Figure 185), the curve breaks into two separate branches: a discontinuity is observed at $T_n = T_p$, in accordance with equation (34).

Garton obtained similar curves for a number of metals (see §37). These curves pinpoint the position of the perturbing terms, whose presence modifies the wave functions of the atomic states and affects the oscillator strengths of the individual spectral lines. Oscillator strength measurements for the lines of the principal series of alkaline earth metals have shown that the nonmonotonic variation of the $f$ vs. $n$ curves always involves a nonmonotonic variation of the quantum defect $n-n^*$ [41]. This explains why the higher terms in a series in absorption spectra are stronger than the lower terms [42, 43].

## 37. ABSORPTION SPECTRA OF METAL VAPORS

The first work in this direction was carried out by Beutler and co-workers [22–30]. Their results were highly qualitative, but the originality of their approach is worth noting: for the first time the absorption spectra associated with the excitation of inner electrons were studied. Numerous autoionization lines were detected and

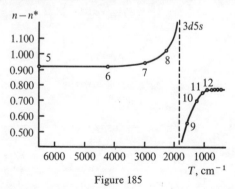

Figure 185

Perturbation of $4snd\ {}^3D_3$ terms in the calcium spectrum (the figures near the curves mark the principal quantum numbers).

---

* This equality can be generalized to the case of a series of perturbing terms (see [17]).
† The difference $n-n^*$ is called the quantum defect.

classified. Table 21 lists Beutler's principal results for metal vapor absorption spectra.

We will briefly describe the experimental procedure employed by Beutler. The sources for absorption spectroscopy in most cases were provided by inert gas continua (see § 4) and by the hydrogen line spectrum (see § 2). A normal-incidence vacuum spectrograph was used with reciprocal dispersion of 17.5 Å/mm and 20 micron slit. The spectra were recorded photographically. A diagram of the experimental setup is shown in Figure 186.

The light from the discharge tube 5 was passed through the absorption tube 6, placed in a furnace, to reach the spectrograph 10. Helium was circulated by the pump 1; the gas was cleaned in a liquid-air coal trap. Traces of hydrogen were removed from helium by copper oxide heated to high temperatures. Part of the helium was pumped out by a two-stage pump from the space between the discharge tube and the absorption volume. The countercurrent of helium suppressed the diffusion of metal vapor from the tube. The pump 3 produced a countercurrent of helium through the space 7, preventing the diffusion of metal vapor toward the slit. Pumps 4 and 8 maintained the vacuum in the spectrograph.

Later works of Ditchburn, Garton, Hudson, and co-workers [6, 7, 38, 42, 44–65] give detailed information on the absorption spectra of metal vapors and provide

Table 21

| Element | Ground state configuration (abbreviated) | Observed terms | $n$ | Spectral region, Å | Number of autoionization lines |
|---|---|---|---|---|---|
| Hg | $\ldots 5d^{10}6s^2\,{}^1S_0$ | $5d^96s^2np^3P_1^0,\,{}^1P_1^0,\,{}^3D_1^0$ | 6–18 | | |
| | | $nf\,{}^3P_1^{01}P_1^0$ | 5–10 | 745–1301 | 40 |
| Cd | $\ldots 4d^{10}5s^2\,{}^1S_0$ | $4d^95s^2np^3P_1^0,\,{}^1P_1^0,\,{}^3D_1^0$ | 5–14 | | |
| | | $nf\,{}^3P_1^{01}P_1^0$ | 4–7 | 683–1023 | 27 |
| Zn | $\ldots 3d^{10}4s^2\,{}^1S_0$ | $3d^94s^2np^3P_1^0,\,{}^1P_1^0.\,{}^3D_1^0$ | 4–12 | | |
| | | $nf\,{}^3P_1^{01}P_1^0$ | 4–5 | 714–1109 | 24 |
| K | $\ldots 3p^64s^2S_{1/2}$ | $3p^54s^2\,{}^2P^0$ | | 653, 662 | 2 |
| Cs | $\ldots 5p^66s^2S_{1/2}$ | $5p^56sns$ | 6–13 | 640–1008 | 119 |
| | | $nd$ | 5–12 | | |
| Rb | $\ldots 4p^65s^2S_{1/2}$ | $4p^55sns$ | 5–8 | 595–810 | 39 |
| | | $nd$ | 4–7 | | |
| Tl | $\ldots 5d^{10}6s^26p^2P_{1/2}$ | $6s6pnp$ | | 1490, 1610 | 2 |
| | | $5d^96s^26pnp$ | | 651–891 | 9 |

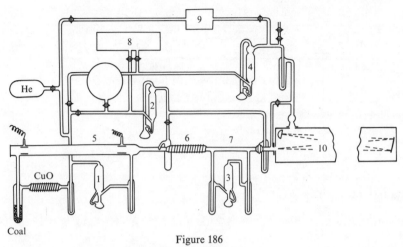

Figure 186

Beutler's experimental setup:

1,2,3,4) diffusion pumps,   5) discharge tube,   6) absorption tube,   8) forevacuum pump,
9) McLeod manometer,   10) spectrograph.

sufficient data for measuring the photoionization cross sections of a number of atoms.

The main experimental difficulty in the study of absorption in metal vapor is how to obtain an absorbing column of known vapor density distribution.

Ditchburn [66] originally used an absorption tube with the test metal placed in the middle, so that the vapor was allowed to spread freely to the cold ends of the tube. In this setup, it was impossible to calculate the density distribution in any given section of the tube. The tube (cuvette) shown on Figure 187, on the other hand, permits calculating the vapor pressure [6]. Here the metal is placed in two "boats", and the vapor diffuses in two directions from each boat. The tube is made of steel. A necking is provided in the tube to prevent the metal vapor from damaging the windows. An inert gas (mostly helium) is pumped into the tube at a pressure slightly higher than the metal vapor pressure. In this way the pressure distribution in the tube could be calculated.

The pressure in the section between the two "boats" was virtually equal to the saturated vapor pressure at the corresponding temperature. The main pressure drop is observed in the necked section and in the part of the tube where the metal vapor condenses. The pressure distribution can be found if one remembers that the sum of the partial pressures of the inert gas and the metal vapor is constant, being equal to the total pressure. Another point to be considered is that the concentration gradients of the inert gas and the metal vapor are equal. Proceeding from these considerations, Ditchburn et al. [6] developed a procedure for calculating the pressure distribution, which is applicable to tubes of any geometry with two "boats".

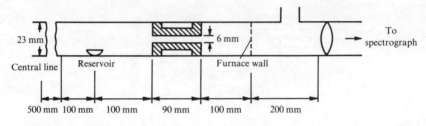

Figure 187

Cross section through absorption cuvette (only the right half of the tube is shown).

## Lithium [60, 64, 67–69]

The absorption was studied between 2300 and 1450 Å [60] and between 2300 and 1150 Å [64].

Figure 188 shows two experimental curves.* The data obtained by the different authors show a good fit. Theoretical calculations [68, 69] are also in good agreement with the experimental findings. The experimental photoionization cross section corresponding to the ionization limit (2300 Å) is (1.54 ± 0.23) Mbarn [64].

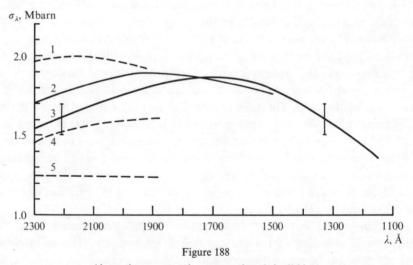

Figure 188

Absorption cross section vs. wavelength for lithium:

1,5) Tait's theoretical calculations [69],   4) theoretical calculations of Burgess and Seaton [68],   2) Marr's experimental data [60],   3) experimental data of Hudson and Carter [64].

* The absorption cross sections were obtained by reducing different experimental data with the same equation of saturated vapor pressure.

**Sodium** [7, 59, 68, 70, 71]

Carefully purified sodium was placed in nickel boats in a nickel tube. Helium was introduced as the inert gas after cleaning in a liquid-air trap of activated coal. The measurements were made photographically [59] using two spectrographs between 2500 and 1600 Å; the wavelengths between 2250 and 2005 Å were covered by both spectrographs, and the results showed a good fit between the measured absorption coefficients. The fluorite spectrograph used in the vacuum ultraviolet had a reciprocal dispersion of 34 Å/mm at 2000 Å and 15 Å/mm at 1600 Å.

The absorption spectrum of sodium was also studied in [7]. The results do not fully agree with those of [59]. For example, at 1950 Å, the absorption cross section is virtually zero, at variance with the findings of [59]. The results in [7] are more reliable, since more accurate thermochemical values were used. A hydrogen discharge tube and a condensed argon discharge were used as light sources. The measurements were carried out photoelectrically. The monochromator had a reciprocal dispersion of 7.5 Å/mm and a bandwidth of 1 Å.

An original illumination system was developed, using a mirror condenser, which markedly reduced the scattered light component (Figure 189). The mirror transformed a divergent beam into a convergent one, so that narrow apertures could be placed before the photomultiplier.

Figure 190 shows some curves plotting the experimental and the theoretical results for sodium [7, 70]. The experimental curve closely follows the theoretical.

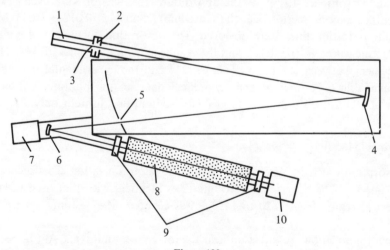

Figure 189

Experimental setup for absorption measurements in sodium vapor:

1) source,   2) differential pumpout slits,   3) entrance slit,   4) grating,   5) exit slit,   6) mirror,
7,10) photomultipliers,   8) furnace,   9) water cooling.

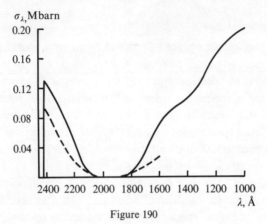

$\sigma_\lambda,$Mbarn

Figure 190

Absorption cross section vs. wavelength for sodium (dashed curve—theoretical).

The experimental photoionization cross section near the series limit (2412 Å) is (0.12 ± 0.012) Mbarn [59] and (0.130 ± 0.018) Mbarn [7].

### Potassium [6, 63, 63a, 68, 69, 71]

Potassium was among the first elements whose absorption coefficients were measured in vapor phase. A hydrogen source was used, and the spectra were recorded photographically [6]. Figure 191 plots the absorption cross section vs. wavelength. The photoionization cross section near the series limit (2860 Å) is (0.012 ± 0.003) Mbarn.

No autoionization lines were observed. The obsorption coefficient of potassium was again measured in [63, 63a], and the results show a good fit with [6]. There is no agreement between the theory [68, 69, 71] and the experimental findings.

The available experimental and theoretical data on the photoionization cross sections of alkali metals show a good fit for sodium and lithium only.

### Magnesium [54, 58]

The absorption spectrum of magnesium and the photoionization cross section were studied in [58]. The experimental technique is identical with that used in [6, 59]. The spectral region from 1620 to 1450 Å was covered. Magnesium vapor pressure reached 0.5–1.3 T.

The photoionization cross section near the ionization limit (1620 Å, Figure 192) is (1.18 ± 0.25) Mbarn. The experimental data show a good fit with the theory [71a].

The absorption spectrum of magnesium was also studied by Codling [54]. He measured the wavelengths of 27 lines of the principal magnesium series $3s^2 S_1-3Snp\ {}^1P_1$ and six lines of the $3s^2\ {}^1S_0-3Snp\ {}^3P_1$ series (with $n$ going from 21 to 26). The spectrum

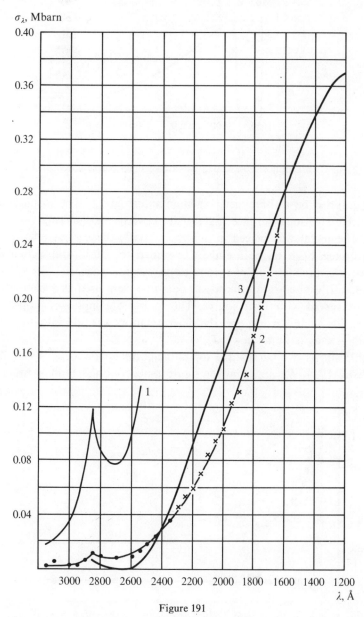

Figure 191

Absorption cross section vs. wavelength for potassium. The vertical scale for curve 1 has been blown up by a factor of 10 [6]. Curve 2 from [6], curve 3 from [63a].

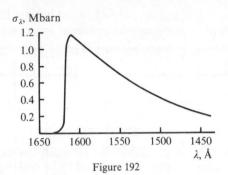

Figure 192

Absorption cross section vs. wavelength for magnesium.

was photographed on a three-meter vacuum spectrograph. The magnesium vapor was produced in King's furnace (a graphite cuvette 330 cm long and 20 mm in diameter). The metal was placed in a nickel "boat", the helium pressure reached 2 T. The furnace, open on both ends, was heated to 750°C; differential pumpout was applied (the pressure in the spectrograph was less than $10^{-3}$ T). Copper lines (Cu I and Cu II) excited in a hollow-cathode tube were used as a comparison. The Lyman tube served as a light source. The ionization limit was pinpointed with higher precision in this work, and the determination was additionally checked by plotting $n^* - n$ as a function of $T_\infty - T_n$.

Figure 193 shows two curves: the top curve corresponds to the series limit from Moore's work [72]. We see from the figure that Codling's limit is more reliable,

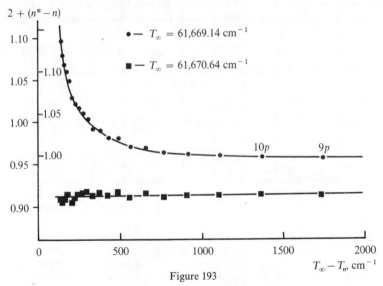

Figure 193

Quantum defect vs. term difference.

since his plot is a straight line almost parallel to the horizontal axis. This indicates that the principal series of magnesium was free from any perturbations in this case.

The experimental technique described in [54] was also used in the later work of Garton and Codling.

## Calcium [6, 50, 53, 56, 57, 59, 61]

The absorption spectrum of calcium was studied by a number of authors [50, 53, 56, 57, 61]. Continuous absorption beyond the ionization limit was studied in [57]. The experimental technique is described in detail in [6, 59].

The metal was heated in an iron tube, with one "boat" at the center. The one-boat tube is simpler to work with, but it is by no means certain that we can obtain a homogeneous vapor column. Its application, however, is justified in view of the good fit between the results obtained with two-boat and one-boat tubes [59].

Molecular absorption in the relevant spectral region is negligible. The absorption was measured between 2030 and 1950 Å. The absorption cross section at the series limit (2028 Å) was $(0.45 \pm 0.07)$ Mbarn. The absorption spectrum between 2028 and 1080 Å was investigated in [53]. General curves of the absorption cross section vs. wavelength are shown in Figure 194. The trend of the curves and the numerical values of the absorption coefficient at the series limit between 2028–1950 Å on the whole fit the results of [57]. The absorption cross sections at wavelengths corresponding to the first two lines are exceedingly high, 30 and 70 Mbarn, respectively. Numerous autoionization lines are observed between 1900 and 1600 Å [50, 53, 56, 61].

Garton and Codling [50, 55] established that the $4snp\ ^1P_1^0$ series is perturbed by the term $3d4p\ ^1P_1^0$. Calcium and other alkali metals have 6 perturbed series of the form $4s^2\ ^1S_0 - 3dnp\ ^1P_1^0,\ ^3P_1^0,\ ^3D_1^0,\ 4s^2\ ^1S_0 - 3dnf\ ^1P_1^0,\ ^3P_1^0,\ ^3D_1^0$.

Ditchburn and Hudson [53] studied in detail two of these series, $4s^2\ ^1S_0 - 3dnp\ ^1P_1^0$ and $4s^2\ ^1S_0 - 3dnp\ ^3P_1^0$, found their limits, and measured the oscillator strengths from the line profiles (Table 2).

Considerable continuous absorption is observed between 1600 and 1080 Å. Near 1589 Å, a second limit is observed, with an absorption cross section of 0.9 Mbarn.

Table 22

| Transition | $f$ | Transition | $f$ |
|---|---|---|---|
| $4s^2\ ^1S_0 - 3d5p\ ^1P_1$ | 0.024 | $4s^2\ ^1S_0 - 3d11p\ ^1P_1$ | 0.00006 |
| $-3d6p\ ^1P_1$ | 0.004 | $-3d5p\ ^3P_1$ | 0.0002 |
| $-3d7p\ ^1P_1$ | 0.002 | $-3d6p\ ^3P_1$ | 0.0001 |
| $-3d8p\ ^1P_1$ | 0.001 | $-3d7p\ ^3P_1$ | 0.0001 |
| $-3d9p\ ^1P_1$ | 0.0005 | $-3d8p\ ^3P_1$ | 0.00005 |
| $-3d10p\ ^1P_1$ | 0.00016 | $-3d9p\ ^3P_1$ | 0.00003 |

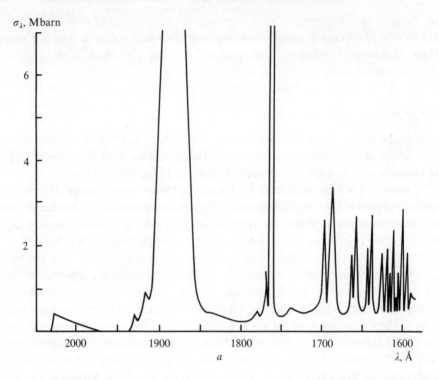

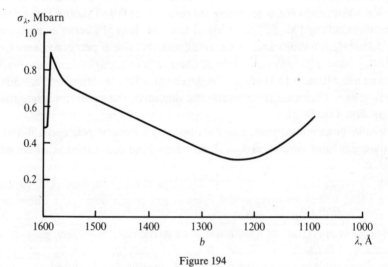

Figure 194

Absorption cross section vs. wavelength for calcium between 2000 and 1600 Å (*a*) and between 1600 and 1000 Å (*b*).

It seems that this figure is equally distributed between the continua $4s^2\,{}^1S_0-4snp\,{}^1P$ and $4s^2\,{}^1S_0-3dnp\,{}^1P_1,\,{}^3P_1$.

The theoretical absorption cross sections [73] show a poor fit with the experiment [53, 57]. This is not surprising, because theory ignores autoionization.

## Barium [42, 43, 48, 50, 51]

The absorption spectrum of barium, like that of calcium, has 7 perturbed series. The perturbation is highly pronounced, since the ground state of the Ba II ion $(6s\,{}^2S_{1/2})$ coincides with the doubly excited state of the neutral atom Ba I $(5d8p\,{}^1P_1)$. As a result, some of the high members in the principal series of barium are stronger than the low members. All the perturbed series of barium fall between 2450 and 2100 Å.

## Aluminum [50, 51, 65]

The absorption spectrum of aluminum in the vacuum ultraviolet was studied in [50, 51]. The ionization limit of aluminum is at 2070 Å. The high members of the $3s^2 3p\,{}^2P-nd\,{}^2D$, $ns\,{}^2S$ series were observed, and also a diffuse doublet with the upper term 0.05 eV above the ionization limit. It is not clear to what series this doublet actually belongs. The less diffuse doublet near 1930 Å corresponds to the terms $3s3p^2\,{}^2S$. The upper limit for the lines of this doublet is 0.4 eV above the ionization limit. Special experiments [65] gave the oscillator strengths of the lines of this doublet. At 1936 Å, $f = 0.033$, and at 1932 Å, $f = 0.049$. The experiments were carried out in a shock tube; the absorption spectrum was photographed and the shape of the autoionization lines was studied. The main difficulty is how to determine the concentration of aluminum atoms. It was calculated using the known oscillator strengths of the calcium lines. An aluminum–calcium compound with a known aluminum-to-calcium mass ratio was introduced into the shock tube. Boltzmann distribution over the energy levels was assumed, and the concentration of aluminum atoms was calculated using Saha's equation and the quasineutrality equation of the plasma. The temperature was determined by the reversal method. This procedure is far from being free from errors, and there is not much hope that the oscillator strengths were reliably determined.

The absorption spectrum of aluminum is of particular interest at present, since the attenuation of the solar continuum at wavelengths shorter than 2100 Å may be due to the absorption by aluminum [74]. A theoretical calculation of the photoionization cross section for aluminum at the series limit was published [75], but no experimental check was attempted.

## Gallium [46, 50, 51]

The absorption spectrum of gallium was studied between 1100 and 2200 Å. The graphite cuvette was placed in King's furnace; the furnace temperature was varied from 1100 to 1610°C, which corresponded to vapor pressures from 0.01 to 5 T.

A hydrogen lamp was used as the source. King's furnace had lithium fluoride windows; a countercurrent of a few torr of helium was set up in the tube, to protect the windows against contamination. Six absorption lines were observed between 1500 and 1630 Å, four of which were markedly broadened by autoionization.

## Indium [44, 49–52]

The absorption spectrum of indium was studied in great detail. It is of considerable importance for understanding the phenomenon of autoionization.

The absorption spectra [44] were photographed with a one-meter normal-incidence spectrograph between 1070 and 2200 Å. A hydrogen lamp and a Lyman tube were used as light sources.

The absorption spectrum between 1170 and 1760 Å shows 14 absorption lines, five of which are strong diffuse lines between 1640 and 1760 Å. They correspond to the $5s^2 5p\ ^2P_{1/2,\ 3/2}$–$5s 5p^2\ ^2S_{1/2}\ ^2P_{1/2,\ 3/2}$ transitions.

Perturbations of the indium series were studied in considerable detail. Some of these series fall in the vacuum ultraviolet. Figure 195 plots the curves $n^* - n = f(T)$,

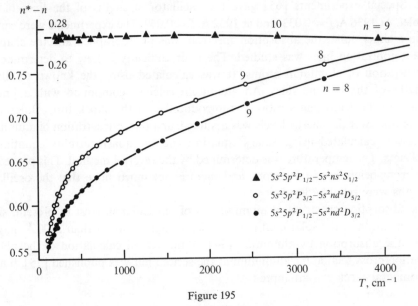

Figure 195

Quantum defect vs. term energy.

where $T$ is the term energy in cm$^{-1}$. We see from the figure that the $5s^25p\,^2P_{1/2}-$ $5s^2ns\,^2S_{1/2}$ series is free from any perturbations, whereas the two series $5s^25p\,^2P_{3/2}-$ $5s^2nd\,^2D_{5/2}$ and $5s^25p\,^2P_{1/2}-5s^2nd\,^2D_{3/2}$ are perturbed: the perturbing term lies above the ionization limit and interacts with the continuum beyond the limit of the two series.

The photoionization cross section is maximum at a distance of 0.33 eV from the series limit (and not at the series limit), which is also associated with the presence of the perturbing term $5s5p^2\,^2D$.

The spectrum of indium shows another effect predicted by the Fano theory [40]. Whenever the transitions from an energy level which is the upper level for a given absorption line terminate in one continuum only, a local reduction of the absorption coefficient on one of the sides of the absorption line is observed. For indium, this reduction is observed on the short-wave side of the absorption line.

## Thallium [45, 50, 51]

The absorption spectrum of thallium was studied between 2050 and 1450 Å [45]. Two series of measurements were carried out between 2050 and 1700 Å and between 1700 and 1450 Å. The thallium vapor pressure in the first series was varied from 0.02 to 0.1 T, and in the second from 0.005 to 0.015 T.

Figure 196 plots the absorption cross section against the wavelength. The absorption cross section at the photoionization limit (2030 Å) is (4.5 ± 0.8) Mbarn.

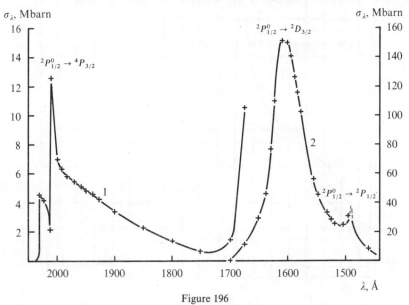

Figure 196

Absorption cross section vs. wavelength for thallium (left scale for curve 1, right scale for curve 2).

We see from the figure that there are three photoionization lines, 2007 Å, 1610 Å, and 1490 Å. The oscillator strengths were determined from the area inside the line profile (Table 23).

The oscillator strength for the 1610 Å line is higher than for all the other lines of thallium [76].

In thallium, like in indium, a marked drop of the absorption coefficient is observed on one side of the absorption line (the long-wave side in this case, see Figure 197).


### Lead [50, 77]

The absorption lines of lead were observed between 1672 and 1353 Å. This region corresponds to two limits of the series $^2P_{1/2}Pb^+$ and $^2P_{3/2}Pb^+$. The autoionization lines of lead are not unlike emission lines; this is due to the overlapping of three series and the reduction of the absorption coefficient near the absorption line.

Autoionization lines and series perturbations were also observed in the spectra of other metals, e. g., Sn [49], Ag [49], Cu [47, 59], Au [48, 50], Yb [48], Sr [48, 50, 51], Zn, Cd, and Hg [38, 49].

Table 24 is a summary of the principal measurement results for the absorption spectra of metals.

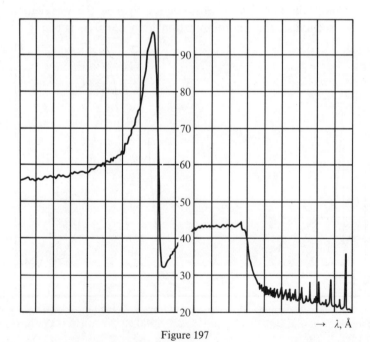

Figure 197

Reduction of absorption coefficient near the series limit in thallium (a microphotometer tracing).

Table 23

| $\lambda$, Å | $f$ | Transition |
|---|---|---|
| 2007 | 0.005 ± 0.001 | $^2P^0_{1/2} - {}^4P_{3/2}$ |
| 1610 | 0.52 ± 0.09 | $^2P^0_{1/2} - {}^2D_{3/2}$ |
| 1490 | ≈ 0.005 | $^2P^0_{1/2} - {}^2P_{1/2}$ |

Table 24

| Metal | Absorption spectrum, Å | Wavelength corresponding to ionization potential, Å | Absorption cross-section at ionization limit, Mbarn | Autonioization lines in the vacuum UV, Å | References experimental | References theoretical** |
|---|---|---|---|---|---|---|
| Li | 2300–1450* | 2300 | 1.54 ± 0.23 | None | [60, 64, 67] | [68, 69] |
| Na | 2412–1600* | 2412 | 0.12 ± 0.012 | None | [7, 59] | [68, 70, 71] |
| K | 2860–1600* | 2860 | 0.012 ± 0.003 | None | [6, 63] | [68, 70, 71] |
| Mg | 1620–1450 | 1620 | 1.18 ± 0.25 | None | [54, 58] | [71a] |
| Ca | 2028–1950 | 2028 | 0.45 ± 0.07 | Numerous | | [77] |
| | 1589–1080 | 1589 | ~0.9 | see [53, 56, 61] | [50] | |
| | | | | | [53] | |
| | | | | | [56] | |
| | | | | | [57, 61] | |
| Al | Below 2070 | 2070 | — | 1936 | [50, 51] | [75] |
| | | | | 1932 | | |
| Ga | Below 2070 | 2070 | — | 1506 | [46, 50, 51] | [75] |
| | | | | 1520 | | |
| | | | | 1525 | | |
| | | | | 1539 | | |
| | | | | 1610 | | |
| | | | | 1632 | | |
| In | 2140–1070 | 2140 | — | 1757† | [44] | |
| | | | | 1741 | [49] | |
| | | | | 1711 | [50] | |
| | | | | 1676 | [51] | |
| | | | | 1649 | [52] | |
| Tl | 2030–1440 | 2030 | 4.5 ± 0.8 | 2007 | [45] | |
| | | | | 1610 | [50] | |
| | | | | 1490 | [51] | |
| Cd | 1400–1150 | 1360 | 0.32 ± 0.03 | | [62] | |

* The shorter wavelengths were not investigated, although they reveal considerable absorption.

** Only references published after 1950 are included in this column; references to earlier work can be found in [71].

† A total of 14 autoionization lines were measured, but only the strongest are listed here.

## 38. ABSORPTION SPECTRA OF INERT GASES

The first studies of the absorption spectra of inert gases were undertaken by Beutler [31], who used the spectrograph itself as the absorption cell; the gas pressure in the spectrograph reached $10^{-3}$–$10^{-2}$ T. A current of gas was pumped through the spectrograph, and the pressure was therefore not entirely constant throughout the system; this naturally somewhat interfered with quantitative measurements. Nevertheless, Beutler's experiments remain of considerable interest to this day, since he was the first to discover asymmetric autoionization lines in the spectra of the heavy inert gases. Table 25 is a summary of Beutler's results.

Detailed quantitative measurements have since been carried out in various laboratories for all the inert gases, except radon, and the results show a good fit.

### Helium [78–97]

Helium is transparent at all wavelengths above 504 Å. This explains the considerable attraction of helium for all work in vacuum ultraviolet.

The absorption cross section of helium has been determined in a number of experimental studies [78–83]. We will consider in some detail the measurement procedure described in [79]. (The same procedure was applied in photoionization measurements of neon and argon atoms.) Baker et al. were the first to use closed cuvettes for absorption measurements at wavelengths shorter than 1050 Å. (The manufacture of these cuvettes is described in §10.) The cuvette windows were made of organic films. The application of these cuvettes permitted making measurements under much cleaner conditions than when the entire spectrograph was filled with the absorbing gas. Moreover, the small size of the absorption cuvette made it possible to raise the pressures to several torr, so that the pressure could be measured with much higher precision than the pressures of a few hundredths of a torr used in other absorption measurements.

The light source between 180 and 600 Å was a condensed spark discharge in an argon-filled glass capillary. The spectrum showed the lines of O III, O IV, O V,

Table 25

| Gas | Absorption spectrum, Å | Number of lines |
|-----|------------------------|-----------------|
| Ar  | 781–879                | 23              |
| Kr  | 850–1003               | 36              |
| Xe  | 926–996                | 18              |

N III, N IV, N V, C III, C IV, Ar II, Ar III, Ar IV, Ar V, Ar VI, Ar VII, and other lines of highly ionized ions. Wavelengths of 180 Å were obtained using the $L_{2,3}$ emission band of aluminum (see §6) [84].

All measurements, except those at 180 Å, were carried out photographically. A normal-incidence spectrograph with an aluminum grating of 1.62 m radius of curvature was used. The grating was ruled with 1200 lines/mm, the reciprocal dispersion of the system was 5.25 Å/mm. The cuvette was placed behind the entrance slit.

At 180 Å, photoelectric measurements were made and the cuvette was placed behind the exit slit of the monochromator.

In helium absorption measurements, the cuvette was 1.27 cm thick and 1.91 cm in diameter. To avoid damage to cuvette windows before it was filled with gas, pumpout proceeded simultaneously on both sides of each window. The window thickness was chosen so that the transmittance at 350 Å was 30%. These cuvettes were not entirely free from leakage (a slight leakage not exceeding $3 \cdot 10^{-4}$ T was observed during the tests). The helium pressure was less than 5 T, and at this pressure the leakage rate was sufficiently slow. Higher pressures are inadmissible, because of possible mechanical damage to the windows. Photometry was done by the method of Woodruff and Givens [85].

Figure 198 plots the absorption cross section (or, equivalently, the photoionization cross section) of helium as a function of wavelength [79]. The accuracy of the corresponding measurements was of the order of 5%. The number of decimal places in the construction of the characteristic curve and in absorption recording varied from 50 tp 1000 (this large number of places is associated with the application of a normal-incidence spectrograph in [79]). Figure 198 also lists the results of other theoretical and experimental studies in which the absorption coefficient of helium was measured.

In [88] the calculations were carried out by nine different methods, and only the averaged figures show a good fit with the experiment. The divergence between the results of individual methods is very large.

Autoionization lines in the absorption spectrum of helium were studied using synchrotron radiation as a continuous spectrum source [89, 90]. A grazing-incidence spectrograph was used (84.5° incidence), the grating was ruled with 600 lines/mm and its radius of curvature was 3 m. The reciprocal dispersion reached 1 Å/mm at 200 Å, resolving power 0.06 Å. An aluminum foil filtered the radiation from 170 to 825 Å. The helium pressure in the spectrograph reached a few tenths of a torr, the absorbing layer was about 83 cm thick. A differential pumpout system was used, since the pressure in the synchrotron was $5 \cdot 10^{-6}$ torr. The spectral region with autoionization lines lies 35–40 eV above the first ionization potential of helium (24.6 eV).

We see from Figure 199a that the discrete absorption lines are superimposed on a continuous absorption spectrum. A total of 21 lines were observed (Table 26).

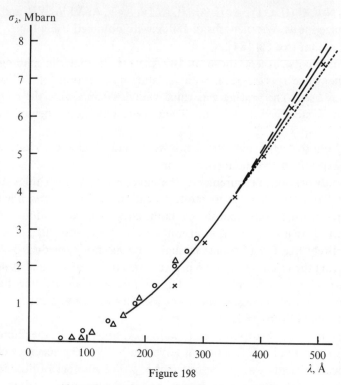

Figure 198

Absorption cross section of helium vs. wavelength:

O from [78]; solid curve, from [79]; dashed curve, from [86]; dotted line, from [87]; Δ from [83];
X from [82].

The observed lines received adequate theoretical interpretation [91–94] which was verified experimentally [95–97].

Silverman and Lassetre [95] and Simpson et al. [97] studied the small-angle scattering of electrons by helium atoms. Rudd [96, 96a] studied the scattering of protons and molecular hydrogen ions by helium atoms. The resonance curve of these experiments gives the energy levels of the scattering atoms, and we can thus observe even the levels corresponding to forbidden transitions. The energy levels recovered from scattering experiments are listed in Table 27. The fit between the theoretical results and the findings of various experimental works is brilliant. It has been established that the absorption lines discovered in [89, 90] correspond to two-electron excitation and are thus regarded as autoionization lines.

The autoionization lines recorded in these experiments form several series. Helium should have two series $2s2s–2snp$ and $2s2s–2pns$, converging to a common limit at 189.6 Å (65.4 eV, $n = 2$). Both series have the same lower term.

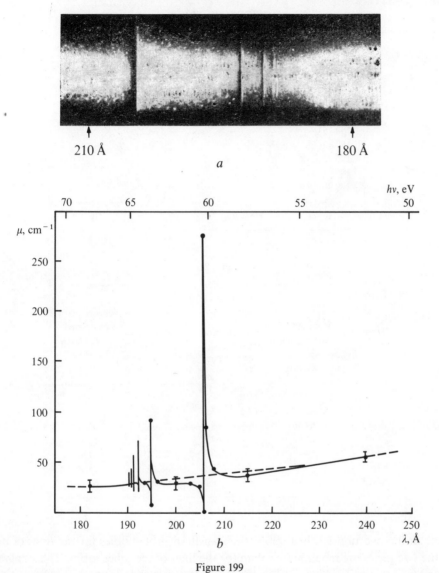

Figure 199

Autoionization lines of helium: *a* spectrum, *b* absorption coefficient of helium vs. wavelength between 180 and 240 Å.

The high levels of $2snp^1P$ and $ns2p^1P$ with $n > 2$ reveal a definite interaction between states with the same $n$. In the limit, the strong coupling actually produces two series in which the level widths are equal to a sum and a difference of the widths of the unperturbed $2snp^1P$ and $2pns^1P$ levels. Since the level width is almost the

Table 26 [89]

| Series I | Series II | Series III | Series IV |
|---|---|---|---|
| 206.21 | 197.56 | 177.26 | 168.09 |
| 194.78 | 193.30 | 173.01 | 166.10 |
| 192.33 | 191.73 | 171.71 | 165.31 |
| 191.29 | — | 171.09 | |
| 190.75 | — | 170.75 | |
| 190.43 | — | 170.53 | |
| 190.22 | | | |
| 190.08 | | | |
| 189.98 | | | |
| Limit of series He$^+$, $n = 2$ | He$^+$, $n = 2$ | He$^+$, $n = 3$ | He$^+$, $n = 4$ |

Table 27

| Term | Energy levels (eV) | | | | Theoretically calculated energy levels [92, 93] (eV) |
|---|---|---|---|---|---|
| | from optical absorption spectra [89, 90] | from electron scattering [95]    [97] | | from ion scattering [96, 96a] | |
| $2s2p\,^1P$ | 60.12 | 60.0 | 60.1 | 60.1 | 60.26 |
| — | 63.65 | 63.5 | 63.6 | — | 63.68 |
| — | 64.46 | — | 64.5 | — | 64.47 |
| — | 64.81 | — | 64.8 | — | 64.82 |
| $2s^2\,^1S$ | — | — | 57.9 | 57.82 | 57.87 |
| $2s2p\,^3P$ | — | — | 58.5 | 58.34 | 58.36 |
| $2s3s\,^1S$ | — | — | — | 62.95 | 62.99 |

same in the two unperturbed series, the transition probabilities for the lines of one of the two series are much higher than for the lines of the other series. This explains why Madden and Codling [90] in their first experiments observed only one of the two series converging to the state (He$^+$, $n = 2$). Later both series were observed (see Table 26). In complete agreement with the theory, the lines of one series are markedly weaker than the lines of the other series. Alongside with these two series, there are also series converging to (He$^+$, $n = 3$) and (He$^+$, $n = 4$) (see Table 26).

Special experiments were carried out in order to determine the level widths [89]. For the $2s2p\,^1P$ level it was found to be $(0.038 \pm 0.004)$ eV (Figure 200), and the width of the level corresponding to 63.65 eV was $(0.008 \pm 0.004)$ eV.

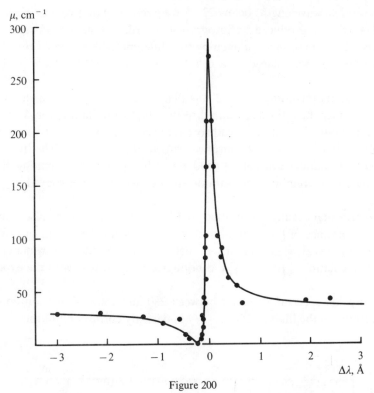

Figure 200

An absorption line of helium at 206.21 Å ($1s^2\ {}^1S_0-2s2p\ {}^1P$).

The probabilities of autoionization for these two states obtained from the above data are found to be $(5.8 \pm 0.6) \cdot 10^{13} \text{sec}^{-1}$ and $(1.2 \pm 0.6) \cdot 10^{13} \text{sec}^{-1}$. The width of the $2s2p\ {}^1P$ level was also calculated by Fano [40] from electron scattering experiments [95]. It was found to be 0.04 eV. Cooper [94] estimates this level width at 0.07–0.09 eV.

The discovery of autoionization lines in the helium spectrum and the exact fit between these lines with theoretical calculations is one of the remarkable results of vacuum UV spectroscopy in the recent years.

## Neon [98–103]

The continuous absorption spectrum of neon was studied in a number of experimental works [98–100a]. We will describe in some detail the procedure developed for the measurement of photoionization cross sections in [98].

The spectral region from 80 to 575 Å (the ionization limit) was studied. The wavelengths from 575 to 225 Å were recorded photographically with a normal-incidence spectrograph. The wavelengths below 226 Å were recorded on two grazing-incidence instruments: the first produced a photographic record, and the second used a Geiger counter (see §26). The results obtained by two different methods could thus be compared. The test gas was placed in a cell 1.0 cm thick and 1.6–1.9 cm in diameter (see §21).

In photographic recording, the cell was placed directly behind the slit, and with the Geiger counter the cell was held in direct contact with the counter. The window thickness was chosen so that the film absorbance between 200 and 700 Å was 25–50% and at 100 Å, about 5%. The pressure was varied from 2 to 15 T. The light sources were a condensed capillary discharge producing a line spectrum, a Penning discharge (see §6), and an aluminium anticathode giving the characteristic Al $L_{2,3}$ band ($\lambda = 180$ Å).

The experimental results are plotted in Figure 201. This figure also shows the experimental findings of [100, 100a] and the theoretical calculations of [101]. The various curves reveal a satisfactory fit between theory and experiment. Earlier theoretical calculations [102, 103a] did not agree quite so well with the experiment [98].

The absorption spectrum of neon between 280 and 250 Å shows autoionization lines converging to the limit at 256 Å; they apparently correspond to the transitions

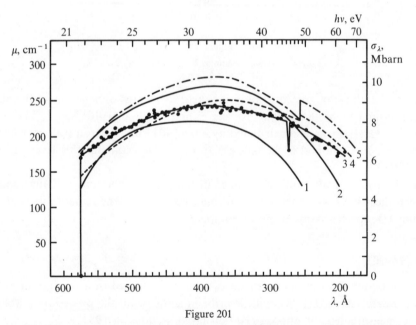

Figure 201

The absorption cross section and the absorption coefficient of neon vs. wavelength:

1) data of [100],   2) data of [98],   3) data of [100a],   4,5) data of [101].

$2s^2 2p^6\ {}^1S_0 - 2s2p^6 np\ {}^1P$. The wavelengths of nine lines were measured (Figure 202). The energy levels in the neon spectrum can be determined from optical experiments [90] and from electron scattering measurements [97]. Table 28 reveals a satisfactory fit for the data obtained by various methods.

276 Å                                                   250 Å

Figure 202

Autoionization lines of neon (only part of the lines are visible).

Table 28

| Term | Energy levels (eV) | |
|---|---|---|
| | from optical absorption spectra [90] | from electron scattering [97] |
| — | — | 43.6 |
| — | 44.9 | 45.0 |
| $2s2p^6 3p\,^1P$ | 45.6 | 45.6 |
| — | — | 46.5 |
| $2s2p^6 4p\,^1P$ | 47.1 | 47.1 |
| $2s2p^6 5p\,^1P$ | 47.7 | 47.7 |

## Argon

The absorption spectrum of argon was studied experimentally in [80, 104–109]. The spectral region from 800 to 360 Å was measured in [80]; the measurements were made with a line spectrum source [5]. The absorption spectrum was recorded photographically, and the spectrograph itself acted as the absorption volume.

The spectral region from 800 to 600 Å was covered in [106]. The experimental procedure is described in detail in [111]. The helium continuum was used as the radiation source [110]; the differential pumpout made it possible to reduce the monochromator pressure to $10^{-3}$ T, while keeping the source pressure as high as 1 atm. The aluminized monochromator grating had $R = 2$ m, 1200 lines/mm and was coated with a layer of $MgF_2$. The absorbing cell and the photomultiplier were placed behind the monochromator. A current of gas was driven through the chamber, and the pumpout was done through the monochromator. The narrow slit, on the one hand, and the high speed of pumping, on the other, permitted obtaining a pressure of a few torr in the chamber, while the pressure in the spectrograph was negligible.

The main error of this method is associated with pressure measurements: there naturally was a certain pressure gradient in the chamber. To pinpoint the exact error, the absorption coefficient of $CO_2$ obtained with this setup was compared with the results of measurements with a closed cuvette. The figures were found to be 15% too low.

The photoionization cross section of the argon atom was also measured by Samson [104], who used two ionization chambers. He worked with the half-meter Seya–Namioka monochromator with a 1200 lines/mm platinized grating. The resolving power of his setup reached 1.3 Å. A high-voltage condensed argon arc served as a light source. The cell was 10 cm long, the argon pressure reached 0.05–0.5 T. The spectral region from 800 to 300 Å was covered. The accuracy of the absolute measurements was about 5%, and the accuracy of the relative measurements about 3%.

Similar measurements were also carried out by Rustgi [105]. He studied the spectral region from 800 to 170 Å. The line source in his experiments was a condensed discharge in a boron nitride capillary. The capillary was filled with nitrogen to 0.1 T. A differential pumpout arrangement was used. A 0.1 $\mu$F capacitor was charged to 18 kV, the discharge recurred 44 times each second. The source gave a bright spectrum to 170 Å. The recording was done with a one-meter monochromator using a 1200 lines/mm grating and 1 Å bandwidth. The absorbing cuvette was placed behind the exit slit; the pressure was measured with a thermocouple gauge calibrated against a McLeod manometer. The gas from the absorption cell virtually did not leak into the spectrometer, as a separate pumpout system was provided.

The short-wave region was studied in [107]. Measurements between 100 and 300 Å were carried out with photon counters. Be $K$ and Al $L_{2,3}$ bands were used as the line sources (see §6), and also the He II Lyman series. The cell was placed inside a grazing-incidence spectrometer.

The results obtained for the photoionization cross section of argon atoms are also given in [109]. An 8 kV condensed discharge in a ceramic capillary was used as the source. The capillary was filled with a 0.2 T mixture of air and argon, and its radiation was passed through a shock tube* serving as an open cuvette. The light entered through a 1 mm aperture; the thickness of the absorbing layer was equal to the diameter of the shock tube. A half-meter normal-incidence monochromator with a 1200 lines/mm aluminized grating was used; dispersion 16 Å/mm. Figure 203 plots the experimental curves of various authors. We see that although entirely

---

* The shock tube was actually intended for a different experiment, and the absorbance was measured only as a check on the plasma absorption coefficient.

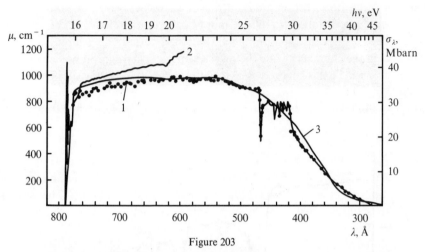

Figure 203

Absorption cross section and absorption coefficient of argon vs. wavelength:

1) data of [104],    2) data of [106],    3) data of [105].

different measurement techniques were used, the results are quite consistent. This apparently proves that the measurements of photoionization cross sections have reached a sufficiently high level.

Numerous autoionization lines were discovered in argon [90, 104, 106, 112, 113]. They were first discovered between 420 and 470 Å by Madden and Codling [90]. The pressure inside the spectrograph in their experiments was 0.01 T, the optical path reached 105 cm. These lines correspond to the $3s^2 3p^6 \, {}^1S_0 - 3s3p^6 np \, {}^1P_1$ transitions. Samson [104, 112] also observed these lines and arranged them in a Rydberg series:

$$v = 235,832 - \frac{R}{(n-1.53)^2} , \qquad (35)$$

where $n = 4, 5, \ldots$ A total of 11 lines were observed. The first of these eleven lie at 466 Å, 442.8 Å, and 434.8 Å. The wavelengths of all the measured lines fit the results of calculations.

The energy levels corresponding to $ms-np$ transitions can be readily calculated for any inert gas by subtracting from the ionization potential of the $s$ electron of the alkali metal immediately following the inert gas the energies corresponding to the excitation potentials of the resonance lines of the metal [114]. The autoionization lines in the argon spectrum, in accordance with the Fano theory [40], appear like emission lines, since the absorption markedly decreases at the corresponding wavelengths (Figure 204).

Autoionization lines lying between two ionization limits were recorded in [106,

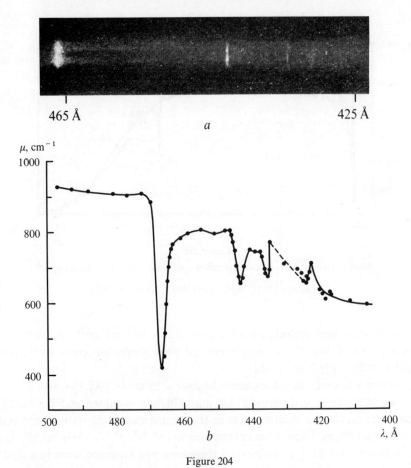

Figure 204

Autoionization lines of argon: *a* spectrum, *b* absorption coefficient of argon vs. wavelength.

113]. These lines were originally observed by Beutler [31]. Figure 205 shows the absorption spectrum of argon between these ionization limits [106]. The measurements were made photoelectrically.

Contrary to Beutler's belief, the oscillator strengths were found to be very small (Table 29).

Theoretical calculations of photoionization cross sections were carried out in [102, 115]. Cooper [102] predicted with fair accuracy the wavelength corresponding to the minimum photoionization cross section (290 Å). The measurements of Alexander et al. [107] give 270 Å for this wavelength.

The general trend of the curve of photoionization cross sections obtained by Cooper [102], however, is at variance with numerous experimental data. Dalgarno

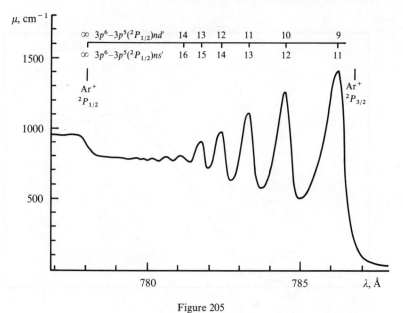

Figure 205

Absorption coefficient of argon vs. wavelength between 777 and 788 Å.

Table 29

| $\lambda$, Å | $f$ [106] | $f$ [113] |
|---|---|---|
| 786.6 | 0.00575 | 0.0039 |
| 784.9 | 0.00244 | 0.0011 |
| 783.6 | 0.00157 | 0.0006 |
| 782.7 | 0.00072 | 0.0002 |
| | $\sum f = 0.0105$ | $\sum f = 0.0058$ |

[115] obtained 30 Mbarn for the photoionization cross section corresponding to the ionization limit. This figure is in excellent agreement with the experimental results (see Figure 203).

## Krypton [83, 109, 111–114, 116–119a]

The absorption measurements in [119] were carried out with fairly low accuracy (errors of the order of 20%), but the results are nevertheless fairly consistent with the findings of other authors (Figure 206). The Lyman continuum was used as the light source, and the spectrograph was filled with a few torr of the absorbing gas. Photo-electric recording was used.

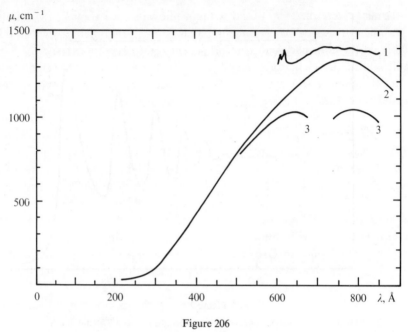

Figure 206

Absorption coefficient of krypton vs. wavelength:

1) data of [111],    2) data of [118],    3) data of [119].

The experimental results of [109, 111–113, 118] are fairly consistent among themselves, and the variances between individual measurements do not exceed 10%. The spectral region from 886 to 600 Å was covered in [111], that from 600 to 400 Å in [112], from 845 to 500 Å in [109], and the region from 845 to 230 Å in [118] (plus a single measurement at 170 Å).

The measurement technique was the same as in argon absorption measurements of the same authors. Some experimental results on the photoionization cross sections are given in Figure 206. We see that, as for argon, the results of Huffman et al. [111] are too high, and the results of Pery-Thorne et al. [119] are conversely too low compared to the data of Rustgi et al. [118].

Cooper's theoretical cross sections [102] do not coincide with the experimental data: there is a difference by more than a factor of 2.

The autoionization lines of krypton were studied in [111–114, 116, 117, 119]. After Beutler's classical work [31], the autoionization lines between 886 and 845 Å were first measured in [111, 113, 119]. In [111] the autoionization line profiles were recorded photoelectrically and in [119] photographically. Photoionization technique was used in [113]. The helium continuum was used as the source.

The shapes of the absorption lines were measured in all the three sources. The measurements were made with and without allowance for the $^2P_{3/2}$ continuum. It is very difficult to say which of these methods is the more reliable, since no data are available on the continuous absorption near the autoionization lines.

Table 30 lists the oscillator strengths from the three sources. The data in columns two and three show an excellent fit. The variance between the figures in columns three and four does not exceed the margin of error.

All the observed absorption lines belong to two series, $4p^6\,{}^1S_0-4p^5({}^2P_{1/2})md$ and $4p^6\,{}^1S_0-4p^5({}^2P_{1/2})ns$. The autoionization lines show asymmetric broadening, i.e., their short-wave half is substantially wider than the long-wave half, and the lines of the $d$ series are on the whole wider than the lines of the $s$ series. Figure 207 identifies the autoionization lines. The lines in both series overlap, and only the first members can be resolved.

The autoionization lines of krypton between 498 and 456 Å were observed in [112, 114, 117]. The light source in [117] was a 180 MeV synchrotron radiation. A three-meter incidence spectrograph was used, with a resolving power of 0.06 and 1.45 Å/mm dispersion at 500 Å. The optical path length was 100 cm, and the krypton pressure in the spectrograph $5 \cdot 10^{-2}$ torr.

Samson observed the same lines.* He used a 2.2-meter normal-incidence spectrograph. The grating was ruled with 1200 lines/mm, the dispersion was 3.76 Å/mm, slit width 30 $\mu$, resolution 0.1 Å, gas pressure $10^{-3}$ torr. A 10 kV Garton tube was used as the source (9 $\mu$F capacitor). Helium was used as the discharge medium [114].

Table 30

| $\lambda_{av}$, Å | $f$ from [119] | $f$ from [113] | $f$ ignoring continuum [111] | $f$ with allowance for continuum [111] |
|---|---|---|---|---|
| 886.5† | | | | 0.0087 |
| 880 | 0.0431 | 0.0431 | 0.0666 | 0.0934 |
| 869 | 0.0235 | 0.0231 | 0.0378 | 0.0529 |
| 863 | 0.0143 | 0.0168 | 0.0227 | 0.0341 |
| 858 | 0.0086 | 0.0088 | 0.0130 | 0.0237 |
| 856 | 0.0051 | 0.0050 | 0.0083 | 0.0180 |
| 854 | 0.0032 | 0.0024 | 0.0052 | 0.0121 |
| 852 | 0.0021 | 0.0017 | 0.0030 | 0.0077 |
| 851 | 0.0013 | 0.0008 | 0.0017 | 0.0060 |
| 850.6† | | | | 0.0300 |
| | $\sum f = 0.1012$ | $\sum f = 0.1017$ | $\sum f = 0.158$ | $\sum f = 0.287$ |

† The maximum wavelength of the autoionization line.

* The measurement technique using two ionization chambers is described in §26.

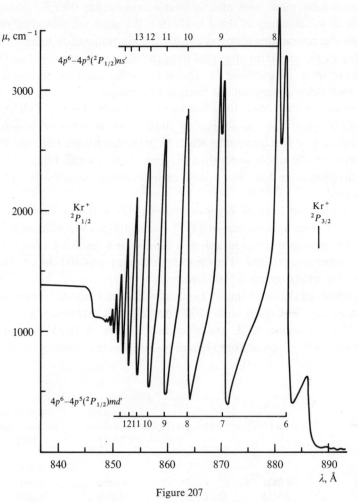

Figure 207

Absorption coefficient of krypton vs. wavelength between 840 and 886 Å.

Theoretical calculations fitted all the autoionization lines with the series expression [112]

$$v = 221{,}917 - \frac{R}{(n - 2.53)^2}, \tag{36}$$

where $n = 5, 6, \ldots$ .

The energy levels of the krypton atom were predicted in [114]. The results of calculations and experimental measurements from [114] are listed in Table 31.

The autoionization lines form the series $4s^2 4p^6\,{}^1S_0 - 4s4p^6 np\,{}^1P_1$, with its limit at 450.6 Å (Kr II $4s4p^6\,{}^2S$). They appear as emission lines, since the absorption

Table 31

| Transition | $\lambda_{theor}$, Å | $\lambda_{exp}$, Å |
|---|---|---|
| $4s^24p^6 - 4s4p^65p$ | — | 501.11 |
| $4s^24p^6 - 4s4p^65p$ | 498.0 | 497.46 |
| $4s^24p^6 - 4s4p^65p$ | 497.4 | 496.87 |
| | — | 496.04 |
| $4s^24p^6 - 4s4p^66p$ | 471.8 | 471.54 |
| $4s^24p^6 - 4s4p^67p$ | 462.8 | 462.75 |
| $4s^24p^6 - 4s4p^68p$ | 458.6 | 457.85 |
| $4s^24p^6 - 4s4p^69p$ | 456.2 | 456.14 |

coefficient at the relevant wavelengths is substantially lower than in the continuum (see [401]).

Still another series was discovered, corresponding to the two-electron excitation $4s^24p^6\ {}^1S_0 - 4s^24p^45snp\ {}^1P_1^0$, with its limit at 386.5 Å.

The krypton spectrum shows lines between 132 and 136 Å [116]. They were recorded photographically on a three-meter grazing-incidence spectrograph with 0.06 Å resolution at 150 Å; the krypton pressure in the spectrograph was 0.07 T. The lines were identified and measured with fair accuracy; they can be arranged in two series, $3d^{10}4s^24p^6\ {}^1S_0 - 3d^94s^24p^6({}^2D_{3/2})np\ {}^1P_1$ and $3d^{10}4s^24p^6\ {}^1S_0 - 3d^94s^24p^6\ ({}^2D_{5/2})np\ {}^1P_1$. A $3d$ electron is thus excited, i.e., one of the inner deep-lying electrons. Table 32 lists the measured wavelengths of these lines and the corresponding quantum numbers.

The krypton spectrum shows still another series between 110 and 115 Å [119a].

**Xenon**

The absorption spectrum of xenon and its autoionization lines were studied in numerous experiments [8, 83, 106, 109, 113, 116–118, 119a, 120–123]. The spectral

Table 32

| $n$ | $\lambda$ of ${}^2D_{5/2}$ series, Å | $\lambda$ of ${}^2D_{3/2}$ series, Å |
|---|---|---|
| 5 | 135.88 | 134.09 |
| 6 | 133.90 | 132.12 |
| 7 | 133.17 | 131.43 |
| 8 | 132.82 | 131.09 |
| | 132.14 (98.82)* | 130.45 (95.04)* |

\* This wavelength corresponds to the limit of the series. The figure in parentheses is the energy in eV.

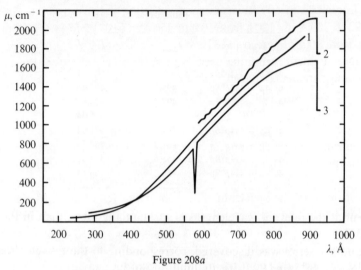

Figure 208*a*

Absorption coefficient of xenon vs. wavelength:

1) data of [118],    2) data of [106],    3) data of [120].

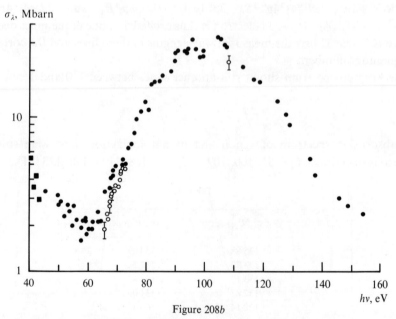

Figure 208*b*

Absorption cross section of xenon vs. wavelength:

■ data of [120],  ● data of photographic measurements [122], O results obtained with a counter [122].

region from 1023 to 600 Å was covered in [106], that from 922 to 280 Å in [118], from 922 to 230 Å in [120], from 922 to 450 Å in [109] and [121], from 250 to 20 Å in [83], from 300 to 80 Å in [122].

The measurement technique used in [106, 109, 118, 120] was the same as in absorption measurements of argon and krypton by the same authors. Figure 208 plots the data of some experimental studies. The results show an excellent fit, especially if we remember that the work has been carried out by different methods in different laboratories. The absorption coefficients obtained in [106] were somewhat too high. Photoionization cross sections at 170 Å for krypton and xenon are compared in [118]; the photoionization cross section of xenon is found to be almost 300 times as high as that of krypton, which is probably associated with the presence of auto-ionization lines in the spectrum of xenon at the relevant wavelengths. The auto-ionization lines of xenon were observed in [106, 113, 114, 116, 117].

The $f$ numbers of the autoionization lines between $^2P_{1/2}$ and $^2P_{3/2}$ were recorded and measured in [106, 113]. The $f$ numbers were measured from the line widths, assuming that the $^2P_{3/2}$ continuum did not introduce any distortion. Figure 209 [8] plots the absorption coefficient of xenon as a function of wavelength in the relevant region, and Table 33 lists the wavelengths with the corresponding $f$ numbers. The lines form two series, $5p^6\ ^1S_0-5p^5\ ^2P_{1/2}nd^1$ and $5p^6\ ^1S_0-5p^5\ ^2P_{1/2}ns^1$, with over-lapping $ns^1$ and $nd^1$ lines. These lines are asymmetric: they are markedly broadened on the short-wave side. The wavelengths between 860 and 1022 Å were studied in

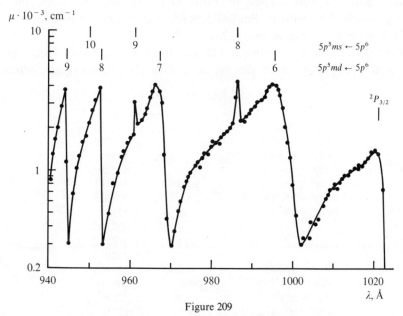

Figure 209

Absorption coefficient of xenon vs. wavelength between 940 and 1022 Å.

Table 33

| $\lambda$, Å | $ns^1$ | $nd^1$ | $f$ [106] | $f$ [113] |
|------|------|------|------|------|
| 995 | 8 | 6 | 0.288 | 0.116 |
| 966 | 9 | 7 | 0.145 | 0.088 |
| 952 | 10 | 8 | 0.077 | 0.042 |
| 943 | 11 | 9 | 0.047 | 0.028 |
| 938 | 12 | 10 | 0.029 | 0.014 |
| 935 | 13 | 11 | 0.017 | 0.007 |
| | | | $\sum f = 0.603$ | $\sum f = 0.295$ |

particularly great detail in [8]. The quantum yield of photoionization was checked for the wavelengths between $^2P_{1/2}$ and $^2P_{3/2}$ and found to be unity.

The autoionization lines between 535 and 600 Å were observed in [114, 117, 120]. They can be fitted by a Rydberg series relation [112]

$$v = 188{,}708 - \frac{R}{(n - 3.53)^2}, \tag{37}$$

where $n = 6, 7, \ldots$ .

The xenon energy levels were predicted by Samson. The results of his calculations and experiments are summarized in Table 34 [114]. The lines form the series $5s5p^6\,^1S_0 - 5s5p^6np\,^1P_1$, with its limit at 529.9 Å. Autoionization lines between 600 and 535 Å were also observed in [123].

New autoionization lines between 179 and 191 Å in the xenon spectrum were observed in [116]. They were discovered with a three-meter grazing-incidence

Table 34

| Transition | $\lambda_{\text{theor}}$, Å | $\lambda_{\text{exp}}$, Å |
|------|------|------|
| $5s^2 5p^6 - 5s5p^5 6p$ | — | 599.95 |
| $5s^2 5p^6 - 5s5p^5 6p$ | 593.5 | 595.92 |
| $5s^2 5p^6 - 5s5p^5 6p$ | 591.6 | 591.81 |
| $5s^2 5p^6 - 5s5p^5 6p$ | — | 589.62 |
| $5s^2 5p^6 - 5s5p^5 7p$ | — | 579.25 |
| | — | 570.90 |
| | 558.5 | 557.92 |
| | — | 552.07 |
| $5s^2 5p^6 - 5s5p^5 8p$ | 546.5 | 546.16 |
| $5s^2 5p^6 - 5s5p^5 9p$ | 540.7 | 540.71 |
| $5s^2 5p^6 - 5s5p^5 10p$ | 537.6 | 537.40 |
| $5s^2 5p^6 - 5s5p^5 11p$ | 535.6 | 535.62 |

spectrograph with $0.06\,\text{Å}$ resolution at $150\,\text{Å}$ and $0.07$ torr pressure. These lines were identified and arranged in two series, $4d^{10}5s^25p^6\ {}^1S_0-4d^95s^25p^6({}^2D_{3/2})np\ {}^1P_1$ and $4d^{10}5s^25p^6\ {}^1S_0-4d^95s^25p^6({}^2D_{5/2})np\ {}^1P_1$. They correspond to $4d-np$ transitions, which involve excitation of very deep-lying electrons. Table 35 lists the measured wavelengths and the energies corresponding to the series limits.

Table 35

| $n^*$ | $\lambda$ of ${}^2D_{5/2}$ series. Å | $\lambda$ of ${}^2D_{3/2}$ series. Å |
|---|---|---|
| 6 | 190.41 | 184.94 |
| 7 | 186.81 | 181.42 |
| 8 | 185.47 | 180.14 |
| 9 | — | 179.53 |
| 10 | 184.45 | — |
| | 183.55 (67.55)* | 178.33 (69.52)* |

* This wavelength corresponds to the limit of the series, The figure in parentheses is the energy in eV.

A new series in the spectrum of xenon was observed between 145 and $160\,\text{Å}$ [119a].

The theory interpreting the shape of the autoionization lines in the absorption spectra of inert gases was developed by Fano and Cooper [40, 124]. Table 36 is a summary of the various data on the absorption spectra of the inert gases.

# 39. ABSORPTION SPECTRA OF MOLECULAR AND ATOMIC GASES

Although we are mainly concerned with atomic spectroscopy in the vacuum ultraviolet, this section briefly discusses some data on the absorption of molecular gases frequently encountered in experimental practice. These are primarily the atmospheric gases—nitrogen, oxygen, water vapor, NO, hydrogen, $CO_2$, ozone, ammonia, $N_2O$, carbon monoxide. The absorption spectrum of hydrogen is of particular interest because $H_2$ is used to fill the discharge tubes of continuous spectrum sources.

Various review papers have been published on the absorption spectra of these common gases [2, 125, 126]. In what follows we will only concentrate on the determination of the absorption cross sections of molecular gases; the methods for the determination of the photoionization cross sections are not discussed.

### Nitrogen

Numerous experimental studies deal with the absorption spectrum of nitrogen [127–142a]. After all, nitrogen is the main constituent of air and its absorption therefore

Table 36

| Gas | Spectral region, Å | Wavelength corresponding to ionization potential, Å | Spectral region showing autoionization lines, Å | References | |
|---|---|---|---|---|---|
| | | | | theoretical | experimental |
| He | 600–100 | 504 | 207–165 | [86–88, 91–94] | [78–83, 89, 90] |
| Ne | 600–80 | 575 | 280–250 | [101–103a] | [98–100a] |
| Ar | 800–100 | 787 | 787–782 | [102, 115] | [80, 90, 104–109, |
| | | | 470–420 | | 112, 113] |
| Kr | 886–200 | 886 | 886–850 | [102, 115] | [83, 109, 111–114, |
| | | | 501–456 | | 116–119a] |
| | | | 136–130 | | |
| Xe | 1022–200 | 1022 | 995–935 | | [8, 83, 106, 109, 113, |
| | | | 600–535 | | 116–118, 119a, |
| | | | 191–179 | | 120–123] |

affects the composition of radiation reaching the observer from the Sun and other celestial bodies. Moreover, the experimental physicist should know to what vacuum to pump out the spectroscopic instruments, i.e., to what extent nitrogen absorption may distort the source intensity.

The absorption spectrum of nitrogen can be divided into three regions: from 1450 to 1000 Å, from 1000 to 796 Å, and from 796 to 160 Å.

Figure 181 is the energy level diagram of a nitrogen molecule, explaining the origin of these three regions. The 1450–1000 Å region corresponds to the $x\ ^1\Sigma_g^+ - a\ ^1\Pi_g$ transitions (Lyman–Birge–Hopfield bands) and the $x\ ^1\Sigma_g^+ - c\ ^3\Pi_u$ transitions; no continuous absorption is observed in this region. Since the absorption in this region is very weak, the absorption spectrum at atmospheric pressure can be photographed only if a nitrogen layer of a few centimeters is used.

Table 37 lists the wavelengths of the absorption bands in accordance with Tanaka's measurements [129]. The continuous spectrum source in Tanaka's work was a slightly condensed argon discharge at 200 T pressure, 15 kV voltage, and 1 kW supply transformer. The spectrum was recorded with a two-meter normal-incidence spectrograph with 8 Å/mm dispersion.

The data on the absorption cross sections in this region are not always consistent [125]. At the maxima of the Lyman–Birge–Hopfield bands, the absorption cross sections are of the order of $10^{-2}$ Mbarn, and between the bands of the order of $10^{-4}$ Mbarn.

The 1450–1000 Å region contains several strong lines of the solar spectrum whose absorption cross sections have been measured [131]. Some characteristic data are the following: at 1025.72 Å, $\sigma = 10^{-3}$ Mbarn; at 1031.91 Å, $\sigma = 7.4 \cdot 10^{-4}$ Mbarn;

Table 37

| Wavelengths of Lyman–Birge–Hopfield lines, Å | Wavelengths corresponding to the $x\,^1\Sigma_g^+ - c\,^3\Pi_u$ transitions, Å |
|:---:|:---:|
| 1450.4 | 1123 |
| 1416.1 | 1099 |
| 1384.0 | 1076 |
| 1353.8 | |
| 1325.4 | |
| 1298.6 | |
| 1273.4 | |
| 1249.4 | |
| 1226.9 | |
| 1205.6 | |
| 1185.2 | |
| 1165.9 | |
| 1147.6 | |
| 1130.4 | |
| 1114.2 | |

at 1037.61 Å, $\sigma = 7.4 \cdot 10^{-4}$ Mbarn. These cross sections have been measured with high accuracy and, unlike the previous figures, they are definitely not semiqualitative.

Between 1000 and 796 Å, strong absorption bands are observed, but there is no continuous absorption. This region has been studied in detail by various experimentalists [127, 131–137, 139, 142].

The wavelength of 796 Å corresponds to the first ionization potential ($N_2^+ x^2\Sigma_g$). The 1000–800 Å region was studied in the greatest detail in [139, 142], where the helium continuum was used as the source (see §4). A vacuum monochromator with 1200 lines/mm grating (2.2 m radius of curvature) was used in [139]; its entrance and exit slits had bandwidths of 0.5 Å.

The spectrograph used in [142] had a 1200 lines/mm grating with 1 m radius of curvature, 40 micron entrance slit, 30 micron exit slit, and 0.5 Å bandwidth. The pressure was varied from 0.01 to 0.1 T, the radiation was recorded with a closed photomultiplier and a sodium salicylate layer. Figure 210 plots the absorption coefficient of nitrogen as a function of wavelength [139]. The curves were obtained by scanning the spectrum at four different pressures between 0.04 and 0.17 T. The absorption cross sections at certain wavelengths reached tens of barns.

The absorption coefficients are tabulated for various wavelengths in [139] and in [142]. The results of these tables, however, are not always consistent (either between themselves or with the findings of other authors). This is primarily due to the pressure dependence of the absorption coefficients of individual bands.

To reduce the error associated with pressure variation, the luminous fluxes should be measured either at the minimum of the absorption band or precisely at the maximum. Highly reliable measurements were carried out for individual spectral lines in [131].

Starting with 796 Å, the spectrum of nitrogen develops an ionization continuum which corresponds to the transition of the nitrogen molecule from the ground state to the state $N_2^+ x^2\Sigma_g^+$. A number of Rydberg bands are superimposed on the continuum. The wavelengths and the absorption coefficients for $\lambda > 600$ Å are given in [142] (see Figure 210c and Figure 210d).

The absorption spectrum between 700 and 600 Å is not unlike the atomic spectrum of autoionization lines (see §38). Figure 210e plots the absorption coefficients of nitrogen for wavelengths shorter than 600 Å, according to the measurements of a number of authors [135, 138, 141, 142a]. The results show a very poor fit.

Unfortunately, despite the great number of experimental studies, the existing determinations of the absorption coefficient and the absorption cross section of molecular nitrogen are far from reliable. The great difficulties involved in these measurements are evident from the fact that the results of [139] and [142], although obtained under completely analogous conditions, are by no means consistent and the divergence far exceeds the margin of experimental error (Table 38).

Autoionization in molecular nitrogen was studied by Codling and Madden [140]. They used synchrotron radiation as a continuous spectrum source.

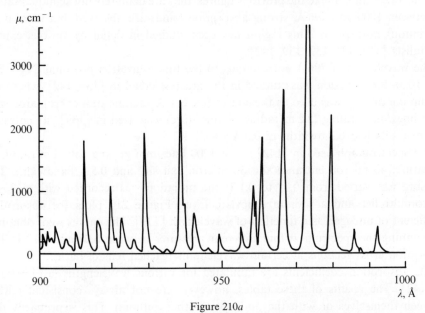

Figure 210a

Absorption coefficient of nitrogen vs. wavelength between 1000 and 900 Å.

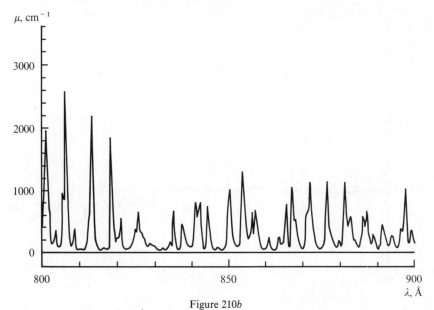

Figure 210*b*

Absorption coefficient of nitrogen vs. wavelength between 900 and 800 Å.

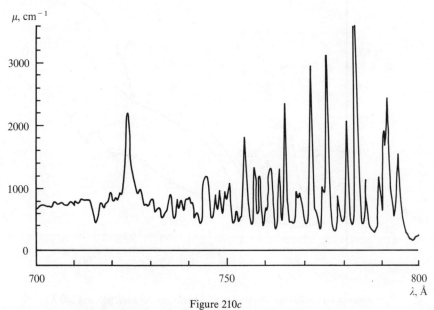

Figure 210*c*

Absorption coefficient of nitrogen vs. wavelength between 800 and 700 Å.

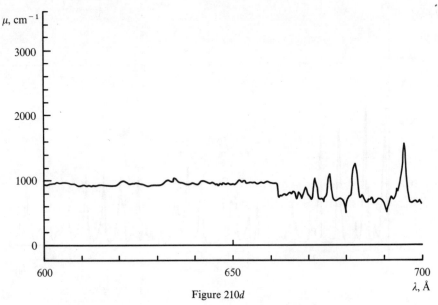

Figure 210*d*

Absorption coefficient of nitrogen vs. wavelength between 700 and 600 Å.

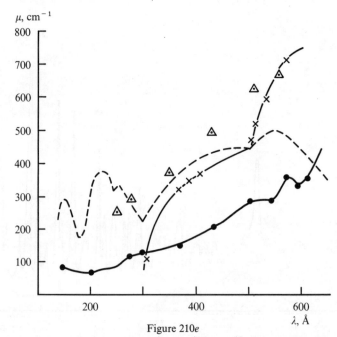

Figure 210*e*

Absorption coefficient of nitrogen vs. wavelength between 600 and 200 Å:

dashed line, data of [138]; ● data of [141]; × data of [135]; △ data of [142a].

Table 38

| $\lambda$, Å | $\mu$, cm$^{-1}$ | |
|---|---|---|
| | [142] | [139] |
| 912.6 | 960 | 1860 |
| 920.0 | 450 | 1060 |
| 949.2 | 18.9 | 310 |
| 958.0 | 500 | 1120 |
| 970.0 | 5.0 | 23 |
| 972.5 | 5200 | 8120 |

**Oxygen** [3, 125, 134, 136, 137, 142–155a]

The absorption spectrum of oxygen has also been very little studied (for the same reasons as the nitrogen spectrum).

The absorption between 2500 and 1850 Å was discovered by Herzberg [143], who assigned it to the dissociation $O_2\,^3\Sigma_g \to O\,^3P + O\,^3P$. Absorption measurements in this region were carried out in [144]. The absorption is very weak (of the order of $10^{-5}$ Mbarn). Measureable absorption is observed at atmospheric pressure in tubes about 7 m long. A hydrogen lamp was used as the source. Exposure times of about one hour were required.

A fundamental experimental difficulty is associated with ozone production: the absorption coefficient of ozone is $10^5$ times as high as the absorption coefficient of oxygen. To avoid the ozone absorption, its content in oxygen must be reduced to a minimum. This is done either by passing a jet of gas through the tube and pumping out the ozone, or filtering off the wavelengths which induce ozone production. These special measures made it possible to determine the absorption cross section between 1900 and 2500 Å. It varied from $1.5 \cdot 10^{-5}$ Mbarn at 1900 Å to $3 \cdot 10^{-7}$ Mbarn at 2500 Å.

Schumann–Runge bands are observed between 1950 and 1750 Å. The absorption curve in this region is plotted in Figure 211a from the data of [145].

The spectral region from 1750 to 1250 Å has been studied partly or completely by various authors [3, 125, 137, 145–151]. Continuous absorption is noted in this region. Three diffuse bands are clearly distinguishable in the short-wave part of this region: 1293 Å, 1332 Å, and 1352 Å. Figure 211b shows a general absorption curve for this part of the spectrum [145].

The results of [145] and [137] were tabulated in [125], and they seem to agree with the measurements of [3].

Numerous absorption bands with prominent absorption minima (so-called "windows") are observed between 1250 and 1050 Å. This region was studied in

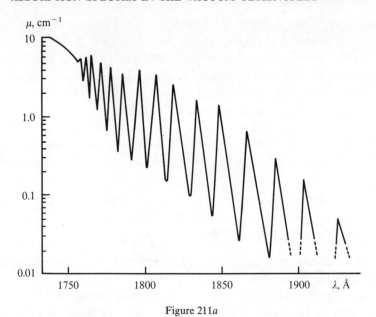

Figure 211*a*

Absorption coefficient of oxygen vs. wavelength between 1950 and 1750 Å.

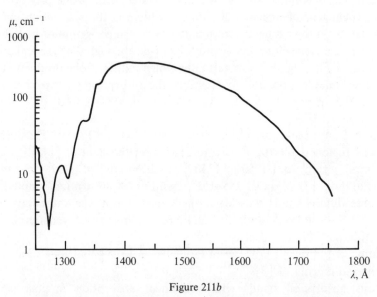

Figure 211*b*

Absorption coefficient of oxygen vs. wavelength between 1750 and 1250 Å.

particularly great detail in [137, 145, 148, 150, 151] (Figures 211c and 211d). The absorption coefficients in the seven oxygen "windows" are listed in Table 39.

Of particular interest is the absorption coefficient for $L_\alpha$. It was measured in [136, 145, 149, 152], and some results are summarized in Table 38. This absorption cross section is dependent on pressure (Figure 212) [125]. The absorption cross section of oxygen for $L_\alpha$ is of the order of $10^{-2}$ Mbarn.

Note that the spectrometer bandwidth in [148] was 0.5 Å, and this resolution was quite sufficient for correct measurements, i.e., the absorption coefficients showed a good fit with Watanabe's results [125] obtained with 0.1–0.2 Å resolution.

Table 39

| $\lambda$, Å | $\mu$, cm$^{-1}$ | | |
|---|---|---|---|
| | [3] | [136] | [125] |
| 1215.7 | 0.28 | 0.23 | 0.27 |
| 1187.1 | 0.20 | 0.35 | 0.18 |
| 1166.8 | 0.29 | 0.28 | 0.27 |
| 1157.0 | 0.44 | — | 0.51 |
| 1142.8 | 0.31 | — | 0.26 |
| 1126.9 | 0.62 | — | 0.53 |
| 1108.3 | 0.20 | 0.44 | 0.11 |

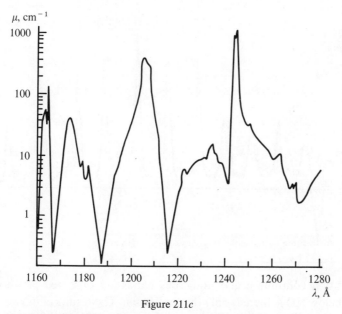

Figure 211c

Absorption coefficient of oxygen vs. wavelength between 1280 and 1160 Å.

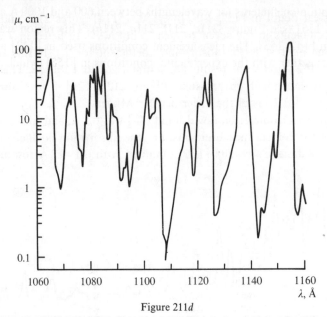

Figure 211*d*

Absorption coefficient of oxygen vs. wavelength between 1160 and 1060 Å.

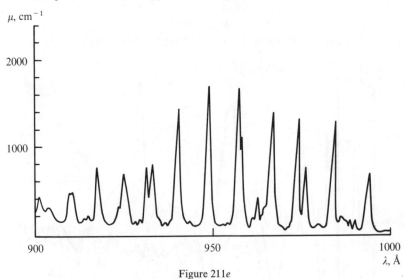

Figure 211*e*

Absorption coefficient of oxygen vs. wavelength between 1000 and 900 Å.

An ionization continuum and numerous bands are observed between 1050 and 200 Å, and below 600 Å there is only the continuum. The results of oxygen absorption measurements in this region can be found in [134, 136, 137, 142, 142a, 151, 153–155a].

The absorption coefficients for wavelengths between 600 and 1000 Å are tabulated in [125, 142, 155] (see Figures 211e, 211f, 211g, 211h). This region was studied in great detail in [142, 155]. The measurement conditions used in [142] are described on page 275, together with the experimental conditions in [155] (which are the same as in [139]).

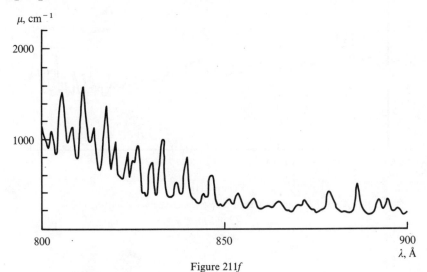

Figure 211f

Absorption coefficient of oxygen vs. wavelength between 900 and 800 Å.

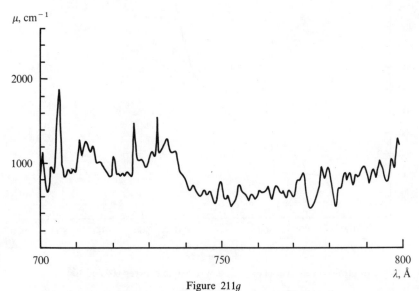

Figure 211g

Absorption coefficient of oxygen vs. wavelength between 800 and 700 Å.

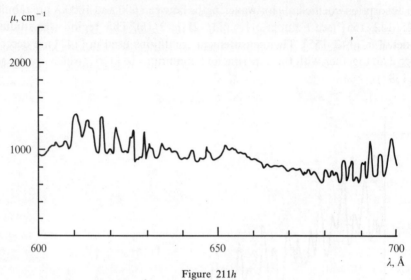

Figure 211*h*

Absorption coefficient of oxygen vs. wavelength between 700 and 600 Å.

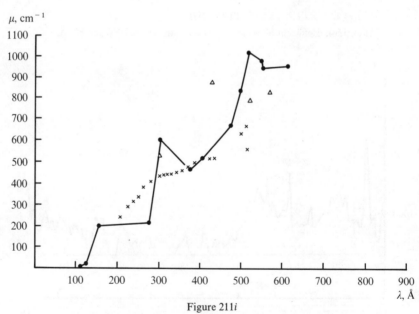

Figure 211*i*

Absorption coefficient of oxygen vs. wavelength between 600 and 100 Å:

●data of [153], △data of [136], × data of [142*a*].

The absorption curves were obtained at pressures between 0.5 and 0.34 T [155] and between 0.01 and 0.1 T [142]. Many of the oxygen bands are wide, and their absorption coefficient is thus independent of pressure. There are divergences of some 20–30% between the results of [142, 155]. These deviations are quite random.

Figure 211*i* plots the experimental curves for wavelengths shorter than 600 Å [136, 142a, 153]. The data show a poor agreement between themselves; the results of [142a] apparently should be preferred.

**Water vapor**

The absorption spectrum of water was studied experimentally in [156–167]. The region between 1850 and 200 Å was covered. Figure 213 plots the experimental curves. Although there is no perfect fit between the results of various authors, the different sets of data are not too widely divergent. Exact determination of the absorption coefficients of water vapor is impossible, because of pressure measurement inaccuracies, especially in open cuvette experiments. Therefore the following technique is often used: the absorption coefficient is measured for a spectral region where it is known from other measurements, and the results are applied to determine the exact pressure [137].

The wavelengths from 1850 to 1450 Å were studied in [160–163, 167], the wavelengths from 1450 to 1100 Å in [160, 163], from 1100 to 850 Å in [166], from 1100 to 160 Å in [160, 164, 165].

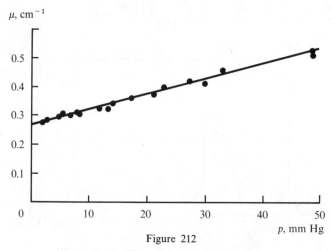

Figure 212

Absorption coefficient of oxygen in $L_\alpha$ vs. pressure.

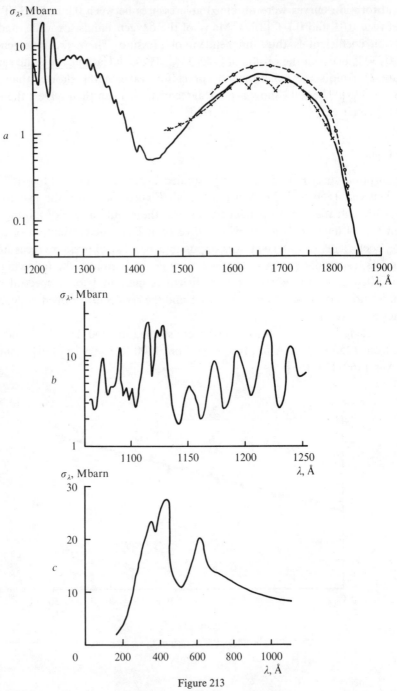

Figure 213

Absorption coefficient of water vapor vs. wavelength:

a   1900–1200 Å (✕ data of [161], ◯ data of [162], solid curve from [163])
b   1250–1000 Å;   c   1000–200 Å.

The curves of Figure 213 show that the absorption in water vapor is strong in the entire vacuum ultraviolet, and no spectrometer should be used without first freezing out the water vapor, especially when line intensities are to be measured.

### Nitrogen monoxide NO [168–174]

The absorption spectrum of NO was studied in great detail, since this gas is used as a filling for various counters and ionization chambers.

The absorption and photoionization cross sections were measured in [168–174]. The wavelengths from 150 to 2300 Å were studied. The region with $\lambda > 1400$ Å was investigated in [170, 173], but the results are not always consistent and are only semiquantitative. The most reliable measurements are available between 1050 and 1350 Å [168–170] (Figure 214, which also gives the photoionization cross sections).

According to Watanabe's measurements, the quantum yield in this region is constant, being equal to 81% (see §27). The absorption and photoionization cross section for this region of the spectrum are tabulated in [125].

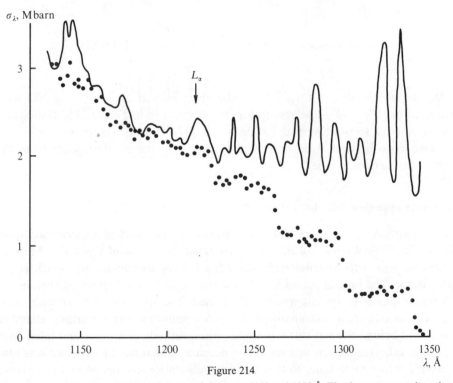

Figure 214

Absorption cross section of NO vs. wavelength between 1150 and 1350 Å. The dots correspond to photo-ionization cross section values.

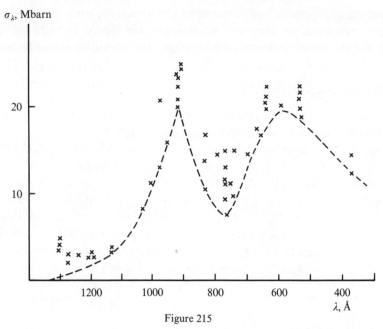

Figure 215

Absorption cross section of NO vs. wavelength between 1200–400 Å [171].

At wavelengths shorter than 1000 Å, the absorption cross sections of NO were measured in [171, 172]. The absorption curve is shown in Figure 215. The photo-ionization cross sections were also measured in [174], but the results are apparently too low, since between 1350 and 1050 Å there is a distinct divergence from the highly reliable data of [168].

**Molecular hydrogen** [108, 142a, 175–180]

The absorption spectrum of molecular hydrogen was studied experimentally in [142a, 175–180]. We will consider in some detail the results of Cook and Metzger [179] and their experimental technique. The helium continuum was used as the light source. The helium pressure in the source reached a few hundred torr, and a differential pumpout system was therefore used. The spectrum was recorded with a Seya–Namioka monochromator with 0.5 Å resolution. The absorbing chamber was placed behind the exit slit. A platinum photocathode or a photomultiplier with a sodium salicylate screen was used as a detector. The ionization current was also measured at the same time, so that both the absorption coefficient and the photo-ionization coefficient could be determined.

The measurements were carried out at wavelengths from 1000 to 580 Å. Figure 216 plots the photoionization and absorption cross sections as a function of wavelength. We see from the curves that the absorption spectrum between 860 and 710 Å is highly complex: bands are superimposed on the continuum. Weak absorption in the form of isolated absorption bands is observed between 1000 and 860 Å ($\mu \leq 20$ cm$^{-1}$, occasionally falling to 1 cm$^{-1}$). It was detected at pressures of about 2–3 T in an absorbing column 87 cm long. A predissociation continuum was observed at 844.8 Å. This continuum corresponds to the dissociation of a hydrogen molecule into a normal and an excited hydrogen atom according to the following scheme:

$$H_2 \rightarrow H(1\,^2S) + H(2\,^2P).$$

The lower limit of this continuum is shifted to 858 Å, because the low rotational sublevels of the hydrogen molecule are fully occupied at room temperature [182].

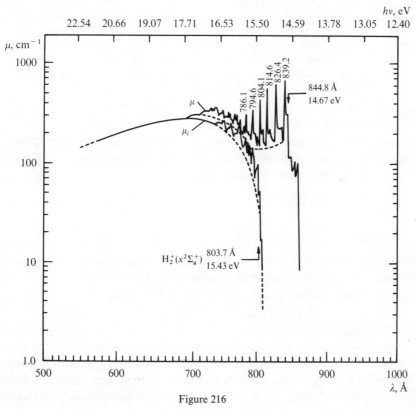

Figure 216

Absorption cross section and photoionization cross section of hydrogen vs. wavelength between 900 and 560 Å ($\mu$ is the absorption coefficient, $\mu_i$ is the photoionization coefficient).

The absorption coefficient at 844.8 Å is 320 cm$^{-1}$. At wavelengths from 844.8 to 803 Å a continuum with an absorption coefficient of about 150 cm$^{-1}$ is observed (maximum absorption coefficient about 300 cm$^{-1}$), and several absorption bands are superimposed on the continuum (for one of the absorption bands the absorption coefficient is as high as 860 cm$^{-1}$). The cell length in these measurements was about 40 cm, and the pressure varied from 0.005 to 0.1 T. The absorption spectrum of deuterium is not unlike the absorption spectrum of hydrogen. The results of Lee and Weissler [178] show good agreement with the curve of Figure 216, and there is substantial divergence only near 720 Å. Table 40 lists the absorption coefficient of individual absorption bands.

Table 40

| $\lambda$, Å | $\mu$, cm$^{-1}$ | $\lambda$, Å | $\mu$, cm$^{-1}$ | $\lambda$, Å | $\mu$, cm$^{-1}$ |
|---|---|---|---|---|---|
| 868.8 | $\approx 20$ | 814.7 | max 560 | 786.1 | max 330 |
| 853.3 | 105 | 813.0 | min 150 | 785.0 | min 190 |
| 839.2 | max 680 | 804.1 | max 440 | 778.3 | max 260 |
| 838.0 | min 180 | 802.0 | min 145 | 777.0 | min 150 |
| 826.4 | max 610 | 794.6 | max 350 | 771.5 | max 300 |
| 823.0 | min 160 | 793.0 | min 165 | 770.0 | min 230 |

The photoionization cross section at 763 Å is 9.7 Mbarn, which is fairly close to the cross section measured by Wainfan et al. [108].

The absorption coefficient at $\lambda < 860$ Å is so small that a hydrogen lamp can be safely used as a source, without the danger of self-absorption distorting the energy distribution in the hydrogen emission spectrum.

**Ozone** [183]

The most detailed study of the ozone absorption spectrum was carried out by Tanaka et al. [183]. Figure 217 plots the results of these authors. Between 1050 and 2200 Å, only continuous absorption is observed. The absorption cross section of ozone for $L_\alpha$ is 24 Mbarn.

**Carbon dioxide** [161, 184–187]

The absorption spectrum of carbon dioxide was studied by various authors. The region from 1440 to 1700 Å was investigated in [161], the region from 1050 to 1800 Å in [186], that from 1330 to 370 Å in [184], from 1050 to 300 Å in [185], and from 160 to 1000 Å in [187].

Figure 218 plots the experimental curves based on the results of [186].

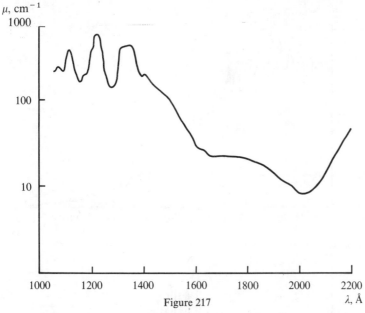

Figure 217

Absorption coefficient of ozone vs. wavelength.

### Ammonia [168, 188–190]

In the absorption spectrum of ammonia, continua are superimposed on discrete bands. The absorption spectrum was qualitatively studied by Duncan [188, 189]. Quantitative results were obtained by Watanabe [168] for wavelengths between 1050 and 2200 Å, by Sun and Weissler [190] between 370 and 1300 Å. An overall absorption curve is shown in Figure 219 [168].

### Carbon monoxide [184, 185, 185a, 191]

The absorption spectrum of carbon monoxide and the absorption coefficient at various wavelengths were studied experimentally by various authors [184, 185, 185a, 191].* However, the results of [184] and [191] are inconsistent. The results of [185] occupy an intermediate position between the two, with deviations not exceeding 20–25%.

### Nitrous oxide $N_2O$ [192, 194]

The absorption cross sections of $N_2O$ were measured between 100 and 2200 Å [192, 194]. The measurement results are plotted in Figure 221. There are several

* Reference to all previous work is given in [191].

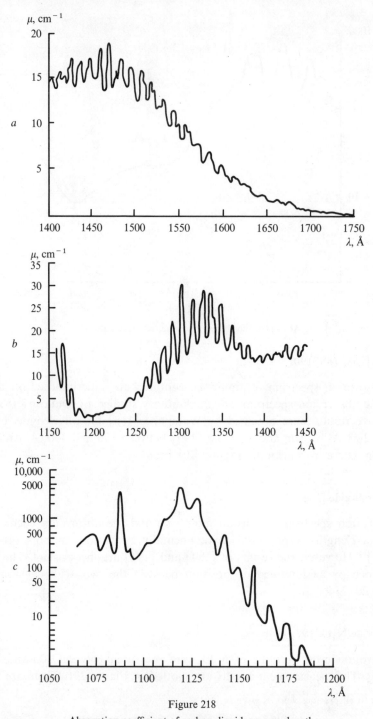

Figure 218

Absorption coefficient of carbon dioxide vs. wavelength:

*a*   1750–1400 Å;   *b*   1450–1150 Å;   *c*   1200–1075 Å.

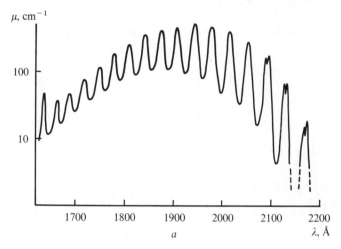

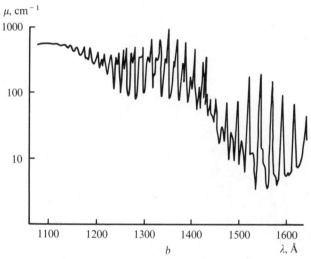

Figure 219

Absorption coefficient of ammonia vs. wavelength:

a   2100–1600 Å,   b   1600–1100 Å.

continua with maxima at 1820 Å, 1450 Å, 1275 Å, and 1080 Å. Three additional continua are observed at wavelengths shorter than 1000 Å.

## Atomic nitrogen [195–197]

The absorption cross sections of atomic nitrogen were measured using a Philips ionization pressure gauge. A spark discharge in a ceramic capillary was used as the

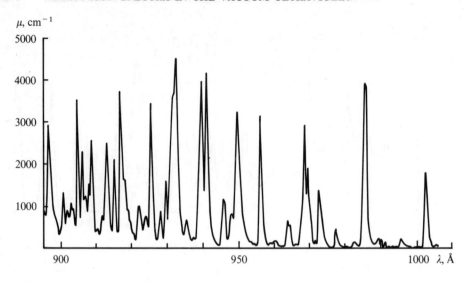

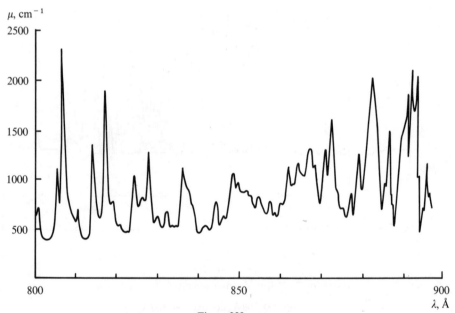

Figure 220a

Absorption coefficient of carbon monoxide vs. wavelength:

top, 1000–900 Å; bottom, 900–800 Å.

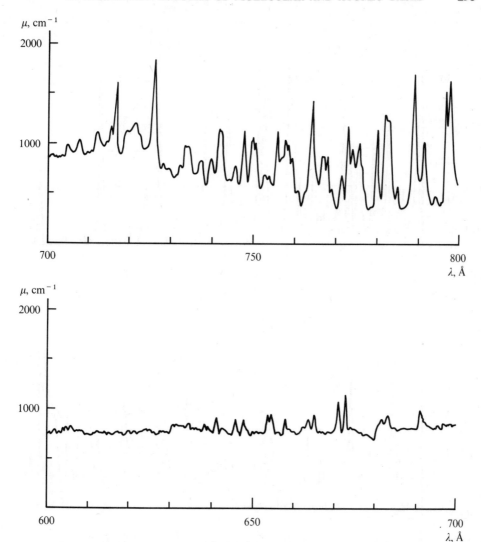

Figure 220*b*

Absorption coefficient of carbon monoxide vs. wavelength:

top, 800–700 Å; bottom, 700–600 Å.

light source. The column length in the ionization gauge reached 58 cm, the current was 30 mA, the pressure 3 kV. Differential pumpout controlled independently the pressure in the source, the spectrograph, and the ionization gauge.

The light intensity was measured when the discharge was turned on and off in the ionization gauge; the absorption coefficient of the plasma itself could thus be

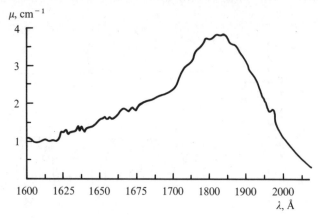

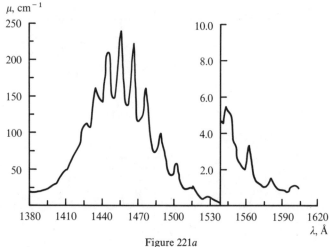

Figure 221a

Absorption coefficient of $N_2O$ vs. wavelength:

top, 2000–1600 Å; bottom, 1600–1380 Å.

found. The absorption of the plasma is probably associated with the absorption of radiation in atomic nitrogen, which produces nitrogen ions:

$$N + h\nu = N^+ + e.$$

This assumption gives 14.4 Mbarn for the absorption cross section of nitrogen between 750 and 450 Å (Figure 222).

In control experiments the absorption of the plasma in the ionization gauge was recorded 4.5 msec after turning off the discharge. This time is long enough for the metastable states to decay, but too short for nitrogen molecules to form, so that the radiation is absorbed by nitrogen atoms only. The results of these experiments

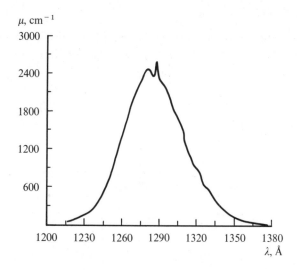

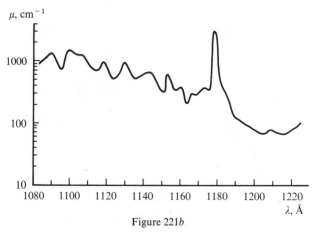

Figure 221*b*

Absorption coefficient of $N_2O$ vs. wavelength:

top, 1380–1220 Å; bottom, 1220–1080 Å.

all gave an absorption cross section of 12.8 Mbarn within the margin of experimental error. These results are close to the theoretical values of $\sigma_\lambda$ obtained in [196], and are much higher than the results of [197].

## Atomic hydrogen [197a–200]

The absorption cross section of atomic hydrogen was experimentally determined in [197a], and reliable theoretical calculations were published in [198–200].

**Atomic oxygen** [196, 197, 201, 202]

The absorption of atomic oxygen was studied experimentally in [201] and theoretically in [196, 197, 202]. Figure 223 shows the results of [201] and [202]. The fit between theory and experiment is satisfactory.

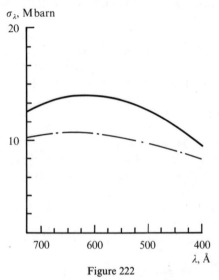

Figure 222

Absorption cross section of atomic nitrogen vs. wavelength (dashed curve—theoretical, solid curve—experimental).

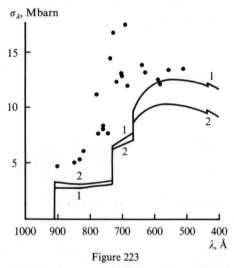

Figure 223

Absorption cross section of atomic oxygen vs. wavelength:
1,2) theoretical curves; ● experimental data.

# BIBLIOGRAPHY

1. COLE, R. *J. Opt. Soc. America,* **41**, 38 (1951).
2. WEISSLER, G.L. *Handbuch der Physik,* S. Flügge, Editor, **XXI**, 304. 1956.
2a. KULIKOV, S.A., YU.A. SNIGIREV, and G.P. STARTSEV. *Optiko-mekhanicheskaya Promysh-lennost',* No. 10, 23 (1965).
3. METZGER, P.H. and G.R. COOK. *J. Quant. Spectr. Rad. Trans.,* **4**, 107 (1964).
4. SAMSON, J.A.R. *J. Opt. Soc. America,* **54**, 6 (1964).
5. PO LEE and G.L. WEISSLER. *J. Opt. Soc. America,* **42**, 80 (1952).
6. DITCHBURN, R.W., J. TUNSTEAD, and J.G. YATES. *Proc. Roy. Soc.,* **A181**, 386 (1943).
7. HUDSON, R.D. *Phys. Rev.,* **135A**, 1212 (1964).
8. MATSUNAGA, F.M., R.S. JACKSON, and K. WATANABE. *J. Quant. Spectr. Rad. Trans.,* **5**, 329 (1965).
9. WOOD, R.W. *Philos. Mag.,* **20**, 707 (1910).
10. WOOD, R.W. and G.A. HEMSALECH. *Philos. Mag.,* **27**, 899 (1914).
11. MEYER, C.F. and R.W. WOOD. *Philos. Mag.,* **30**, 449 (1915).
12. OLDENBURG, O. *Z. Phys.,* **38**, 370 (1926).
13. MCLENNAN, J.C., R. RUEDY, and F.H. CLEMENTS. *Trans. Roy. Soc. Can.,* Section III, **22**, 253 (1928).
14. SCHOEN, R.J., D.L. JUDGE, and G.L. WEISSLER. *Proc. V Intern. Conf. Ioniz. Phenom. Gases,* 1961, **I**, 25.
15. HUFFMAN, R.E., Y. TANAKA, and J.C. LARRABEE. *J. Chem. Phys.,* **38**, 1920 (1963).
16. JUDGE, D.L., A.L. MORSE, and G.L. WEISSLER. *Proc. VI Intern. Conf. Ioniz. Phenom. Gases, Paris,* 1963, **III**, 373.
17. FRISH, S.E., *Opticheskie spektry atomov (Optical Spectra of Atoms).* Fizmatgiz. 1963.
18. EL'YASHEVICH, M.A. *Atomnaya i molekulyarnaya spektroskopiya (Atomic and Molecular Spectroscopy).* Fizmatgiz. 1962.
19. HERZBERG, G. *Atomic Spectra and Atomic Structure.* N. Y., Dover. 1944.
20. SHENSTONE, A.G. *Phys. Rev.,* **38**, 873 (1931).
21. SHENSTONE. A.G. *Phys. Rev.,* **37**, 1701 (1931).
22. BEUTLER, H. *Z. Phys.,* **86**, 495 (1933).
23. BEUTLER, H. *Z. Phys.,* **86**, 710 (1933).
24. BEUTLER, H. *Z. Phys.,* **87**, 19 (1933).
25. BEUTLER, H. and K. GUGGENHEIMER. *Z. Phys.,* **87**, 176 (1933).
26. BEUTLER, H. and K. GUGGENHEIMER. *Z. Phys.,* **87**, 188 (1933).
27. BEUTLER, H. and K. GUGGENHEIMER. *Z. Phys.,* **88**, 25 (1934).
28. BEUTLER, H. *Z. Phys.,* **91**, 131 (1934).
29. BEUTLER, H. and W. DEMETER. *Z. Phys.,* **91**, 202 (1934).
30. BEUTLER, H. and W. DEMETER. *Z. Phys.,* **91**, 218 (1934).
31. BEUTLER, H. *Z. Phys.,* **93**, 177 (1935).
32. SHENSTONE, A.G. *Repts. Progr. Phys.,* **5**, 214 (1938).
33. BOYCE, J.C. *Revs. Mod. Phys.,* **13**, 1 (1941).
34. EDLÉN, B. *Handbuch der Physik,* S. Flügge, Editor, **XXVII**, 80, 1963.
35. ALLEN, C.W. *Phys. Rev.,* **39**, 42, 55 (1932).

36. SHENSTONE, A.G. *Philos. Trans. Roy. Soc.*, **A241**, 297 (1948).
37. SHENSTONE, A.G. *Phys. Rev.* **57**, 894 (1940).
38. GARTON, W.R.S. and A. RAJARATNAM. *Proc. Phys. Soc.*, **A68**, 1107 (1955).
39. TILFORD, S.G. and P.G. WILKINSON. *J. Opt. Soc. America*, **54**, 322 (1964).
40. FANO, U. *Phys. Rev.*, **124**, 1866 (1961).
41. PENKIN, N.P. and L.N. SHABANOVA. *Optika i Spektroskopiya*, **18**, 941 (1965).
42. GARTON, W.R.S., and K. CODLING. *Proc. Phys. Soc.*, **75**, 87 (1960).
43. PENKIN, N.P. and L.N. SHABANOVA. *Optika i Spektroskopiya*, **12**, 3 (1962).
44. GARTON, W.R.S. *Proc. Phys. Soc.*, **A67**, 864 (1954).
45. MARR, G.V. *Proc. Roy. Soc.*, **A224**, 83 (1954).
46. GARTON, W.R.S. *Proc. Phys. Soc.*, **A65**, 268 (1952).
47. GARTON, W.R.S. *Proc. Phys. Soc.*, **A65**, 461 (1952).
48. GARTON, W.R.S., A. PERY, and K. CODLING. *Proc. IV Intern. Conf. Ioniz. Phenom. Gases*, **I**, 206. Amsterdam, North-Holland Publ. Co. 1960.
49. GARTON, W.R.S. In: *Na poroge v kosmos*, B.A. Bagritskii, Editor, p. 218. IL 1960.
50. GARTON, W.R.S. *J. Quant. Spectr. Rad. Trans.*, **2**, 335 (1962).
51. GARTON, W.R.S. *Proc. V Intern. Conf. Ioniz. Phenom. Gases*, **II**, 1884. Amsterdam, North-Holland Publ. Co. 1962.
52. GARTON, W.R.S. and K. CODLING. *Proc. Phys. Soc.*, **78**, 600 (1961).
53. DITCHBURN, R.W. and R. HUDSON. *Proc. Roy. Soc.*, **A256**, 53 (1960).
54. CODLING, K. *Proc. Phys. Soc.*, **77**, 797 (1961).
55. GARTON, W.R.S. and K. CODLING. *Proc. Phys. Soc.*, **86**, 1067 (1965).
56. KAISER, T.R. *Proc. Phys. Soc.*, **75**, 152 (1960).
57. JUTSUM, P.J. *Proc. Phys, Soc.*, **A67**, 190 (1954).
58. DITCHBURN, R.W. and G.V. MARR. *Proc. Phys. Soc.*, **A66**, 655 (1953).
59. DITCHBURN, R.W., P.J. JUTSUM, and G.V. MARR. *Proc. Roy. Soc.*, **A219**, 89 (1953).
60. MARR, G.V. *Proc. Phys. Soc.*, **81**, 9 (1963).
61. GARTON, W.R.S. and K. CODLING. *Mém. Soc. Roy. Sci. Liège*, **4**, 193 (1961).
62. ROSS, K.J. and G.V. MARR. *Proc. Phys, Soc.*, **85**, 193 (1965).
63. HUDSON, R.D. and V.L. CARTER. *J. Opt. Soc. America*, **54**, 1403 (1964).
63a. HUDSON, R.D. and V.L. CARTER. *Phys. Rev.* **139A**, 1426 (1965).
64. HUDSON, R.D. and V.L. CARTER. *Phys. Rev.* **137A**, 1648 (1965).
65. GARTON, W.R.S., W.H. PARKINSON, and E.M. REEVES. *Astrophys. J.*, **140**, 1269 (1964).
66. DITCHBURN, R.W. *Proc. Roy. Soc.*, **A117**, 486 (1928).
67. TUNSTEAD, J. *Proc. Phys. Soc.*, **A66**, 304 (1953).
68. BURGESS, A. and M.J. SEATON. *Monthly Notices Roy. Astron. Soc.*, **120**, 121 (1960).
69. TAIT, J.H. *Atomic Collision Processes*, M.R.C. McDowell, Editor, p. 586. Amsterdam, North-Holland Publishing Co. 1964.
70. SEATON, M.J. *Proc. Roy. Soc.*, **A208**, 418 (1951).
71. DITCHBURN, R.W. and U. OPIK. *Photoionization Processes*, p. 79. In: *Atomic and Molecular Processes*, D. Bates, Editor, p. 79. New York–London, Academic Press. 1962.
71a. PEACH, G. *Monthly Notices Roy. Astron. Soc.*, **124**, 371 (1962).
72. MOORE, C.E. *Circ. Nat. Bur. Stand.*, **1**, No. 467 (1949).

73. BATES, D.R. and H.S.W. MASSEY. *Proc. Roy. Soc.,* **A177**, 329 (1941).
74. TOUSEY, R. In: *Kosmicheskaya astrofizika,* W. Liller, Editor, p. 11. IL. 1962.
75. VAINSHTEIN, L.A. and G.E. NORMAN. *Optika i Spektroskopiya,* **8**, 149 (1960).
76. PENKIN, N.P. and L.N. SHABANOVA. *Optika i Spektroskopiya,* **14**, 167 (1963).
77. KREMENEVSKII, N.V. *Doklady AN SSSR,* **3**, 251 (1935).
78. LOWRY, J.F., D.H. TOMBOULIAN, and D.L. EDERER. *Phys. Rev.,* **137**, 1054 (1965).
79. BAKER, D.J., D.E. BEDO, and D.H. TOMBOULIAN. *Phys. Rev.,* **124**, 1471 (1961).
80. PO LEE and G.L. WEISSLER. *Phys. Rev.,* **99**, 540 (1955).
81. AXELROD, N. and M.P. GIVENS. *Phys. Rev.,* **115**, 97 (1959).
82. SAMSON, J.A.R. *J. Opt. Soc. America,* **54**, 876 (1964).
83. LUKIRSKII, A.P., I.A. BRYTOV, and T.M. ZIMKINA. *Optika i Spektroskopiya,* **17**, 438 (1964).
84. BEDO, D.E. and D.H. TOMBOULIAN. *Rev. Scient. Instrum.,* **32**, 184 (1961).
85. WOODRUFF, R.W. and M.P. GIVENS. *Phys. Rev.,* **97**, 52 (1955).
86. HUANG, S. *Astrophys. J.* **108**, 354 (1948).
87. STEWART, A.L. and W.J. WILKINSON. *Proc. Phys. Soc.,* **75**, 796 (1960).
88. STEWART, A.L. and G. WEBB. *Proc. Phys. Soc.,* **82**, 532 (1963).
89. MADDEN, R.P. and K. CODLING. *Astrophys. J.,* **141**, 364 (1965).
90. MADDEN, R.P. and K. CODLING. *Phys. Rev. Lett.,* **10**, 516 (1963).
91. COOPER, J.W., U. FANO, and F. PRATS. *Phys. Rev. Lett.,* **10**, 518 (1963).
92. BURKE, P.G. and D.D. MCVICAR. *Phys Rev. Lett.,* **11**, 559 (1963).
93. BURKE, P.G. and D.D. MCVICAR. *Proc. Phys. Soc.,* **84**, 749 (1964).
94. COOPER, J.W. *Atomic Collision Processes,* M.R.C. McDowell, Editor, p. 595. Amsterdam, North-Holland Publishing Co. 1964.
95. SILVERMAN, S.M. and E.N. LASSETRE. *J. Chem. Phys.* **40**, 1265 (1964).
96. RUDD. M.E. *Phys. Rev. Lett.,* **13**, 503 (1964).
96a. RUDD, M.E. *Phys. Rev. Lett.,* **15**, 580 (1965).
97. SIMPSON, J.A., S.R. MIELCZAREK, and J.W. COPPER. *J. Opt. Soc. America,* **54**, 269 (1964).
98. EDERER, D.L. and D.H. TOMBOULIAN. *Phys. Rev.* **133A**, 1525 (1964).
98a. CODLING, K. and R.P. MADDEN. *J. Opt. Soc. America,* **56**, 552 (1966).
99. PO LEE and G.L. WEISSLER. *Proc. Roy. Soc.,* **A220**, 71 (1953).
100. DITCHBURN, R.W. *Proc. Phys. Soc.,* **75**, 461 (1960).
100a. SAMSON, J.A.R. *J. Opt. Soc. America,* **55**, 935 (1965).
101. SEWELL, K.G. *Phys. Rev.,* **138A**, 418 (1965).
102. COOPER, J.W. *Phys. Rev.,* **128**, 681 (1962).
103. MCGUIRE, E.J. and D.H. TOMBOULIAN. *Bull. Amer. Phys. Soc.,* **8**, 75 (1963).
103a. SEATON, M.J. *Proc. Phys. Soc.,* **A67**, 927 (1954).
104. SAMSON, J.A.R. *J. Opt. Soc. America,* **54**, 420 (1964).
105. RUSTGI, O.P. *J. Opt. Soc. America,* **54**, 464 (1964).
106. HUFFMAN, R.E., Y. TANAKA, and J.C. LARRABEE. *J. Chem. Phys.,* **39**, 902 (1963).
107. ALEXANDER, R.W. D.L. EDERER, and D.H. TOMBOULIAN. *Bull. Amer. Phys. Soc.,* **9**, 626 (1964).
108. WAINFAN, N., W.C. WALKER, and G.L. WEISSLER. *Phys. Rev.,* **99**, 542 (1955).
109. BLACKWELL, H.E., G.S. BAJWA, G.S. SHIPP, and G.L. WEISSLER. *J. Quant. Spectr. Rad. Trans.,* **4**, 249 (1964).

110. HUFFMAN, R.E., Y. TANAKA, and J.C. LARRABEE. *Appl. Optics*, **2**, 617 (1963).

111. HUFFMAN, R.E., Y. TANAKA, and J.C. LARRABEE. *Appl. Optics*, **2**, 947 (1963).

112. SAMSON, J.A.R. *Phys. Rev.*, **132**, 2122 (1963).

113. METZGER, P. and G.R. COOK. *J. Opt. Soc. America*, **55**, 516 (1965).

114. SAMSON, J.A.R. *Phys. Lett.*, **8**, 107 (1964).

115. DALGARNO, A. *Proc. Phys. Soc.*, **A65**, 663 (1952).

116. CODLING, K. and R.P. MADDEN. *Phys. Rev. Lett.*, **12**, 106 (1964).

117. MADDEN, R.P. and K. CODLING. *J. Opt. Soc. America*, **54**, 268 (1964).

118. RUSTGI, O.P., E.I. FISCHER, and C.H. FULLER. *J. Opt. Soc. America*, **54**, 745 (1964).

119. PERY-THORNE, A. and W.R.S. GARTON. *Proc. Phys. Soc.*, **76**, 833 (1960).

119a. CODLING, K. and R.P. MADDEN. *Appl. Optics.*, **4**, 1431 (1965).

120. SAMSON, J.A.R. *J. Opt. Soc. America*, **54**, 842 (1964).

121. WEISSLER, G.L. *J. Quant Spectr. Rad. Trans.*, **2**, 383 (1962).

122. EDERER, D.L. *Phys. Rev. Lett.*, **13**, 760 (1964).

123. DAMANY-ASTOIN, N. *C.R. Acad. Sci., Paris*, **259**, 1493 (1964).

124. FANO, U. and J.W. COOPER. *Phys. Rev.*, **137A**, 1364 (1965).

125. WATANABE, K. *Advan. Geophys.*, **5**, 153 (1958).

126. DITCHBURN, R.W. *Proc. Roy. Soc.*, **A236**, 216 (1956).

127. OGAWA, M. and Y. TANAKA, *Canad. J. Phys.*, **40**, 1593 (1962).

128. BIRGE, R.T. and J.J. HOPFIELD. *Astrophys. J.*, **68**, 257 (1928).

129. TANAKA, *J. Opt. Soc. America*, **45**, 663 (1955).

130. WILKINSON, P.G. *Astrophys. J.*, **126**, 1 (1957).

131. SAMSON, J.A.R. and R.B. CAIRNS. *J. Geophys. Res.*, **69**, 4583 (1964).

132. TANAKA,Y. and T. TAKAMINE. *Sci. Pap., Inst. Phys. Chem. Res. Tokyo*, **39**, 427 (1942).

133. WORLEY, R.E. *Phys. Rev.*, **64**, 207 (1943).

134. CLARK, K.C. *Phys. Rev.*, **87**, 271 (1952).

135. WEISSLER, G.L., PO LEE, and E.I. MOHR. *J. Opt. Soc. America*, **42**, 84 (1952).

136. PO LEE. *J. Opt. Soc. America*, **45**, 703 (1955).

137. WATANABE, K. and F.F. MARMO. *J. Chem. Phys.*, **25**, 965 (1956).

138. ASTOIN, N. and J. GRANIER. *C.R. Acad. Sci., Paris*, **244**, 1350 (1957).

139. HUFFMAN, R.E., Y. TANAKA, and J.C. LARRABEE. *J. Chem. Phys.*, **39**, 910 (1963).

140. CODLING, K. and R.P. MADDEN. *J. Opt. Soc. America*, **54**, 1391 (1964).

141. CURTIS, J.P. *Phys. Rev.*, **94**, 908 (1954).

142. COOK, G.R. and P.H. METZGER. *J. Chem. Phys.*, **41**, 321 (1964).

142a. SAMSON, J.A.R. and R.B. CAIRNS. *J. Opt. Soc. America*, **55**, 1035 (1965).

143. HERZBERG, G. *Naturwissenschaften*, **20**, 577 (1932).

144. DITCHBURN, R.W. and P.A. YOUNG. *J. Atmos. and Terr. Phys.*, **24**, 127 (1962).

145. WATANABE, K., E.C.Y. INN, and ZELIKOFF. *J. Chem. Phys.*, **21**, 1026 (1953).

146. WATANABE, K., E.C.Y. INN, and M. ZELIKOFF. *J. Chem. Phys.*, **20**, 1969 (1952).

147. LADENBURG, R. and C.C. VAN VOORHIS. *Phys. Rev.*, **43**, 315 (1933).

148. SCHNEIDER, E.G. *J. Chem. Phys.*, **5**, 106 (1937).

149. DITCHBURN, R.W. and D.W.O. HEDDLE. *Proc. Roy. Soc.*, **A220**, 61 (1953).

150. TANAKA, Y. *J. Chem. Phys.*, **20**, 1728 (1952).

151. KOSINSKAYA, I.V. and G.P. STARTSEV. *Optika i Spektroskopiya*, **18**, 735 (1965).

152. PRESTON, W.M. *Phys. Rev.*, **57**, 887 (1940).

153. ABOUD, A.A., J.P. CURTIS, R. MERCURE, and W.A. RENSE. *J. Opt. Soc. America*, **45**, 767 (1955).

154. WEISSLER, G.L. and PO LEE. *J. Opt. Soc. America*, **42**, 200 (1952).

155. HUFFMAN, R.E., J.C. LARRABEE, and Y. TANAKA. *J. Chem. Phys.*, **40**, 356 (1964).

155a. REILHAC, L. DE and N. DAMANY-ASTOIN. *C.R. Acad. Sci., Paris*, **258**, 519 (1964).

156. PRICE, W.C. *J. Chem. Phys.*, **4**, 147 (1936).

157. LEIFSON, S.W. *Astrophys. J.*, **63**, 73 (1926).

158. HOPFIELD, J.J. *Phys. Rev.*, **77**, 560 (1950).

159. HENNING, H.J. *Ann. Physik*, **13**, 599 (1932).

160. RATHENAU, G. *Z. Phys.* **87**, 32 (1933).

161. WILKINSON, P.G. and H.L. JOHNSTON. *J. Chem. Phys.*, **18**, 190 (1950).

162. HARRISON, A.J., B.J. CEDERHOLM, and M.A. TERWILLIGER. *J. Chem. Phys.*, **30**, 355 (1959).

163. WATANABE, K. and M. ZELIKOFF. *J. Opt. Soc. America*, **43**, 753 (1953).

164. ASTOIN, N., A. JOHANNIN-GILLES, and B. VODAR. *C.R. Acad. Sci., Paris*, **237**, 558 (1953).

165. ASTOIN, N. *C.R. Acad. Sci., Paris*, **242**, 2327 (1956).

166. WATANABE, K. and A.S. JURSA. *J. Chem. Phys.*, **41**, 1650 (1964).

167. JOHANNIN-GILES, A. *C.R. Acad. Sci., Paris*, **236**, 676 (1953).

168. WATANABE, K. *J. Chem. Phys.*, **22**, 1564 (1954).

169. WATANABE, K., F.F. MARMO, and E.C.Y. INN. *Phys. Rev.*, **91**, 1155 (1953).

170. MARMO, F.F. *J. Opt. Soc. America*, **43**, 1186 (1953).

171. SUN, H. and G.L. WEISSLER. *J. Chem. Phys.*, **23**, 1372 (1955).

172. GRANIER, J. and N. ASTOIN. *C.R. Acad. Sci., Paris*, **242**, 1431 (1956).

173. MAYENCE, J. *Ann. phys. (Paris)*, **7**, 453 (1952).

174. WALKER, W.C. and G.L. WEISSLER. *J. Chem. Phys.*, **23**, 1962 (1955).

175. DIEKE, G.H. and J.J. HOPFIELD. *Phys. Rev.*, **30**, 400 (1927).

176. BEUTLER, H., A. DEUBNER, and H.O. JÜNGER. *Z. Phys.*, **98**, 181 (1936).

177. TANAKA, Y. *Sci. Pap., Inst. Phys. Res., Tokyo*, **42**, 49 (1944).

178. PO LEE and G.L. WEISSLER. *Astrophys. J.*, **115**, 570 (1952).

179. COOK, G.R. and P.H. METZGER. *J. Opt. Soc., America*, **54**, 968 (1964).

180. NAMIOKA, T. *J. Chem. Phys.*, **40**, 3154 (1964).

181. TANAKA, Y., R.E. HUFFMAN, and J.C. LARRABEE. *J. Quant Spectr. Rad. Trans.*, **2**, 451 (1962).

182. HERZBERG, G. and A. MONFILS. *J. Mol. Spectr.* **5**, 482 (1960).

183. TANAKA, Y., E.C.Y. INN, and K. WATANABE. *J. Chem. Phys.*, **21**, 1651 (1953).

184. SUN, H. and G.L. WEISSLER. *J. Chem. Phys.*, **23**, 1625 (1955).

185. CAIRNS, R.B. and J.A.R. SAMSON. *J. Geophys. Res.*, **70**, 99 (1965).

185a. CAIRNS, R.B. and J.A.R. SAMSON. *J. Opt. Soc. America*, **56**, 526 (1966).

186. INN, E.C.Y., K. WATANABE, and M. ZELIKOFF. *J. Chem. Phys.*, **21**, 1648 (1953).

187. DAMANY-ASTOIN, N., L. SANSON, and M.C. BONELLE. *C.R. Acad. Sci., Paris*, **250**, 1824 (1960).

188. DUNCAN, A.B.F. *Phys. Rev.*, **47**, 822 (1935).

189. DUNCAN, A.B.F. *Phys. Rev.*, **50**, 700 (1936).

190. SUN, H. and G.L. WEISSLER. *J. Chem. Phys.*, **23**, 1160 (1955).

191. HUFFMAN, R.E., J.C. LARRABEE, and Y. TANAKA. *J. Chem. Phys.*, **40**, 2261 (1964).

192. ZELIKOFF, M., K. WATANABE, and E.C.Y. INN. *J. Chem. Phys.*, **21**, 1643 (1953).

193. ROMAND, J. and J. MAYENCE. *C.R. Acad. Sci., Paris*, **228**, 998 (1949).

194. ASTOIN, N. and J. GRANIER. *C.R. Acad. Sci., Paris*, **241**, 1736 (1955).

195. EHLER, A.W. and G.L. WEISSLER. *J. Opt. Soc. America*, **45**, 1035 (1955).

196. BATES, D.R. and M.J. SEATON. *Monthly Notices Roy. Astron. Soc.*, **109**, 698 (1949).

197. DALGARNO, A. and D. PARKINSON. *J. Atmos. and Terr. Phys.*, **18**, 335 (1960).

197a. BEYNON, J.D.E. and R.B. CAIRNS. *Proc. Phys. Soc.*, **86**, 1343 (1965).

198. MENZEL, D.H. and C.L. PEKERIS. *Monthly Notices Roy. Astron. Soc.*, **96**, 77 (1935).

199. KRAMERS, H.A. *Philos. Mag.*, **46**, 836 (1923).

200. BURGESS, A. *Monthly Notices Roy. Astron. Soc.*, **118**, 477 (1958).

201. CAIRNS, R.B. and J.A.R. SAMSON. *Phys. Rev.*, **139A**, 1403 (1965).

202. DALGARNO, A., R.J.W. HENRY, and A.L. STEWART. *Planetary Space Sci.*, **12**, 235 (1904).

# CHAPTER VIII

# Determination of Atomic Constants from Measurements in the Vacuum Ultraviolet

## 40. MEASUREMENT OF OSCILLATOR STRENGTHS OF LINES IN THE VACUUM ULTRAVIOLET

The fundamental parameters which determine light emission and absorption processes are related by well-known equalities: the transition probability $A_{ki}$ is the proportionality coefficient between the number of spontaneous transitions $n_{ki}$ from excited state $k$ to state $i$ in unit time and the number of atoms in the initial excited state $N_k$:

$$n_{ki} = A_{ki} N_k. \tag{38}$$

The sum of the transition probabilities from level $k$ to all lower-lying levels determines the lifetime $\tau_k$ of the excited state and the width $\Delta E_k$ of the energy level:

$$\tau_k = \frac{1}{\sum\limits_{i=0}^{k-1} A_{ki}} = \frac{h}{\Delta E_k}. \tag{39}$$

The oscillator strength is a well-matured concept borrowed by atomic physics from its classical predecessor. The oscillator strength $f_{ik}$ and the transition probability $A_{ki}$ are related by the equality

$$A_{ki} = \frac{g_i}{g_k} \frac{8\pi^2 e^2 v_{ik}^2}{mc^3} f_{ik}, \tag{40}$$

**305**

where $g_i$ and $g_k$ are the statistical weights (the degeneracies) of the lower and the upper level, $v_{ik}$ is the oscillation frequency, $m$ and $e$ are the electron mass and charge, $c$ is the velocity of light.

Measurements of the $f$ numbers of lines in the vacuum ultraviolet involve certain experimental difficulties, and there are consequently only few published results of such measurements.

### Method of dispersion

This method [1] is concerned with the dependence of refractive index on wavelength near the absorption line. In spectra containing relatively few lines, which are however very strong, the dispersion measurements can be carried out far from the absorption lines. The most accurate results for the refractive indices of gases are obtained using an interferometer in conjunction with a spectrograph.

The limit of application of the interference methods is determined by the transparency threshold of the beam-splitting mirrors in the interferometer. An LiF interferometer, for example, is transparent only to $1400\,\text{Å}$ [2] (see §19). Rozhdestvenskii's "method of hooks", which is the most precise method of dispersion measurement, was applied to measure the oscillator strength of the $1849\,\text{Å}$ mercury line with a fluorite interferometer: the results gave for this oscillator strength $1.3 \pm 0.15$ [3].

The method of dispersion has been applied by various authors [4–7]. It gives reliable results for the oscillator strengths in one of the following two cases: either when the refractive index is measured fairly near the line whose oscillator strength is to be found [5], or if the absorption cross section beyond the limit of the series is known. Wolfsohn [4] measured the refractive index of mercury vapor between 7000 and $2650\,\text{Å}$; his results were insufficient to determine the oscillator strength of the $1849\,\text{Å}$ line, but in a later work [5] he extended his measurements to $1890\,\text{Å}$, which gave 1.19 for the oscillator strength of the line.

Applying the dispersion relations to the resonance lines of inert gases and using the known absorption coefficients in the continuous spectrum, we can find the sum $f_1 + f_2$, since the wavelengths of the two resonance lines are close to each other. These tentative calculations can be made from the equations of the dispersion theory [8]

$$n_0 - 1 = \frac{e^2 N}{2\pi m} \sum \frac{f_i}{v_i^2 - v_0^2} \tag{41}$$

or, taking the continuous absorption into account.

$$n_0 - 1 = \frac{e^2 N}{2\pi m} \left( \frac{f_1}{v_1^2 - v_0^2} + \frac{f_2}{v_2^2 - v_0^2} + \cdots + \frac{f_i}{v_i^2 - v_0^2} \right) + \frac{c}{2\pi^2} \int_v^\infty \frac{\mu_v dv}{v^2 - v_0^2}. \tag{42}$$

In these equations, $n_0$ is the refractive index at frequency $v_0$, $m$ and $e$ are the electron mass and charge, $N$ is the number of atoms in unit volume, $v_1$, $v_2$, ..., $v_i$ are the resonance frequencies, $v$ is the frequency at which the continuous absorption begins, $f_1$, $f_2$, ..., $f_i$ are the oscillator strengths of the resonance lines, $c$ is the velocity of light, $\mu_v$ is the absorption coefficient at frequency $v$.

Oscillator strengths calculated from equation (42) fit the experimental results for helium only. For other inert gases, there is a definite discrepancy between theory and experiment.

Using equation (42), we can also solve the inverse problem: given the oscillator strengths and the absorption coefficient of the gas beyond the ionization limit, we can find the refractive indices at various wavelengths. Such calculations based on experimental data [9, 10] give an excellent fit for the refractive index of helium at 2300 Å [11].

Similar calculations based on old data for the oscillator strengths and absorption coefficients beyond the ionization limit were carried out by Körwien [12]. Between 6300 and 2300 Å the differences between theory and experiment were at most 3% of the experimental values.

### The method of upper level widths

Schütz and Schillbach [13, 14] were the first to measure the width of the upper level for this purpose. They measured the widths of neon lines with a common upper level and different lower levels ($s_2$, $s_3$, $s_4$, and $s_5$). The lines associated with transitions to the $s_2$ level were found to be $(0.8 + 0.4) \cdot 10^9 \ \text{sec}^{-1}$ wider than the other lines. This is so because the $s_2$ level is unstable, giving a single transition which corresponds to the 736 Å resonance line. The width of this level makes it possible to determine the transition probability and the oscillator strength of the 736 Å line. The oscillator strength of this line was found to be $0.2 \pm 0.1$. Recently, Korolev et al. repeated the measurements of the oscillator strength of the 736 Å line [15], using an atomic beam spectroscope to determine the halfwidths of the neon lines in the visible. These results give $0.16 \pm 0.014$ for the oscillator strength of the 736 Å line.

A similar method was applied to measure the transition probability for the 584 Å helium line $(1^1S_0 - 2^1P)$ [16, 17]. All the authors measured the widths of lines in the visible spectrum with $2^1P_1$ as their lower level. Different light sources were used: a microwave helium discharge* (the tube was cooled with liquid helium or liquid nitrogen) [16] and an atomic beam source [17]. The line contours were traced photoelectrically using a Fabry–Perot etalon. The respective results were $f = 0.377 \pm 0.035$ [16] and $f = 0.28 \pm 0.02$ [17].

Vaughan and Kuhn [18a, 18b] later admitted that they had erred in their determina-

---

* The design of this tube is described in [18].

tion of the line widths: it had been assumed [16] that the line width could be found by extrapolating to $p = 0$ the linear plot of line width vs. pressure. Theoretical calculations give $f = 0.276$; this result has been repeatedly checked by various methods, and all fit [19].

The same procedure (though of lower accuracy) was applied by Fursov et al. [20] to determine the oscillator strength of the 1046 Å argon line. As in the case of neon, the measurements were carried out for lines with $s_2$ as their lower level (4510 and 4333 Å). The line widths were found to vary with pressure, and the pressure contribution to broadening could be determined. This component of the line width was identified with resonance broadening [21], and the $f$ number of the 1046 Å line was thus found. This method is far from being unobjectionable, and it can be used only in tentative estimates.

The oscillator strengths of the argon resonance lines were determined with higher precision in [22]. The resonance lines were excited in a capillary discharge, and the observations were carried out at right angles to the capillary axis. The discharge currents reached a few milliamperes. The line contours in the infrared were traced with a Fabry–Perot interferometer. The differences in line widths were used to determine the oscillator strengths of the resonance lines $\lambda = 1048$ Å ($f = 0.275 \pm 0.02$) and $\lambda = 1067$ Å ($f = 0.036 \pm 0.004$).

### The method of linear absorption

The linear absorption method measures the decrease in intensity of individual spectral lines whose radiation is allowed to pass through an absorbing volume. The absorption coefficient at the center of the absorption line is measured. If the shapes of the absorption and emission lines are known, the oscillator strengths can be found.

A detailed treatment of the method of linear absorption is given by Mitchell and Zemansky [23] and by Frish et al. [24, 25]. The method was applied to the measurement of the oscillator strengths of the 1200 Å nitrogen multiplet [26, 27] and of the 1302 Å oxygen multiplet [27, 28] in the vacuum ultraviolet. The light sources used in these measurements were a microwave discharge tube and a hollow cathode tube. A mixture of nitrogen (oxygen) and helium at 1–10 T was pumped through the source tube. The nitrogen (oxygen) concentration in the helium mixture was a few percent. The absorbing tube contained nitrogen atoms pumped from another discharge tube. The atomic nitrogen was produced by the afterglow in the nitrogen gas. Atomic oxygen was the product of the reaction between NO and atomic nitrogen. The concentrations of N and O were determined by chemical methods.

The line shape may be distorted by reabsorption. If reabsorption is neglected, the measured oscillator strengths may differ by several orders of magnitude from the true values [26]. Correction for reabsorption distortion of the line shapes and a lucky choice of the line shape parameters gave satisfactory results for the oscillator strengths of the nitrogen lines [27], which showed a good fit with the theory. The measured oscillator strengths of the oxygen lines agree with the theoretical results to within 25% [30–32]. The oscillator strengths of the nitrogen and oxygen multiplets are listed in Table 41.

Table 41

| Atom or ion | Transition | $\lambda$, Å | $f$ | Method | References |
|---|---|---|---|---|---|
| C IV | $2s^2S_{1/2}-2p^2P_{3/2}$ | 1548.2 | $0.214 \pm 0.007$ | Attenuation of resonance radiation | [46] |
| C IV | $2s^2S_{1/2}-2p^2P_{1/2}$ | 1550.7 | $0.107 \pm 0.004$ | Ditto | [46] |
| N V | $2s^2S_{1/2}-2p^2P_{3/2}$ | 1238.8 | $0.154 \pm 0.006$ | ,, | [46] |
| N V | $2s^2S_{1/2}-2p^2P_{1/2}$ | 1242.8 | $0.077 \pm 0.003$ | ,, | [46] |
| O VI | $2s^2S_{1/2}-2p^2P_{3/2}$ | 1031.9 | $0.126 \pm 0.004$ | ,, | [46] |
| O VI | $2s^2S_{1/2}-2p^2P_{1/2}$ | 1037.6 | $0.063 \pm 0.002$ | ,, | [46] |
| F VII | $2s^2S_{1/2}-2p^2P_{3/2}$ | 883.1 | $0.108 \pm 0.004$ | ,, | [46] |
| F VII | $2s^2S_{1/2}-2p^2P_{1/2}$ | 890.8 | $0.054 \pm 0.002$ | .. | [46] |
| Ne VIII | $2s^2S_{1/2}-2p^2P_{3/2}$ | 770.4 | $0.102 \pm 0.004$ | ,, | [46] |
| Ne VIII | $2s^2S_{1/2}-2p^2P_{1/2}$ | 780.3 | $0.051 \pm 0.002$ | ,, | [46] |
| B II | $2s^2 \, ^1S-2p^1P$ | 1362 | $0.92$†† | Phase shift | [44b] |
| B II | $2p^3 \, ^1P-2p^2 \, ^3P$ | 1624 | $0.39$†† | Phase shift | [44b] |
| Hg I | $6s^2 \, ^1S_0-6p^1P_1$ | 1849 | $1.3 \pm 0.15$ | Anomalous dispersion | [3] |
| Hg I | $6s^2 \, ^1S_0-6p^1P_1$ | 1849 | $1.18 \pm 0.07$ | Hanle | [40] |
| Hg I | $6s^2 \, ^1S_0-6p^1P_1$ | 1849 | $1.19 \pm 0.02$ | Dispersion | [5] |
| B I | $2p^2P-3d^2D$ | 1826 | $0.18$†† | Phase shift | [44b] |
| C II | $2p^2P-2p^2 \, ^2D$ | 1335 | $0.12$†† | Phase shift | [44b] |
| C I | $2p^2 \, ^3P_{012}-5d^3P^0_{12}$ $-5d^1F^0_3$ $-6s^1P^0_1$ $-5d^3D^0_{23}$ $-5d^3F^0_{23}$ | 1156–1159 | $0.021$* | Emission | [43] |
| C I | $2p^2 \, ^3P_{012}-4d^3P^0_{12}$ $-4d^1F^0_3$ $-5s^1P^0_1$ $-4d^3D^0_{123}$ $-4d^3F^0_3$ | 1189–1195 | $0.051$ | Emission | [43] |
| C I | $2p^2 \, ^3P_{012}-3d^3P^0_{12}$ | 1261–1262 | $0.029$ | Emission | [43] |
| C I | $2p^2 \, ^3P_2-3d^1F^0_3$ | 1274 | $2.3 \cdot 10^{-4}$ | Emission | [43] |
| C I | $2p^2 \, ^3P_{012}-3d^3D^0_{123}$ | 1277–1278 | $0.063$ | Emission | [43] |
| C I | $2p^2 \, ^3P_2-3d^3F^0_3$ | 1279 | $3.8 \cdot 10^{-3}$ | Emission | [43] |
| C I | $2p^2 \, ^3P_{012}-4s^3P^0_{012}$ | 1280–1281 | $0.020$ | Emission | [43] |

Table 41 (continued)

| Atom or ion | Transition | $\lambda$, Å | $f$ | Method | References |
|---|---|---|---|---|---|
| C I | $2p^2\,^1D_2 - 5d\,^1P_1^0$ <br> $- 5d\,^1F_3^0$ <br> $6s\,^1P_1^0$ <br> $- 5d\,^3D_3^0$ <br> $- 5d\,^3F_3^0$ | 1311–1313 | 0.010 | Emission | [43] |
| C I | $2p^2\,^3P_{012} - 2p^3\,^3P_{012}^0$ | 1329–1330 | 0.039 | Emission | [43] |
| C I | $2p^2\,^1D_2 - 4d\,^1P_1^0$ <br> $- 4d\,^1F_3^0$ <br> $- 4d\,^3F_3^0$ <br> $- 5s\,^1P_1^0$ | 1354–1350 | 0.029 | Emission | [43] |
| C I | $2p^2\,^1D_2 - 4d\,^1D_2^0$ | 1364 | $1.3\cdot10^{-3}$ | Emission | [43] |
| C I | $2p^3\,^5S_2^0 - 3s\,^5P_3$ | 1431.6 | 0.064 | Emission | [43] |
| C I | $2p^3\,^5S_2^0 - 3s\,^5P_2$ | 1432.1 | 0.043 | Emission | [43] |
| C I | $2p^3\,^5S_2^0 - 3s\,^5P_1$ | 1432.5 | 0.024 | Emission | [43] |
| C I | $2p^2\,^1D_2 - 3d\,^1P_1^0$ | 1459 | $7.0\cdot10^{-3}$ | Emission | [43] |
| C I | $2p^2\,^1D_2 - 3d\,^1P_1^0$ | 1463 | $9.3\cdot10^{-2}$ | Emission | [43] |
| C I | $2p^2\,^1D_2 - 3d\,^1F_3^0$ | 1467 | $8.9\cdot10^{-2}$ | Emission | [43] |
| C I | $2p^2\,^1D_2 - 4s\,^1P_1^0$ | 1469 | $3.6\cdot10^{-4}$ | Emission | [43] |
| C I | $2p^2\,^1D_2 - 3d\,^3F_3^0$ | 1470 | $4.0\cdot10^{-4}$ | Emission | [43] |
| C I | $2p^2\,^1D_2 - 4s\,^3P_1^0$ | 1472 | $1.0\cdot10^{-4}$ | Emission | [43] |
| C I | $2p^2\,^1D_2 - 3d\,^1D_2^0$ | 1482 | $1.1\cdot10^{-2}$ | Emission | [43] |
| C I | $2p^2\,^3P_{012} - 2p^3\,^3D_{123}^0$ | 1560–1561 | 0.078†† | Phase shift | [44b] |
| C I | $2p^2\,^3P_{012} - 2p^3\,^3D_{123}^0$ | 1560–1561 | 0.091 | Emission | [43] |
| C I | $2p^2\,^3P_{012} - 3s\,^3P_0^0$ | 1656–1658 | 0.17 | Emission | [43] |
| C I | $2p^2\,^3P_{012} - 3s\,^3P_{012}^0$ | 1656–1658 | 0.13†† | Phase shift | [44b] |
| C I | $2p^2\,^1S_0 - 3d\,^1P_1^0$ | 1752 | 0.12 | Emission | [43] |
| C I | $2p^2\,^1S_0 - 4s\,^1P_1^0$ | 1764 | $3.1\cdot10^{-3}$ | Emission | [43] |
| C I | $2p^2\,^1S_0 - 3d\,^3D_1^0$ | 1765 | $1.0\cdot10^{-3}$ | Emission | [43] |
| C I | $2p^2\,^1D - 3s\,^1P$ | 1930 | 0.10†† | Phase shift | [44b] |
| N II | $2p^2\,^3P - 2p^3\,^3D$ | 1085 | 0.11†† | Phase shift | [44b] |
| N I | $2p^3\,^2D_{3/2,\,5/2} - 4d\,^2D_{5/2}$ <br> $- 4d\,^2D_{5/2}$ <br> $- 4d\,^4P_{5/2}$ <br> $- 4d\,^2F_{7/2}$ <br> $- 4d\,^2F_{5/2}$ <br> $- 4d\,^4D_{3/2}$ <br> $- 4d\,^4F_{5/2}$ | 1096–1099 | $1.9\cdot10^{-2}$** | Emission | [44a] |
| N I | $2p^3\,^2D_{3/2,\,5/2} - 5s\,^2P_{3/2}$ | 1100.4 | $2.3\cdot10^{-3}$ | Emission | [44a] |
| | $- 5s\,^2P_{1/2}$ | 1101.3 | $1.4\cdot10^{-3}$ | Emission | [44a] |
| N I | $2p^3\,^4S - 2p^4\,^4P$ | 1134 | 0.080†† | Phase shift | [44b] |
| N I | $2p^3\,^4S_{3/2} - 2p^4\,^4P_{1/2,\,3/2}$ | 1134.2; <br> 1134.4 | 0.074 | Emission | [44a] |
| N I | $- 2p^4\,^4P_{5/2}$ | 1135.0 | 0.063 | Emission | [44a] |

Table 41 (continued)

| Atom or ion | Transition | $\lambda$, Å | $f$ | Method | References |
|---|---|---|---|---|---|
| N I | $2p^3\,{}^2D_{3/2,\,5/2}-3d^2D_{5/2,\,3/2}$ | 1163.9; 1164.3 | $9.6\cdot10^{-3}$ | Emission | [44a] |
| N I | $2p^3\,{}^2D_{3/2,\,5/2}-3d^4D_{7/2}$ | 1165.6 | $3.2\cdot10^{-4}$ | Emission | [44a] |
| N I | $2p^3\,{}^2D_{5/2}-3d^2F_{7/2}$ | 1167.4 | 0.018 | Emission | [44a] |
| N I | $2p^3\,{}^2D_{3/2,\,5/2}-3d^2F_{5/2}$ | 1168.3; 1168.5 | 0.018 | Emission | [44a] |
| N I | $2p^3\,{}^2D_{3/2,\,5/2}-3d^4F_{7/2}$ | 1169.7 | $5.0\cdot10^{-4}$ | Emission | [44a] |
| N I | $2p^3\,{}^2P_{1/2,\,3/2}-6d^2D_{5/2}$ | 1170.3 | $2.6\cdot10^{-3}$ | Emission | [44a] |
| N I | $2p^3\,{}^2D_{3/2,\,5/2}-3d^4F_{5/2}$ | 1170.3 | $5.0\cdot10^{-4}$ | Emission | [44a] |
| N I | $2p^3\,{}^2P_{1/2,\,3/2}-6d^2D_{3/2}$ | 1171.1 | $1.4\cdot10^{-3}$ | Emission | [44a] |
| N I | $2p^3\,{}^2D_{3/2,\,5/2}-3d^2P_{3/2}$ | 1171.1 | $2.8\cdot10^{-4}$ | Emission | [44a] |
| N I | $2p^3\,{}^2D_{3/2,\,5/2}-4s^2P_{3/2}$ | 1176.5; 1176.6 | $8.7\cdot10^{-3}$ | Emission | [44a] |
| N I | $2p^3\,{}^2D_{3/2,\,5/2}-4s^2P_{1/2}$ | 1177.7 | $5.5\cdot10^{-3}$ | Emission | [44a] |
| N I | $2p^3\,{}^4S_{3/2}-3s^4P_{5/2}$ | 1199.6 | 0.18 | Emission | [44a] |
| N I | $2p^3\,{}^4S_{3/2}-3s^4P_{5/2}$ | 1199.6 | $0.049\pm0.015$ | Linear absorption | [27] |
| N I | $2p^3\,{}^4S_{3/2}-3s^4P_{3/2}$ | 1200.2 | 0.11 | Emission | [44a] |
| N I | $2p^3\,{}^4S_{3/2}-3s^4P_{3/2}$ | 1200.2 | $0.033\pm0.010$ | Linear absorption | [27] |
| N I | $2p^3\,{}^4S_{3/2}-3s^4P_{1/2}$ | 1200.7 | 0.062 | Emission | [44a] |
| N I | $2p^4S_{3/2}-3s^4P_{1/2}$ | 1200.7 | $0.016\pm0.005$ | Linear absorption | [27] |
| N I | $2p^3\,{}^4S_{3/2}-3s^4P$ | 1200 | 0.26†† | Phase shift | [44b] |
| N I | $2p^3\,{}^2P_{3/2,\,1/2}-4d^2D_{5/2}$ $-4d^2D_{3/2}$ $-4d^4P_{3/2}$ $-4d^4P_{1/2}$ $-4d^4D_{5/2}$ $-4d^2P_{1/2}$ $-4d^2P_{3/2}$ $-4d^4D_{1/2}$ | 1225–1229 | 0.037 | Emission | [44a] |
| N I | $2p^3\,{}^2P_{1/2,\,3/2}-5s^2P_{1/2}$ | 1231.6 | $2.5\cdot10^{-4}$ | Emission | [44a] |
| N I | $2p^3\,{}^2D_{3/2,\,5/2}-3s^1\,{}^2D_{5/2,\,3/2}$ | 1243.2; 1243.3 | 0.11 | Emission | [44a] |
| N I | $2p^3\,{}^2D_{3/2,\,5/2}-3s^1\,{}^2D_{5/2,\,3/2}$ | 1243 | 0.094†† | Phase shift | [44b] |
| N I | $2p^3\,{}^2P_{1/2,\,3/2}-3d^2D_{5/2,\,3/2}$ | 1310.6; 1311.0 | 0.058 | Emission | [44a] |
| N I | $2p^3\,{}^2P_{1/2,\,3/2}-3d^4D_{3/2}$ | 1313.1 | $1.8\cdot10^{-4}$ | Emission | [44a] |
| | $-3d^4P_{1/2}$ | 1315.5 | $2.5\cdot10^{-4}$ | Emission | [44a] |
| | $-3d^2F_{5/2}$ | 1316.3 | $6.4\cdot10^{-4}$ | Emission | [44a] |
| | $-3d^2P_{1/2}$ | 1319.0 | 0.011 | Emission | [44a] |
| | $-3d^2P_{3/2}$ | 1319.7 | 0.023 | Emission | [44a] |
| | $-4s^2P_{3/2}$ | 1326.6 | $3.1\cdot10^{-3}$ | Emission | |
| | $-4s^2P_{1/2}$ | 1328.0 | $2.2\cdot10^{-3}$ | Emission | [44a] |
| | $-3s'\,{}^2D_{3/2,\,5/2}$ | 1411.9 | 0.026 | Emission | [44a] |
| N I | $2p^3\,{}^2D_{3/2,\,\;5/2}-3s^2P_{3/2}$ | 1492 | 0.078†† | Phase shift | [44b] |

Table 41 (continued)

| Atom or ion | Transition | $\lambda$, Å | $f$ | Method | References |
|---|---|---|---|---|---|
| N I | $2p^3\,{}^2D_{3/2,\,5/2} - 3s^2P_{3/2}$ | 1492.6; 1492.8 | 0.077 | Phase shift | [44a] |
|  | $-3s^2P_{1/2}$ | 1494.7 | 0.034 | Emission | [44a] |
| N I | $2p^3\,{}^2P_{1/2,\,3/2} - 3s^2P_{3/2}$ | 1742.7 | 0.064 | Emission | [44a] |
|  | $-3s^2P_{1/2}$ | 1745.3 | 0.029 | Emission | [44a] |
| N I | $2p^3\,{}^2P_{1/2,\,3/2} - 3s^2P_{1/2,\,3/2}$ | 1742 | 0.064†† | Phase shift | [44b] |
| O I | $2p^4\,{}^3P_0 - 3s^3S$ | 1306.0 | 0.033 ± 0.008 | Linear absorption | [27] |
| O I | $2p^4\,{}^3P_1 - 3s^3S$ | 1304.9 | 0.033 ± 0.008 | Linear absorption | [27] |
| O I | $2p^4\,{}^3P_2 - 3s^3S$ | 1302.2 | 0.033 ± 0.008 | Linear absorption | [27] |
| He I | $1s^2\,{}^1S_0 - 2^1P_1$ | 584 | 0.26 ± 0.07 | Line width | [46a] |
| He I | $1s^2\,{}^1S_0 - 2^1P_1$ | 584 | 0.28 ± 0.02 | Upper level width | [17] |
| He I | $1s^2\,{}^1S_0 - 2^1P_1$ | 584 | 0.288 | Inelastic electron scattering | [41] |
| Ne I | $2p^6\,{}^1S_0 - 3s^1P_1$ | 736 | 0.2 ± 0.1 | Upper level width | [13, 14] |
| Ne I | $2p^6\,{}^1S_0 - 3s^1P_1$ | 736 | 0.16 ± 0.014 | Upper level width | [15] |
| Ne I | $2p_6\,{}^1S_0 - 3s^1P_1$ | 736 ⎫ | 0.140 ± 0.01† | Inelastic electron scattering | [42] |
| Ne I | $2p^6\,{}^1S_0 - 3s^3P_1$ | 743 ⎭ | | | |
| Ne I | $2p^6\,{}^1S_0 - 4s^1P_1$ | 736 ⎫ | 0.16† | Inelastic electron scattering | [41] |
| Ne I | $2p^6\,{}^1S_0 - 3s^3P_1$ | 743 ⎭ | | | |
| Ar I | $3p^6\,{}^1S_0 - 4s^1P_1$ | 1048 | 0.28 ± 0.02 | Upper level width | [22] |
| Ar I | $3p^6\,{}^1S_0 - 4s^3P_1$ | 1067 | 0.036 ± 0.004 | Upper level width | [22] |
| Ar I | $3p^6\,{}^1S_0 - 4s^1P_1$ | 1048 ⎫ | 0.233 ± 0.02† | Inelastic electron scattering | [42] |
| Ar I | $3p^6\,{}^1S_0 - 4s^3P_1$ | 1067 ⎭ | | | |
| Kr I | $4p^6\,{}^1S_0 - 5s^1P_1$ | 1165 | 0.135 | Equivalent width | [36a] |
| Kr I | $4p^6\,{}^1S_0 - 5s^3P_1$ | 1235 | 0.158 | Equivalent width | [36a] |
| Kr I | $4p^6\,{}^1S_0 - 5s^3P_1$ | 1235 | 0.166 | Attenuation of resonance radiation | [46b] |
| Kr I | $4p^6\,{}^1S_0 - 5s^1P_1$ | 1165 ⎫ | 0.346 ± 0.06† | Inelastic electron scattering | [42] |
| Kr I | $4p^6\,{}^1S_0 - 5s^3P_1$ | 1235 ⎭ | | | |
| Xe I | $5p^6\,{}^1S_0 - 6s^1P_1$ | 1295 | 0.238 ± 0.015 | Hanle | [39] |
| Xe I | $5p^6\,{}^1S_0 - 6s^1P_1$ | 1295 | 0.23 ± 0.05 | Linear absorption | [34] |
| Xe I | $5p^6\,{}^1S_0 - 6s^3P_1$ | 1470 | 0.256 ± 0.008 | Hanle | [39] |
| Xe I | $5p^6\,{}^1S_0 - 6s^3P_1$ | 1470 | 0.28 ± 0.05 | Linear absorption | [34] |

\* The error in the determination of the C I oscillator strengths by the method of emission is of the order of 25%.

\*\* The error in the determination of the N I oscillator strengths by the method of emission is of the order of 30–40%. The error of the phase shift determination is 10–20%.

† The sum of the oscillator strengths is given.

†† The sum of the oscillator strengths of the multiplet components is given. The transition probability for the entire multiplet is given in [44b]. $L$–$S$ coupling was assumed in the calculation of the oscillator strengths.

Various aspects of the determination of oscillator strengths of oxygen, nitrogen, and hydrogen resonance lines are discussed in [33]. The authors' conclusion is that adequate results can be obtained if $\mu_0 l$ (the product of the absorption coefficient at the line center and the layer thickness) is small.

The method of linear absorption in Zemansky's original version [23] was applied in [34] to determine the oscillator strengths of the xenon resonance lines. The absorbing cell was filled with a xenon–helium mixture at various pressures, and the emission to absorption line width ratios were measured. The measured absorption coefficient at the center of the resonance line was used to calculate the oscillator strengths at the 1470 Å line ($f = 0.28 \pm 0.05$) and the 1295 Å line ($f = 0.23 \pm 0.05$).

### The method of equivalent widths

The equivalent width of a line is defined as the fraction of the continuum energy absorbed in the line. For optically thick layers, when the absorption at the line center is high enough to absorb the entire incident flux, the equivalent widths of lines are measured at the line wings [35, 36]. At the wings, the line shape is entirely determined by damping, so that

$$Nf_{ki}l\gamma = \frac{mc^3}{e^2\lambda^4} A_\lambda^2,^*$$  (43)

where $N$ is the number of atoms in unit volume, $f_{ki}$ is the oscillator strength, $l$ is the length of the absorbing layer, $\gamma$ is the damping constant, $\lambda$ is the wavelength, $c$ is the velocity of light, $m$ and $e$ are the electron mass and charge, $A_\lambda$ is the equivalent width of the line. The damping constant is defined by the equality

$$\gamma = \frac{1}{\tau_i} + \frac{1}{\tau_k} + \gamma_{\text{col}},$$  (44)

where $\tau_i$ and $\tau_k$ are the lifetimes of the upper and the lower level, respectively, and $\gamma_{\text{col}}$ is the damping coefficient contributed by collisions. For resonance lines $1/\tau_k = 0$. If only one transition is observed from a given level $i$ and $\gamma_{\text{col}}$ is small, we can express $1/\tau_i$ in terms of $f_{ki}$ and write the following formula for the oscillator strength:

$$f_{ki} = \frac{mc^2}{2\pi\lambda e^2} A_\lambda \sqrt{\frac{g_i}{g_k 2Nl}},$$  (45)

where $g_i$ and $g_k$ are the statistical weights of the upper and the lower level, respectively.

This method was used by Wilkinson [36a] in a determination of the oscillator strengths of krypton resonance lines. The equivalent width of the lines was measured

---

* The conditions of application of this formula are discussed in detail by Unsöld [35].

at pressures ranging from 4 to 15 T. At these pressures $\gamma_{col} \neq 0$ and equation (45) does not give correct results for the oscillator strength. The measured oscillator strengths are a function of the absorbing gas pressure, and the true oscillator strengths had to be determined by graphic extrapolation of the measurement results to zero gas pressure. Wilkinson obtained $f = 0.158$ for the 1235 Å line and $f = 0.135$ for the 1165 Å line.

### Hanle method

The Hanle method is now widely used for the determination of oscillator strengths of resonance lines [37–40]. The theory of this method is discussed in detail in [37].

The method is based on the decrease in the intensity of a resonance line when the source of resonance radiation is placed in a magnetic field. The direction of the exciting radiation, the direction of observation, and the magnetic field direction are mutually perpendicular. The cell is immersed in a magnetic field and is illuminated with a resonance lamp. The fluorescence line widths are measured for various magnetic field strengths. The magnetic field $H_{1/2}$ required to reduce the line intensity to half its maximum value is related to the lifetime of the upper level (a measurable quantity):

$$\tau = \frac{mc}{egH_{1/2}}, \tag{46}$$

where $m$ is the electron mass, $e$ is the electron charge, $c$ is the velocity of light, and $g$ is the Landé factor. The oscillator strengths are then calculated from the lifetimes.

The Hanle method was applied to determine the oscillator strengths of the xenon resonance lines [38, 39] $\lambda = 1470$ Å $(f = 0.256 \pm 0.008)$ and $\lambda = 1295$ Å $(f = 0.238 \pm 0.015)$. The oscillator strength of the 1849 Å mercury resonance line was also found by this method $(f = 1.18 \pm 0.07)$ [40].

### Method of inelastic electron scattering (nonoptical method)

This method was applied to the measurement of the oscillator strength of the 584 Å helium line and the sum of the oscillator strengths of neon lines [41, 42], argon lines [42], and krypton lines [42]. The results are summarized in Table 41.

### The method of emission

The oscillator strengths in carbon multiplets between 1000 and 2000 Å were measured by Boldt [43, 44]. The carbon lines were excited in a Maecker arc adapted by Boldt for work in the vacuum ultraviolet (see §6). The emission method may be used in transition probability measurements if no reabsorption occurs or alternatively, if the growth curve can be plotted (i.e., the dependence of the line intensity $B_\lambda$ on the concentration of atoms in the discharge).* The line intensity $B_\lambda$ is expressed by the formula

$$B_\lambda = \frac{1}{b_\lambda(T)} \int (1 - \exp[-\mu_\lambda(T)l])d\lambda, \tag{47}$$

where $\mu_\lambda$ is the absorption coefficient inside the source at wavelength $\lambda$, $b_\lambda$ $(T)$ is the blackbody spectral brightness, $l$ is the column length.

Argon and carbon dioxide were fed into the arc. The blackbody radiation was provided by the emission lines 1158 Å, 1193 Å, 1261 Å, 1277 Å, 1463 Å, and 1657 Å. At certain $CO_2$ concentrations the carbon lines were wider than the spectroscope bandwidth and could thus be used as brightness standards. The intensity of the carbon lines at various $CO_2$ concentrations was compared with the blackbody intensity, and the growth curve was thus plotted.

For purposes of photographic density calibration, the blackbody emission spectrum was photographed at various exposures, setting unity for the Schwartzschild constant. The $B_\lambda$ curve was plotted as the function of $CO_2$ concentration, which in its turn is related to the concentration of carbon atoms. The oscillator strength $f_{ki}$ can be found from an equation which is applicable to the linear sections of the growth curve:

$$A_\lambda = \frac{\pi e^2}{mc^2} \lambda^2 \left(1 - e^{-hc/\lambda kT}\right) f_{ki} N(T)l, \tag{47a}$$

where $N$ is the concentration of carbon atoms and $l$ is the column length.

A similar method was applied by Labun [44a] to measure the oscillator strengths of the nitrogen multiplets. Table 41 shows that the oscillator strengths of the nitrogen resonance lines measured by the emission method substantially differ from the results obtained by the method of linear absorption and show a good fit with the results of the phase shift method [44b]. The most difficult problem is apparently an accurate determination of the nitrogen atom concentration. In general, the determination of the concentration of emitting and absorbing particles has remained one of the weakest points in physical experiment.

Table 41 lists the experimental oscillator strengths for lines in the vacuum ultraviolet. The oscillator strengths of autoionization lines are discussed in §37 and §38.

---

* Various problems associated with the emission of optically thick plasmas have been treated in great detail by Sobolev [45].

## 41. VERIFICATION OF THE SUM RULE
## FOR THE ATOMS OF INERT GASES

The Thomas–Kuhn–Reiche sum rule can be stated in the following form [47, 47a]: the sum of oscillator strengths $f$ over all the possible transitions between all the possible configurations is equal to the number of electrons $N$ in the atom.

This sum rule can be written in the form

$$\sum_{n'} f(nn') = N \,, \tag{48}$$

where $n$ and $n'$ are the initial and the final states of the atom.

If the interaction between the outer and the inner electrons is ignored, equation (48) takes the form

$$\sum_{n'} f(nn') = r \,, \tag{48a}$$

where $r$ is the number of valence electrons, and only the various possible transitions are considered. In oscillator strength calculations, the oscillator strength of the continuum must be taken into consideration.

Numerous alternative sum rules are listed and presented in quantum-mechanical form in [47, 48]. These sum rules establish a definite relation between oscillator strengths, magnetic susceptibility, polarizability, and bond energy. The sum rule for the polarizability can be checked, as the Thomas–Kuhn–Reiche rule, without any quantum-mechanical calculations. According to this rule,

$$\sum_{n'} \frac{f(nn')}{(E_n - E_{n'})^2} = \frac{\alpha}{4} \,, \tag{49}$$

where $E_n$ and $E_{n'}$ are the bond energies of levels $n$ and $n'$.

The polarizability can be found if the refractive index for several wavelengths is known. The polarizabilities of all the inert gases were determined in [49]. The sum rule for the polarizability is thus amenable to immediate experimental verification.

In verifying the sum rule, we need the oscillator strength of the continuum

$$f = \frac{mc^2}{e^2 \pi n_0} \int \mu_v dv \,, \tag{50}$$

where $\mu_v$ is the absorption coefficient, $v$ is the wavenumber, $n_0$ is the Loschmidt number. Thus,

$$f = 4.19 \cdot 10^{-8} \int \mu_v dv \,.$$

## Helium

The oscillator strength of the helium continuum is 1.54 [50]. It can be found from the curve in Figure 198. The sum of the $f$ numbers for discrete transitions is 0.45 (according to the data of [9] and [51]). The sum of the oscillator strengths for helium is thus 1.99, which fits the value of 2 derived from the sum rule.

The sum rule for the polarizability gives $\alpha = 0.197 \cdot 10^{-24} \, cm^3$ from the experimental data of [50] and the theoretical calculations of [9, 51]. This result agrees with the polarizability derived from refractive index measurements, $\alpha = 0.204 \cdot 10^{-24} \, cm^3$ [49].

## Neon

The sum rule can also be verified for neon [52, 53]. The continuum oscillator strength is found to be 10.1 [52, 53] and 9.4 [53a]. The sum of the oscillator strengths for discrete transitions is estimated as 0.3–0.4 from theoretical calculations [54], i.e., the final result gives $10.5 \pm 0.4$ [52, 53] or $9.8 \pm 0.5$ [53a], which is sufficiently close to the theoretical value of 10.

The polarizability determined from the sum rule is $(0.430 \pm 0.020) \cdot 10^{-24} \, cm^3$ [52, 53], and the value derived from refractive index measurements is $0.395 \cdot 10^{-24} \, cm^3$ [49, 55]. This fit is fully adequate.

## Argon

Using the data of Figure 203, equation (50) can be applied to calculate the oscillator strength of the continuum ($f = 5.65$) [56]; the additional oscillator strength of the discrete transitions is 0.30 [22, 42, 57]. The oscillator strength for transitions between the valence electrons ($M$ electrons) is thus 5.95, instead of the expected 8.

## Krypton

The continuum oscillator strength is $5.9 \pm 0.5$ [58]. The oscillator strengths of the autoionization lines add up to 0.3. The sum of the oscillator strengths of the discrete transitions is also 0.3 [36a, 42].* These figures add up to 6.5, instead of the expected 8.

## Xenon

The oscillator strength of the continuum is 5.6 [58, 58a]. Adding the oscillator strengths of the autoionization lines (0.5) and the oscillator strengths of the discrete

---

* For both krypton and xenon, only the oscillator strengths of the strongest resonance lines are considered.

transitions (0.5) [34, 39] we get 6.6. As in the case of krypton, the check should be performed for the entire atom as a whole.

The sum rule for the polarizability gives $\alpha = 3.24 \cdot 10^{-24}$ cm$^3$ [34], instead of the theoretical $4.04 \cdot 10^{-24}$ cm$^3$ [49]. This is apparently due to a contribution from discrete transitions which have been ignored.

## 42. REFRACTIVE INDICES OF GASES AND RAYLEIGH SCATTERING CROSS SECTIONS

Classical interferometric methods of refractive index measurement are applicable to wavelengths above 1400 Å (see § 19). We will now describe some methods that can be used to measure the refractive indices in the vacuum ultraviolet.

### The line shift method

The only direct method for measuring the refractive index in the vacuum ultraviolet, at wavelengths shorter than 1400 Å, measures the change in wavelength when the spectrograph is filled with the relevant gas.

Let $\lambda_0$ and $\lambda$ be the wavelengths in vacuum and in medium of refractive index $n$. Then

$$\frac{\Delta\lambda}{\lambda} = \frac{\lambda_0 - \lambda}{\lambda} = n - 1.$$

We can thus find the refractive index at any wavelength in that spectral region where the gas is transparent. This method was originally proposed by Dickey [59] and later used by Wilkinson [59a] to measure the refractive index of nitrogen between 2040 and 1650 Å (Table 42).

The accuracy of the refractive index determination depends on the value of the refractive index and the dispersion of the spectroscopic instrument. For nitrogen and argon between 2000 and 1200 Å, the wavelength difference is a few tenths of an angstrom, and an instrument with a reciprocal dispersion of 1 Å/mm will measure the refraction $(n-1)$ to within 1 %.

### The Cherenkov radiation method [60]

Cherenkov radiation is excited in a variable-pressure gas chamber. Cherenkov radiation of a certain wavelength is observed only starting with a certain value of the refractive index and detectors sensitive to different wavelengths will respond at different gas pressures in the chamber. Let $\beta$ stand for the ratio of the particle velocity to the velocity of light in vacuum. Let $n(p_1, \lambda_1)$ be the refractive index at wavelength $\lambda_1$

Table 42

| Gas | $\lambda$, Å | $(n-1)\cdot 10^5$ | | | |
|---|---|---|---|---|---|
| | | from line shift measurements [59a] | from Cherenkov radiation [60] | from scattering observations [62] | extrapolation of dispersion equations |
| $N_2$ | 1988 | 34.35 | | | |
| | $1860 \pm 80$ | 35.04 | $34.4 \pm 0.3$ | | |
| | $1805 \pm 80$ | 35.53 | $34.7 \pm 0.3$ | | |
| | 1750.04 | 36.16 | | | |
| | 1649.19 | 38.34 | | | |
| | $1220 \pm 30$ | | $57.1 \pm 1.0$ | | |
| Ar | $1850 \pm 80$ | | $32.5 \pm 0.3$ | | 33.15 |
| | $1805 \pm 80$ | | $32.8 \pm 0.3$ | | 33.52 |
| | $1210 \pm 30$ | | $55.9 \pm 1.0$ | $56.5 \pm 1.2$ | 53.60 |
| Kr | 1216 | | | 531 | |
| Xe | 1216 | | | 1720 | |
| $H_2$ | 1216 | | | $32.0 \pm 0.6$ | |

(the visible spectrum) and pressure $p_1$ corresponding to the emission of Cherenkov radiation of wavelength $\lambda_1$; $n(p_2, \lambda_2)$ is the refractive index of the gas at wavelength $\lambda_2$ (the vacuum ultraviolet) and pressure $p_2$ corresponding to the emission of Cherenkov radiation of wavelength $\lambda_2$. Then we have the following equalities:

$$\beta n(p_1, \lambda_1) = 1; \quad \beta n(p_2, \lambda_2) = 1,$$

which give

$$n(p_1, \lambda_1) = n(p_2, \lambda_2). \tag{51}$$

A Jamin interferometer can be used to measure the refraction ratio $F$ at a certain wavelength $\lambda_1$ and at different pressures:

$$\frac{n(p_1, \lambda_1) - 1}{n(p_2, \lambda_1) - 1} = F. \tag{52}$$

Using equation (51), we write equation (52) in the form

$$\frac{n(p_2, \lambda_2) - 1}{n(p_2, \lambda_1) - 1} = F.$$

Hence it follows that if the refractive index of a gas is known at a certain wavelength in the visible spectrum, we can calculate its refractive index in the vacuum ultraviolet.

In practice, the wavelength in the visible spectrum is fixed with an interference filter, and an ionization chamber or a photomultiplier responding in a narrow range of wavelengths acts as a vacuum UV filter. In this setup, the refractive index is measured for the wavelength which corresponds to the peak of the detector response curve. The method has been used in measurements of the refractive index of argon and nitrogen (see Table 41).

**Extrapolation of dispersion equations**

For most gases, refractive indices have been measured in the visible and the near ultraviolet. (see, e.g., [60a]) and interpolation formulas are available for the refractions. As an example, consider the interpolation formula for argon:

$$n-1 = 1.2048 \cdot 10^6 \left( \frac{0.209646}{0.87882 \cdot 10^{10} - v^2} + \frac{0.209646}{0.91001 \cdot 10^{10} - v^2} + \right.$$

$$\left. + \frac{4.941724}{2.6936 \cdot 10^{10} - v^2} \right),$$

where $v$ is the wavenumber in $cm^{-1}$.

Interpolation formulas can also be used at frequencies far from the absorption line, and in this way we obtain the refractive indices of various gases in the vacuum ultraviolet. We have no information on the validity of this extrapolation of the dispersion equations, but judging from the data of Table 42 for the dispersion of argon, the dispersion equation can be extrapolated to wavelengths far from the resonance line.

**Rayleigh scattering [61, 62]***

The process of scattering can be described in terms of two quantities, the scattering cross section $\sigma$ and the number of photons $n_\theta$ scattered per second in a unit solid angle at an azimuthal angle $\theta$ relative to the incident beam with photon flux density $\Phi$. The scattering cross section is expressed by the equality

$$\sigma = - \frac{1}{N\Phi} \frac{d\Phi}{dl},$$

where $N$ is the number of molecules in unit volume, $d\Phi/dl$ is the change in photon flux density per unit length.

The number of scattered photons is given by

$$n_\theta = \Phi \frac{3N\sigma}{16\pi} V \left[ \frac{2}{2 + \rho_n} (1 + \cos^2\theta + \rho_n \sin^2\theta) \right] = \Phi \frac{2\pi^2(n-1)^2 V}{\lambda^4 N} \frac{6}{6 - 7\rho_n}, \quad (53)$$

* On Rayleigh scattering, see Fabelinskii [62a].

where $V$ is the scattering volume, $\rho_n$ is the depolarization factor, defined as the ratio of the number of scattered photons with polarization perpendicular to the plane through the incident beam and the line of observation, to the number of scattered photons with polarization parallel to this plane. The depolarization factor $\rho_n$ depends on the polarizability $\alpha$, which in turn is related to the refractive index:

$$\alpha = \frac{n-1}{2\pi N},\tag{53a}$$

where $n$ is the refractive index and $N$ is the number of molecules in unit volume.

The flux scattered at an angle of 54° is independent of $\rho_n$ ($\cos^2 54° = 1/3$). From (53) and (53a) we can calculate the scattering cross section:

$$\sigma = \frac{4\pi}{NV}\frac{n_{54°}}{\Phi} = \frac{8\pi}{3NV}\frac{2+\rho_n}{1+\rho_n}\frac{n_{90°}}{\Phi} = \frac{128\pi^5\alpha_0^2}{3\lambda^4}\frac{6+3\rho_n}{6-7\rho_n}.\tag{54}$$

The scattering cross section is thus inversely proportional to $\lambda^4$, but only if $\alpha_0$ and $\rho_n$ are constants independent of $\lambda$. From (53a) and (54) we readily find

$$(n-1)^2 = \frac{\lambda^4 N}{2\pi^2 V}\cdot\frac{6-7\rho_n}{6+6\rho_n}\cdot\frac{n_{90°}}{\Phi}.\tag{55}$$

Experimental determination of the scattering cross section and the refractive index of any gas involves measurements of the number of photons scattered in unit time in unit solid angle in any direction. The measurements are best carried out at right angles to the incident beam, but then $\rho_n$ should be found from independent experiments. Therefore, if our aim is to find $\sigma$, the scattered light is best measured at an angle of 54° to the incident beam. In refractive index measurements, the observations are generally made at right angles to the incident beam.

The absolute values of $\sigma$ and $n$ are very difficult to find from these experiments, and the scattering method is therefore applied to relative measurements only, which are much easier to carry out. It is readily seen that measurements at 54° give directly the ratio.

$$\frac{\sigma_I}{\sigma_{II}} = \frac{n_{54°}^I}{n_{54°}^{II}}.\tag{56}$$

The relative refractions of two gases are conveniently compared if their refractions at normal conditions are known:

$$n-1 = (n_0-1)\cdot\frac{p273}{T},\tag{57}$$

where $n_0$ is the refractive index at normal conditions, $p$ is the pressure in atmospheres.

From (55) and (57), taking the detector signals $J_{90°}$ and $J$ to be proportional to $n_{90°}$ and $\Phi$, we find

$$\frac{(n-1)_I^2}{(n_0-1)_{II}^2} = \frac{\left(\dfrac{6-7\rho_n}{6+6\rho_n}\right)_I}{\left(\dfrac{6-7\rho_n}{6+7\rho_n}\right)_{II}} \cdot \frac{\left(\dfrac{J_{90°}}{Jp}\right)_I}{\left(\dfrac{J_{90°}}{Jp}\right)_{II}}. \tag{58}$$

The refraction of one gas thus can be found if the refraction of the other gas is known.

The scattering cross sections have been measured for the $L_\alpha$ line, and the refractive indices of hydrogen, argon, krypton, and xenon at 1216 Å. Nitrogen was used as a reference gas. Its refractive index and depolarization factor $\rho_n$ are known from [60] and [63].

We will now briefly describe the experimental setup used by Gill and Heddle [61, 62]. The light of an electrodeless hydrogen lamp (30 MHz, 0.1 T pressure) was directed in a slightly divergent beam to a polarization chamber filled with nitrogen oxide (Figure 224). The scattered radiation was detected with a photon counter filled with iodine vapor and helium (see §26). Lithium fluoride windows were used in both detectors. The chamber was made of Pyrex glass, and its dimensions are shown in the figure. The scattering volume was about 2 cm$^3$. The solid angle covered by the photon counter was about $2 \cdot 10^{-2}$ sterad. The gases were carefully purified from water vapor. Two signals were simultaneously detected in these measurements: the scattered light signal ($J_{90°}$) and the incident light signal ($J$). The measurements

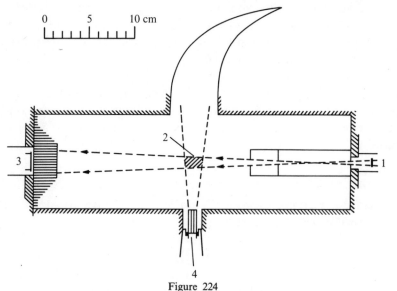

Figure 224

Apparatus for scattering observations:

1) lamp, 2) scattering volume, 3) ionization chamber, 4) photon counter.

were made at various pressures, and $J_{90°}/J$ was plotted as a function of pressure. The slope of the plot gave the sought parameter $J_{90°}/Jp$.

Figure 225 shows a $J_{90°}/J$ vs. $p$ plot for hydrogen. The experimental points closely follow a straight line passing through the origin. Reduction of the experimental data has given the scattering cross sections of $L_\alpha$ radiation for a number of gases and their respective refractions (see Tables 42 and 43).

According to the authors, the error of their measurements is at most 2%.

For helium and neon, the scattering cross sections are very small, and original measurements failed to produce any measurable results. Only further improvement of the experimental technique permitted measuring these cross sections [65].

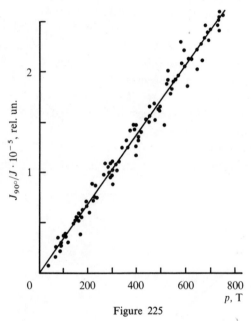

Figure 225

Scattering of $L_\alpha$ by molecular hydrogen.

Table 43

| Gas | $\sigma$ (for $\lambda = 1216$ Å), barn |
|---|---|
| $H_2$ | 2.1 |
| Ar | 6.5 |
| Kr | 680 |
| Xe | 6100 |
| $N_2$ | 7.1 |

The results of measurements for argon show a good fit with the findings of other authors [60a], whereas for xenon and krypton the results are apparently in error, since the calculation of the $f$ numbers from these data gives highly unlikely oscillator strengths [66].

## 43. MEASUREMENT OF EXCITATION CROSS SECTIONS
## IN THE VACUUM ULTRAVIOLET

Unfortunately, there is only a limited number of publications which give any information on short-wave radiation in connection with collisional processes. Although detailed data are currently available on the electronic excitation functions of numerous spectral lines, the corresponding measurements in the vacuum ultraviolet have been carried out for $L_\alpha$ only. These measurements are due to Fite et al. [67–69], who applied the method of crossed beams [69, 70] to the study of the collision of electrons with hydrogen atoms. Atomic hydrogen was produced by thermal dissociation of molecular hydrogen in a vacuum furnace. The radiation was detected with a photon counter filled with iodine vapor; an oxygen filter was used (see §10) [64]. The relative scattering cross sections were measured, and normalized to the Born approximation values for the $1s$–$2p$ transition at energies above 250 eV [71, 72] (Figure 226).

The excitation cross section of the $2s$ state of the hydrogen atom was also studied

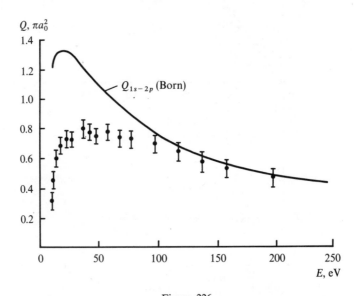

Figure 226

$L_\alpha$ excitation cross section for collisions of electrons with hydrogen atoms.

optically.* These experiments were carried out by Stebbings et al. [69, 74]. They are remarkable for the originality of the optical method developed for determining the concentration of metastable atoms.**

The atomic hydrogen was passed through three chambers with differential pump-out, and in the third chamber it underwent electronic excitation. After that, the atoms reached a uniform electric field between the plates of a condenser, which induced transitions from the 2s state to the 2p state. The $L_\alpha$ excitation cross section was compared with the 2s excitation cross section. The experimental setup is shown in Figure 227. The measurements were carried out with electrons between 11 and 600 eV. First the $L_\alpha$ line produced by primary excitation was recorded. Then the counter was moved to pick up the radiation in the plane passing between the con-denser plates. A special shutter screened off the primary excitation space (without the shutter, the radiation from the collision space was partially detected). The de-tector signal ratio gives the ratio of the two cross sections (1s–2p and 1s–2s).

The excitation cross section of the 2p state of hydrogen atom was also measured by Chamberlain et al. [75]. The energies near the excitation threshold were studied. The measurements were carried out in crossed beams, and the radiation was observed perpendicularly to the beam direction. A NO photon counter with a lithium fluoride window was used (see §26, §27). This counter responds only to the $L_\alpha$ line. The cross

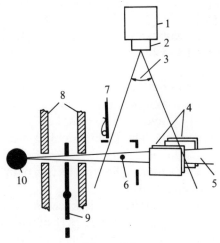

Figure 227

Experimental setup for measuring the ratio of the production cross section of a metastable atom to the $L_\alpha$ excitation cross section:

1) photon counter, 2) filter, 3) counter angle of view, 4) plates, 5) atomic beam, 6) electron beam, 7) shutter, 8) vacuum chamber walls, 9) chopper wheel, 10) furnace.

---

* The excitation cross section of the metastable 2s state was also measured by nonoptical methods [73].
** The concentration of metastable helium ions He$^+$(2s) was also determined by this method [74a].

section markedly increases near the excitation threshold, reaches one third of its maximum value and falls off to a minimum at a distance of 0.3 eV from the threshold; then it again increases. These measurements show only a qualitative fit with the theory as far as the variation of the $1s$–$2p$ cross section near the excitation threshold is concerned [76].

Special experiments were carried out to study the creation and destruction of the metastable hydrogen atoms by a 15 keV proton beam passed through molecular hydrogen [77]. The metastable states were deexcited in an electric field of some 50–500 V/cm. The metastable atoms dropped to the $2p$ state emitting in the $L_\alpha$ line. The excitation cross sections of the metastable $2s$ state were determined as a function of the electric field strength.

The $L_\alpha$ excitation cross sections were studied by bombarding hydrogen atoms with protons at energies between 600 eV and 30 keV [78].

The $L_\alpha$ radiation for excitation cross section measurements was also studied by Geballe et al. [79–82]. The radiation was detected by an iodine vapor counter with an oxygen filter. The following collisions were studied in [79]: $(He^+, H_2)$, $(H_2^+, He)$, $(H^+, He)$, $(H^+, H_2)$, $(H_2^+, H_2)$, $(H_3^+, H_2)$, $(H_3^+, He)$, $(H^+, N_2)$, $(H_3^+, N_2)$, $(He^+, N_2)$, $(H_2^+, N_2)$.

In all these reactions the energy of the primary particles varied from 100 to 6500 eV.

Collisions of protons with energies between 1 and 25 keV with the atoms of inert gases were studied in [80].

The $L_\alpha$ excitation cross sections in the collisions of the molecular ions $H_2^+$ and $D_2^+$ (with energies between 1 and 25 keV) with the atoms of inert gases were measured in [81].

The excitation cross sections for the metastable state $2s$ in the collisions of protons with the atoms of inert gases were studied in [82] and [82a]. The proton energy varied from 1.5 to 23 keV [82] and from 10 to 40 keV [82a]. The metastable states were deexcited in an electric field. The $L_\alpha$ intensity was measured with and without an electric field. The increase in the $L_\alpha$ intensity when the electric field was turned on was associated with $2s$–$2p$ transitions. The cross section of these transitions was thus inferred from the $L_\alpha$ enhancement.

Some authors have studied the excitation cross sections of the lines of inert gases in various collisions. For example, van Eck et al. [83] studied the excitation of atomic inert gases in collisions with protons and helium ions $(He^+)$ and determined the absolute cross sections of the $np^5\,{}^2P$–$np^6\,{}^2S$ and $np^5\,{}^2P$–$(n+1)\,s'\,{}^2D$ transitions for excited $Ne^+$, $Ar^+$, and $Kr^+$ ions. The cross sections of the neon resonance lines were also measured for the excitation of neon atoms by helium ions and protons.

Collisions between singly charge argon ions and various inert gases were studied in [84]. The energy of the ions varied from 5 to 24 keV. Alongside with lines in the visible and the near ultraviolet, lines in the vacuum ultraviolet were recorded $(\lambda > 1000\ \text{Å})$.

Almost all the work on the cross sections of various lines in the vacuum ultraviolet has been carried out in recent years. This is attributed to the considerable advances of vacuum UV spectroscopy and, in particular, development of special methods for the measurements of absolute and relative line intensities. The excitation cross sections of ionic lines cannot be measured at this state. The solution of this problem requires accurate measurements of ion concentrations, which involve considerable difficulties.

## BIBLIOGRAPHY

1. ROZHDESTVENSKII, D.S. *Raboty po anomal'noi dispersii v parakh metallov (Studies of Anomalous Dispersion in Metal Vapors)*, S.E. Frish, Editor. Izdatel'stvo AN SSSR. 1951.
2. PERY–THORNE, A. *J. Quant. Spectr. Rad. Trans.*, **2**, 427 (1962).
3. WOLFSOHN, G. *Z. Phys.*, **85**, 366 (1933).
4. WOLFSOHN, G. *Z. Phys.*, **63**, 634 (1930).
5. WOLFSOHN, G. *Z. Phys.*, **83**, 234 (1933).
6. HERZFELD, K.F. and K.L. WOLF. *Ann. Phys.*, **76**, 71 (1925).
7. HERZFELD, K.F. and K.L. WOLF. *Ann. Phys.*, **76**, 567 (1925).
8. LANDSBERG, G.S. *Optika (Optics)*, p. 477. Gostekhizdat. 1957.
9. DALGARNO, A. and A.L. STEWART. *Proc. Phys. Soc.*, **A76**, 49 (1960).
10. BAKER, D.J., D.E. BEDO, and D.H. TOMBOULIAN. *Phys. Rev.*, **124**, 1471 (1961).
11. LARSEN, T. *Z. Phys.*, **88**, 389 (1934).
12. KÖRWIEN, H. *Z. Phys.*, **91**, (1934).
13. SCHÜTZ, W. *Ann. Physik*, **18**, 705. (1933).
14. SCHILLBACH, H. *Ann. Physik*, **18**, 721 (1933).
15. KOROLEV, F.A., V.I. ODINTSOV, and E.V. FURSOVA. *Optika i Spektroskopiya*, **16**, 555 (1964).
16. KUHN, H.G. and J.M. VAUGHAN. *Proc. Roy. Soc.*, **A277**, 297 (1964).
17. KOROLEV, F.A. and V.I. ODINTSOV. *Optika i Spektroskopiya*, **18**, 968 (1965).
18. VAUGHAN, J.M. *J. Opt. Soc. America*, **54**, 318 (1964).
18a. VAUGHAN, J.M. *Phys. Lett.*, **21**, 153 (1966).
18b. KUHN, H.G., E.L. LEWIS, and J.M. VAUGHAN. *Phys. Rev. Lett.*, **15**, 687 (1965).
19. SCHIFF, B. and C.L. PEKERIS. *Phys. Rev.*, **134A**, 638 (1964).
20. FURSOV, V.S., M.N. OGANOV, and A.R. STRIGANOV. *Doklady AN SSSR*, **101**, 453 (1955).
21. VLASOV, A.A. and V.S. FURSOV. *ZhETF*, **9**, 783 (1939).
22. STACEY, D.N. and J.M. VAUGHAN. *Phys. Lett.*, **11**, 105 (1964).
23. MITCHELL, A.C.G. and M.W. ZEMANSKY. *Resonance Radiation and Excited Atoms*. Cambridge University Press. 1934.
24. FRISH, S.E. and I.P. BOGDANOVA. In: *Sbornik pamyati S.I. Vavilova (S.I. Vavilov Memorial Volume)*, p. 220. Izdatel'stvo ANSSSR. 1952.
25. FRISH, S.E. and O.P. BOCHKOVA. *Vestnik LGU*, chem. phys. ser., No. 16, 40 (1961).

26. FAIRCHILD, C.E. and K.C. CLARK. *Phys. Rev. Lett.*, **9**, 100 (1962).

27. PRAG, A.B., C.E. FAIRCHILD, and K.C. CLARK. *Phys. Rev.*, **137A**, 1358 (1965).

28. PRAG, A.B. and K.C. CLARK. *Phys. Rev. Lett.*, **12**, 34 (1964).

29. KELLY, P.S. and B.H. ARMSTRONG. *Phys. Rev. Lett.*, **9**, 426 (1962).

30. KELLY, P.S. *Astrophys. J.*, **140**, 1247 (1964).

31. GARSTANG, R.H. *Proc. Cambridge Philos. Soc.*, **57**, 115 (1961).

32. KELLY, P.S. and B.H. ARMSTRONG. *Phys. Rev. Lett.*, **12**, 35 (1964).

33. MORSE, F.A. and F. KAUFMAN. *J. Chem. Phys.*, **42**, 1785 (1965).

34. CHASHCHINA, G.I. and E.YA. SCHREIDER. *Optika i Spektroskopiya*, **20**, 511 (1966).

35. UNSÖLD, A. *Physik der Sternatmosphären*, Chapt. 44. Berlin, Springer. 1955.

36. OSTROVSKII, YU.I. and N.P. PENKIN. *Optika i Spektroskopiya*, **11**, 3 (1961).

36a. WILKINSON, P.G. *J. Quant. Spectr. Rad. Trans.*, **5**, 503 (1965).

37. LURIO, A., R.L. DE ZAFRA, and R.J. GOSHEN. *Phys. Rev.*, **134A**, 1198 (1964).

38. ANDERSON, D. and W. LICHTEN. *Bull. Amer. Phys. Soc.*, **9**, 65 (1964).

39. ANDERSON, D.K. *Phys. Rev.*, **137A**, 21 (1965).

40. LURIO, A. *Phys. Rev.*, **140A**, 1505 (1965).

41. KUYATT, C.E. and J.A. SIMPSON. *Proc. III. Intern. Conf. on the Physics of Electronic and Atomic Collisions, Amsterdam*, North-Holland 1964, p. 191

42. GEIGER, J. *Z. Phys.*, **177**, 138 (1963).

43. BOLDT, G. *Z. Naturforsch.*, **18a**, 1107 (1963).

44. BOLDT, G. *J. Quant, Spectr. Rad. Trans.*, **5**, 91 (1965).

44a. LABUHN, F. *Z. Naturforsch*, **20a**, 998 (1965).

44b. LAWRENCE, G.M. and B.D. SAVAGE. *Phys. Rev.*, **141**, 67 (1966).

45. SOBOLEV, N.N. *ZhETF*, **19**, 25 (1949).

46. BERKNER, K., W.S. COOPER III, S.N. KAPLAN, and R.V. PYLE. *Phys. Lett.*, **16**, 35 (1965).

46a. LINCKE, R. and H.R. GRIEM. *Phys. Rev.*, **143**, 66 (1966).

46b. TURNER, R. *Phys. Rev.*, **140A**, 426 (1965).

47. BETHE, H.A. and E. SALPETER. *Quantum Mechanics of One- and Two-Electron Methods*. Berlin, Springer-Verlag. 1957.

47a. ALLER, L.H. *Astrophysics*. London, George Ronald. 1953.

48. DALGARNO, A. and N. LYNN. *Proc. Phys. Soc.*, **A70**, 802 (1957).

49. DALGARNO, A. and A.E. KINGSTON. *Proc. Roy. Soc.*, **A259**, 424 (1960).

50. SAMSON, J.A.R. *J. Opt. Soc. America*, **54**, 876 (1964).

51. SALPETER, E. and M.H. ZAIDI. *Phys. Rev.*, **125**, 248 (1962).

52. EDERER, D.L. and D.H. TOMBOULIAN. *Phys. Rev.*, **133A**, 1525 (1964).

53. PIECH, K.R. and J.S. LEVINGER. *Phys. Rev.*, **135A**, 332 (1964).

53a. SAMSON, J.A.R. *J. Opt. Soc. America*, **55**, 935 (1965).

54. COOPER, J.W. *Phys. Rev.*, **128**, 681 (1962).

55. CUTHBERTSON, C. and M. CUTHBERTSON. *Proc. Roy. Soc.*, **A84**, 13 (1911).

56. SAMSON, J.A.R. *J. Opt. Soc., America*, **54**, 420 (1964).

57. KNOX, R.S. *Phys. Rev.*, **110**, 375 (1958).

58. RUSTGI, O.P., E.I. FISHER, and C.H. FULLER. *J. Opt. Soc. America*, **54**, 745 (1964).

58a. SAMSON, J.A.R. *J. Opt. Soc. America*, **54**, 842 (1964).

59. DICKEY, R.W. *Astrophys. J.*, **45**, 189 (1917).

59a. WILKINSON, P.G. *J. Opt. Soc. America*, **50**, 1002 (1960).

60. HEDDLE, D.W.O., R.E. JENNINGS, and A.S.L. PARSONS. *J. Opt. Soc. America,* **53**, 840 (1963).

60a. LARSEN, T. *Zur Kenntnis der Refraktion und Dispersion von Edelgasen and edelgasähnlichen Hydriden und Deutriden.* Lund. 1938.

61. HEDDLE, D.W.O. *J. Quant. Spectr. Rad. Trans.,* **2**, 349 (1962).

62. GILL, P. and D.W.O. HEDDLE. *J. Opt. Soc. America,* **53**, 847 (1963).

62a. FABELINSKII, I.L. *Molekulyarnoe rasseyaniye sveta (Molecular Light Scattering).* Izdatel'stvo "Nauka." 1965.

63. BHAGAVANTAM, S. *Scattering of light and the Raman Effect,* Waltair, India, Andhra Univ. 1940.

64. BRACKMAN, R.T., W.L. FITE, and K.E. HAGEN. *Rev. Scient. Instrum.,* **29**, 125 (1958).

65. MARMO, F.F. and Y. MIKAWA. *Bull. Amer. Phys. Soc.,* **9**, 626 (1964).

66. KINGSTON, A.E. *J. Opt. Soc. America,* **54**, 1145 (1964).

67. FITE, W.L. and R.T. BRACKMANN. *Phys. Rev.,* **112**, 1151 (1958).

68. FITE, W.L., R.F. STEBBINGS, and R.T. BRACKMANN. *Phys. Rev.,* **116**, 356 (1959).

69. FITE, W.L. In: *Atomic and Molecular Processes,* D.R. Bates, Editor. N.Y., London, Academic Press. 1962.

70. FITE, W.L. and R.T. BRACKMANN. *Phys. Rev.,* **112**, 1141 (1958).

71. MASSEY, H.S.W. *Handbuch der Physik,* S. Flügge, Editor, XXXVI, 354. Berlin. 1956.

72. SEATON, M.J. In: *Atomic and Molecular Processes,* D.R. Bates, Editor. N.Y., London, Academic Press. 1962.

73. LICHTEN, W. and S. SCHULTZ. *Phys. Rev.,* **116**, 1132 (1959).

74. STEBBINGS, R.F., W.L. FITE, D.G. HUMMER, and R.T. BRACKMANN. *Phys. Rev.,* **119**, 1939 (1960).

74a. HARRISON, M.F.A., D.F. DANCE, K.T. DOLDER, and A.C.H. SMITH. *Rev. Scient. Instrum.,* **36**, 1460 (1965).

75. CHAMBERLAIN, G.E., S.J. SMITH, and D.W.O. HEDDLE. *Phys. Rev. Lett.,* **12**, 647 (1964).

76. DAMBURG, R. and M. GAILITIS. *Proc. Phys. Soc.,* **82**, 1068 (1963).

77. SELLIN, I.A. *Phys. Rev.,* **136A**, 1245 (1964).

78. STEBBINGS, R.F., R.A. YOUNG, C.L. OXLEY, and H. EHRHARDT. *Phys. Rev.,* **138A**, 1313 (1965).

79. DUNN, G.H., R. GEBALLE, and D. PRETZER. *Phys. Rev.,* **128**, 2200 (1962).

80. PRETZER, D., B. VAN ZYL, and R. GEBALLE. *Phys. Rev. Lett.,* **10**, 340 (1963).

81. ZYL, B. VAN, D. JAECKS, D. PRETZER, and R. GEBALLE. *Phys. Rev.,* **136A**, 1561 (1964).

82. JAECKS, D., B. VAN ZYL, and R. GEBALLE. *Phys. Rev.,* **137A**, 340 (1965).

82a. ANDREEV, E.P., V.A. ANKUDINOV, and S.V. BOBASHEV. *ZhETF,* **50**, 565 (1966).

83. ECK, J. VAN, F.J. DE HEER, and J. KISTEMAKER. *Phys. Rev.,* **130**, 656 (1963).

84. SLUYTERS, T.J.M. and J. KISTEMAKER. *Physica,* **25**, 1389 (1959).

# CHAPTER IX

# Plasma Diagnostics

## 44. DETERMINATION OF THE ELECTRON TEMPERATURE OF A PLASMA

Plasma diagnostics using the plasma emission in the vacuum ultraviolet is of a fairly recent origin: its advent is closely linked with controlled thermonuclear fusion research.

A "hot" plasma emits mainly in the vacuum ultraviolet, and this emission can be effectively utilized to study the various physical processes in the plasma, to determine the particle concentrations, and to establish the velocity distribution of the plasma particles.

This section is concerned with spectroscopic methods for the determination of electron temperatures, which make use of the plasma emission in the vacuum ultraviolet.

### The continuum intensity distribution

At high current densities, the gas discharge plasma emits a continuous spectrum. This spectrum is produced by transitions between the continuum states and the discrete states of the electron system (free-bound transitions) and by free-free transitions between different continuum states.

Free-bound transitions, emitting recombination radiation, are observed when a free electron is captured by an ion into a discrete level.

Free-free transitions—bremsstrahlung—arise when electrons collide with ions and when electrons jump between different states in a continuous sequence of terms.

The energy $dE_v$ emitted in free-free transitions by a unit plasma volume in unit time in a frequency interval $dv$ is given for hydrogen-like atoms by the relation [1]

$$dE_v = CN_eN_iZ^2\left(\frac{\chi_H}{kT_e}\right)^{1/2} ge^{-hv/kT_e}\, dv, \tag{59}$$

where $C$ is a proportionality coefficient, $N_e$ is the electron concentration, $N_i$ is the ion concentration, $\chi_H$ is the ionization energy of the hydrogen atom, $T_e$ is the electron temperature, $g$ is the Gaunt factor (a factor of the order of unity, which is introduced as a quantum-mechanical correction into classical calculations; it has been tabulated by Allen [2] for various configurations of the hydrogen atom).

At low frequencies (in the visible and especially in the infrared spectrum), $hv \leq kT_e$, and $dE/dv$ is virtually independent of the electron temperature. When $hv$ is comparable with $kT_e$, a definite dependence on the electron temperature is observed, and equation (59) can be used to calculate the electron temperature (see the curve and the calculations in [3]).

The quantity of energy emitted by a unit plasma volume in unit time in a frequency interval $dv$ by free-bound transitions of hydrogen-like ions is given by [4]

$$dE_{v_n} = C_1N_eN_i\frac{Z^4}{T_e^{3/2}}\frac{g}{n^3}e^{-h(v-v_n)/kT_e}\, dv, \tag{60}$$

Here $C_1$ is a proportionality coefficient, $n$ is the principal quantum number, $hv_n$ is the ionization energy from the $n$-th level; the other notation is as in equation (59).

At frequencies higher than $v_n$ the frequency dependence of the emitted energy is the same as for free-free transitions. Therefore, the temperature can be found from the intensity of the continuous spectrum without going into the whole problem of free-free or free-bound transitions. It follows from equations (59) and (60) that the plot of $\log(dE/dv)$ vs. $v$ is a straight line with a slope depending on $T_e$.

The intensity distribution in the continuum has been measured in a number of experimental studies [5–8]. The following technique was used for the determination of the electron temperature on the Scylla machine [6–8]: the radiation was passed through various absorbing films, such as Be, polyethylene, Al, and Ni. The absorption coefficients of the films were known, and the energy transmitted through the film could thus be calculated as a function of the film thickness for various electron temperatures.

Figure 228 is a comparison of the theoretical absorption curves of a polyethylene film with experimental data. Similar curves were constructed for other films also. We see from the figure that the temperature $T_e$ lies between 200 and 300 eV. The

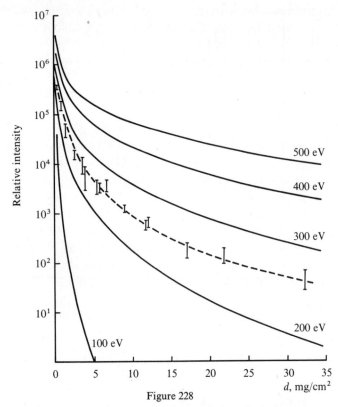

Figure 228

Experimental absorption curve of polyethylene (dashed) and theoretical absorption curves for various electron temperatures.

spectral composition of the incident radiation can be recovered graphically from the absorption curves, and the points marked on Figure 229 are thus obtained. The same figure shows the theoretical lines for three temperatures. The slope of the line which provides the best fit to the experimental data gives the electron temperature of the plasma, which is found to be 240 eV.

### Intensity comparison of two continua

Another method of temperature determination is based on measuring the ratio of the bremsstrahlung intensity near the series limit (on the long-wave side) to the total intensity of bremsstrahlung and recombination radiation just beyond the series limit. The measurements can be made near the Lyman limit (912 Å), as well as near the Balmer limit (3646 Å) [9–11]. The intensity ratio can also be calculated theoretically [9, 10]. The corresponding curves are shown in Figure 230, and the electron

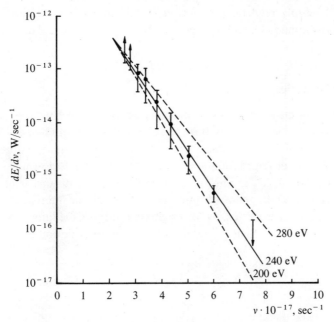

Figure 229

The emission spectrum of plasma in the Scylla machine at various electron temperatures (dots with error bars correspond to the experimental data).

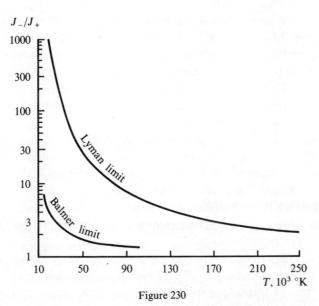

Figure 230

The intensity ratio of continua near the Lyman and the Balmer limits.

temperature is simply read off these curves. The method was applied in practice on the ZETA machine [11], and it received considerable impetus from astrophysical research [12, 13].

## Relative lines intensities

A third method of electron temperature determination which is applicable in the vacuum ultraviolet calls for theoretical calculations of line intensities [10, 14–24]. The intensity ratio of two lines can be computed if certain assumptions are made concerning the state of the plasma and the excitation processes in it.

The intensity ratio $J_{ki}/J_{li}$ is most easily calculated if the plasma is in thermodynamic equilibrium and the self-absorption is low enough for the true intensity ratio to be equal to the apparent intensity (or brightness) ratio of the lines. The concentrations of the excited atoms then follow the Boltzmann distribution and

$$\frac{J_{ki}}{J_{li}} = \frac{g_k}{g_l} \frac{A_{ki}}{A_{li}} \frac{\lambda_{li}}{\lambda_{ik}} e^{-(E_k - E_l)/kT} , \qquad (61)$$

where $g_k$ and $g_l$ are the statistical weights of the upper levels, $A_{ki}$ and $A_{li}$ are the transition probabilities, $\lambda_{li}$ and $\lambda_{ki}$ are the wavelengths, $E_k$ and $E_l$ are the energies of the upper levels, $k$ is Boltzmann's constant, $T$ is the electron temperature. Given the transition probabilities of the corresponding lines, we can find the temperature by measuring their intensity ratio.

The assumption of thermodynamic equilibrium always requires a thorough experimental verification. Mandel'shtam [23] has shown that a linear dependence between $\log (J_{ki}\lambda_{ki}/A_{ki}g_k)$ and $E$ is not a sufficient sign of thermodynamic equilibrium. Moreover, $T$ is usually determined from the strongest lines and there is always a danger of reabsorption. If the temperature is measured from the apparent intensities of two lines, no check of thermodynamic equilibrium can be made, and these measurements are therefore highly questionable.

The above procedure was applied to electron temperature determination of a linear pinch [24]. The machine parameters were as follows: condenser voltage 40 kV, capacitance 36 $\mu$F, inductance $5 \cdot 10^{-7}$ H, hydrogen pressure 0.05 T. The electron temperature determined from various impurity ion lines differed by more than a factor of 2, which clearly establishes the inconsistency of this method. It is apparently applicable only when lines of various elements and ions of various multiplicities give close electron temperatures.

In nonequilibrium plasmas, the intensity ratio can be calculated if some particular excitation mechanism is assumed [25]. For example, ignoring cascade transitions and assuming that all transitions from levels $k$ and $l$ terminate at level $i$ and that the atoms are excited from the ground state, we can show that the intensity ratio

$J_{ki}/J_{li}$ is determined by the number of exciting collisions:

$$\frac{J_{ki}}{J_{li}} = \frac{N_i N_e \lambda_{li} \int\limits_{v_{ik}}^{\infty} Q_{ik}(v) f(v) dv}{N_i N_e \lambda_{ki} \int\limits_{v_{il}}^{\infty} Q_{il}(v) f(v) dv}, \tag{62}$$

where $N_i$ is the concentration of ground state atoms, $N_e$ is the electron concentration, $Q_{ik}(v)$ and $Q_{il}(v)$ are the effective cross sections of the atom for the different collisions, and $f(v)$ is the electron velocity distribution.

Using Seaton's relations [26] for the cross sections and assuming a Maxwellian velocity distribution for the electrons, we get

$$\frac{J_{ki}}{J_{li}} = \frac{A_{ki} g_k}{A_{li} g_l} \frac{E_l}{E_k} \frac{\lambda_{ki}}{\lambda_{li}} e^{-(E_k - E_l)/kT}, \tag{63}$$

(the notation as before, see equation (61)).

The method of relative line intensities has been repeatedly applied to the visible spectrum [17–19]. For example, the intensity ratio of the Fe X and Fe XIV lines made it possible to determine the electron temperature of the solar corona [17]. Kaufman and Williams [18, 19] measured the electron temperature on the Sceptre machine using the relative intensities of C V and B IV lines. The lines whose intensities were measured lay in the near ultraviolet. In the vacuum ultraviolet, this method was applied by Heroux [14, 15], who measured the intensity ratio of two lines with a common lower level and different upper levels. The lines were selected from among the ions in the lithium isoelectronic series. These ions are simple systems for which the line intensities can be computed theoretically with high accuracy. However, even for these systems, the excitation cross sections cannot be determined with sufficient accuracy, and this introduces a source of error.

A higher accuracy in temperature measurements is attained if the upper levels of the comparison lines are very distant from each other. In this case, the lines have markedly different wavelengths and their relative intensities are found by solving a complex problem of heterochromatic photometry in the vacuum ultraviolet (see §33).

Figure 231 plots the ratio $J_{ki}/J_{kl}$ as a function of temperature. It is thus sufficient to determine experimentally the intensity ratio of two lines of ions from the lithium isoelectronic series, and $T_e$ is read off the curve.

In [14], $T_e$ was determined from relative intensities of the N V lines at 1238 Å and 209 Å. These measurements were carried out on the ZETA machine, and the electron temperature was varied from 21 to 25 eV depending on the operating conditions. In measurements of the nitrogen line intensities, the monochromator was calibrated by the method described in §33; alternative calibration techniques included relative

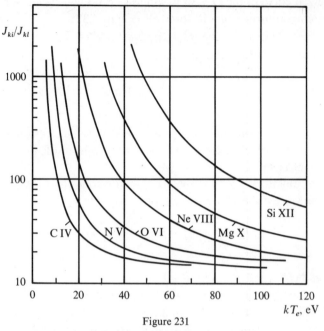

Figure 231

Theoretical ratios of the line intensities corresponding to the transitions $2s\,^2S_{1/2}-2p\,^2P^0_{3/2}$ ($J_{ki}$) and $2s\,^2S_{1/2}-3p\,^2P^0_{1/2,\,3/2}$ ($J_{kl}$) as a function of temperature.

and absolute calibration of the monochromator with a tungsten cathode of known photoelectric quantum yield (see §23).

A similar method of $T_e$ determination was applied by Schwob [16]. He measured the intensity ratio of the N V lines at 1238 Å, 209 Å, and 162 Å. The method will determine temperatures from about 7 eV to 70 eV. At lower temperatures, the intensity ratio of the N V lines is too high, and at higher temperatures it is hardly dependent on temperature. For the 162 Å line ($2s\,^2S_{1/2}-4p\,^2P_{1/2,\,3/2}$) and the 209 Å line, the sensitivity of the method is less than that for the 1238 Å line, but the correction for the change in monochromator transmission is not as significant and can often be omitted. The method was applied to a plasma in the TA-2000 toroidal machine, and the dependence of the electron temperature on pressure was studied.

Hinnov [27] applied the same method to determine the electron temperature in the Stellarator. The electron temperature was measured from O III and O IV lines. Note that these temperature measurements are less reliable than the results of Heroux [14], since the calculation of the O III and O IV excitation cross sections may involve a larger error than the corresponding calculations for the ions of the lithium iso-electronic series. Hinnov's oscillator strengths were also less reliable.

Griem [10] studied in detail some aspects of the application of the method of relative line intensities to electron temperature determination. In particular, he published a theoretical curve of the O V/O VI intensity ratio which can be used to determine electron temperatures from 10 to 40 eV (Figure 232).

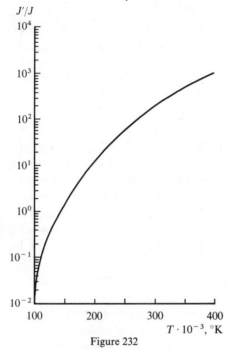

Figure 232

Intensity ratio of the lines O VI (1032 Å) and O V (1371 Å).
$N_e \leq 10^{17} \text{ cm}^{-3}$.

## 45. LINE SHAPES

Measurements of line shapes permit the determination of the temperatures of atoms and ions and the concentrations of charged particles (see, e.g., [21, 28]).

The width of a spectral line emitted by a plasma is determined primarily by the Doppler effect and the Stark effect, although in some cases collisional broadening or broadening through self-absorption may prove significant.*

If the conditions are such that Doppler broadening makes the major contribution, and all the other effects are negligible, the gas temperature can be recovered from the line profile.

The line half-width (the width between half-intensity points) is

$$\Delta\lambda = 7.16 \cdot 10^{-7}\lambda_0 \sqrt{T/\mu}, \tag{64}$$

* See reviews on line broadening [29–31].

where $\lambda_0$ is the wavelength of the relevant line, $T$ is the temperature, $\mu$ is the molecular weight.

We see from this equation that the thermal velocities of the emitting particles can be found if the line half-width has been measured. This method was applied by various authors to measure the thermal velocities of atoms and ions (see, e.g., [21, 32]). In addition to measurements of line widths in the visible spectrum appropriate measurements have been carried out in the vacuum ultraviolet. These measurements were done photographically on ZETA [33] and ALPHA [34] machines and on a linear pinch machine [24]. Measurements in the vacuum ultraviolet are essential because the strong lines of multiply charged ions fall in this particular spectral region. Measurements on the ALPHA machine [34] have shown that the half-widths increase with the increase in the ionic charge. This tendency was confirmed by measurements of line half-widths in the vacuum ultraviolet.

The line profile gives the electron concentration if the half-width is primarily determined by the Stark broadening. At high electron concentrations ($N_e > 10^{17} \text{cm}^{-3}$) and moderate temperatures ($T < 10^{5\circ}\text{K}$), the shape of most lines is insignificantly distorted by Doppler broadening. At the line wings, the line profile is determined exclusively by the Stark effect (even when Doppler broadening is comparable with Stark broadening). The electron concentrations are mostly determined from hydrogen lines, which are characterized by a linear Stark effect.

The theory of Stark broadening of the hydrogen lines was developed in some detail by Griem et al. [10, 35, 36], who introduced substantial corrections to Holtsmark's theory [37]. Griem's theory was applied to tabulate the theoretical shapes of hydrogen lines ($H_\alpha$, $H_\beta$, $H_\gamma$, $H_\delta$, $L_\alpha$, $L_\beta$) at various electron temperatures and concentrations [10].

Other tables, based on Griem's theory, are also available [38]. These tables give the electron concentration as a function of the line widths of $L_\alpha$, $L_\beta$, $H_\alpha$, $H_\beta$, $H_\gamma$, $H_\delta$.

In order to find the electron concentration from tables, we first have to plot the experimental line profile or find its half-width. The temperature has but a slight effect on the Stark line width, but in more exact investigations the temperature must be determined independently. The simultaneous effect of Doppler and Stark broadening and the shapes of various hydrogen lines, $L_\alpha$ included, are discussed in [39].

The $L_\alpha$ and $L_\beta$ line shapes were calculated and compared with experimental findings [36]. The $L_\alpha$ line shape provides an excellent means of checking the theory of collisional broadening of lines. Indeed, two thirds of the total intensity of this line are concentrated in components which are not shifted by random fields, and these components are therefore affected only by electron collisions. The $L_\beta$ line, on the other hand, has no unshifted component, and the correction for electron collisions is therefore negligible: the entire line shape is determined by quasistatic ionic fields. The central parts of resonance lines are greatly distorted by reabsorption, and the theory therefore can be checked only for the line wings. Verification of the theory requires plasma close to local thermodynamic equilibrium. Partly ionized helium plasma was used in the experiments; the plasma was excited in a shock tube 75 cm long, 24 mm in diameter, with initial gas pressure of 40 T.

Comparison of the helium line intensity with the intensity of the adjoining continuum gave temperatures of about 20,000°K. The electron density determined from absolute measurements of the continuum intensity was found to be $3 \cdot 10^{17} \mathrm{cm}^{-3}$. The reproducibility of the flashes was exceptionally good, and the individual points of the line profile could be recovered from different flashes.

The $L_\alpha$ and $L_\beta$ line shapes were determined using a normal-incidence vacuum monochromator with a grating of 2.2 m radius of curvature and 3.75 Å/mm reciprocal dispersion. The long-wave wing of the line was measured, since the short-wave wing is greatly distorted by overlapping of the Si III line. Exact measurements were begun at a distance of $-2$ Å from the line center, and readings were taken each 0.25 Å in the direction of increasing wavelengths. The $L_\alpha$ line shape without any corrections is shown in Figure 233 for a hydrogen pressure of 0.015 T. The cold wall layers produce reabsorption and thus lead to a dip at the line center. The line profile was corrected by introducing reabsorption and background corrections. We see from the

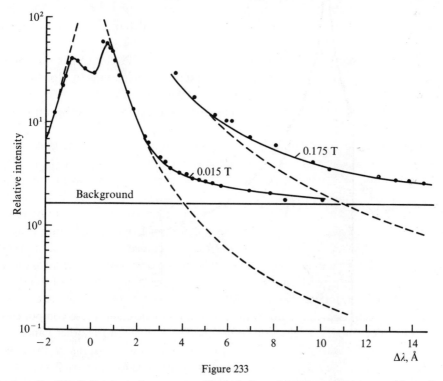

Figure 233

Stark profile of the $L_\alpha$ line for various pressures (the dashed curves are line profiles corrected for reabsorption and background).

figure that the background is exceptionally strong, and the accuracy (especially far from the line center) is very low. To improve the measurement accuracy, the line shapes were studied for hydrogen pressure of 0.175 T and measurements were made from +4 Å to +16 Å from the line center (Figure 233).

The Stark half-width was calculated to be 0.15 Å, and the Doppler half-width 0.12 Å. Doppler broadening substantially distorts the Stark dispersion contour only at distances less than a few tenths of an angstrom from the line center, i.e., its effect on the line wings is negligible. Figure 234 gives a comparison of the theoretical contours with experimental results. The fit is quite adequate. The theoretical contours were calculated for $\Delta\lambda < 2.5$ Å with an accuracy of 10% from the relations of [35]

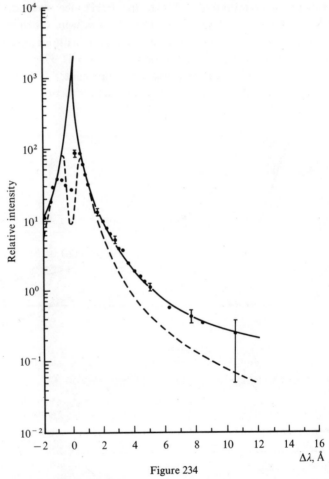

Figure 234

Comparison of the theoretical $L_\alpha$ profiles with experimental (dashed curve—from Holtsmark's theory, solid curve—Elton and Griem's theory, dots—experimental data).

and for $\Delta\lambda > 2$ Å using the asymptotic expression from [40]. A good fit between theory and experiment is also observed for the $L_\beta$ line.

The $L_\alpha$ line shape was also measured by Boldt and Cooper [41]. The aim of their work was to determine the $L_\alpha$ absorption coefficient. They used a Maecker carbon arc described in §6 [42]. The arc burnt in a mixture of hydrogen and argon. The current reached 80–89 A, and the total pressure of the mixture was 1 atm. The plasma was in thermal equilibrium. The spectrum was recorded on a one-meter vacuum monochromator. A photomultiplier with a sodium salicylate screen was used as a detector. The observations were made in reflected light, so that the scattering effects were reduced (the scattered intensity near $L_\alpha$ was 2.5% of the peak intensity). The central part of the line was highly distorted by reabsorption. The absorption coefficient was therefore measured at distances from 3 to 12 Å from the line center.

The brightness $B_\lambda$ of the $L_\alpha$ line emitted by a layer of equilibrium plasma of thickness $l$ is expressible in terms of the blackbody radiation brightness $b_\lambda$ (see, e.g., [43]):

$$B_\lambda = b_\lambda(1 - e^{-\mu_\lambda l}), \qquad (65)$$

where

$$b_\lambda = \frac{2hc^2}{\lambda^5} (e^{hc/\lambda kT} - 1)^{-1},$$

$\mu_\lambda$ is the absorption coefficient at wavelength $\lambda$, corresponding to hydrogen atom concentration $n_H$.

Using (65), we can find the absorption coefficient at any hydrogen pressure (if the concentration of hydrogen atoms is known).

The concentration of hydrogen atoms is determined from the total partial pressures of hydrogen and argon and from the partial pressure of argon at zero hydrogen concentration. The arc temperature is inferred from the absolute intensities of the argon lines in the visible spectrum and from the absolute intensity of the continuum. The temperatures derived from various lines all cluster around 12,000°K; the electron density was found to be about $8.4 \cdot 10^{16}$ cm$^{-3}$.

The $L_\alpha$ absorption coefficient does not quite correspond to its calculated value [35, 37, 40, 44]. The best fit is observed between the experiment and Griem's theory [40].

## 46. IMPURITY EMISSIONS IN HOT-PLASMA MACHINES

The emission of impurities in a gas has been studied in considerable detail in different spectral regions by various authors. These studies also have been carried out in the vacuum ultraviolet, where the strong lines of most multiply charged ions are observed. For example, Burton and Wilson [45, 46] used the ZETA machine to study the time sweeps of a number of resonance lines: $L_\alpha$, C IV (1548 Å), N V (1239 Å), O VI (1032 Å), Ar I (1067 Å), Ar II (920 Å), Ar III (883 Å), Ar IV (801 Å), Ar V (827 Å),

Ar VI (597 Å), Ar VII (586 Å), Ar VIII (700 Å). The time sweeps revealed a number of regular features; for example, the oscillograms of the O VI, N V, C IV and $L_\alpha$ lines showed that the line intensities of these ions reach their maximum after the intensity of $L_\alpha$ starts decreasing, i.e., when hydrogen is completely ionized. The intensity of the O VI line is the last to attain its maximum, and the oscillogram even shows a second maximum, associated with the injection of impurities from the walls.

Figure 235 shows oscillograms of the spectral lines of atomic and ionized argon; the higher the ionic charge, the later is the maximum.

Time sweeps of various spectral lines were also studied on the Stellarator. Figure 236 shows that $L_\beta$ is the first line to be emitted, followed by O II, O III, O IV, and O V [27].

The time variation of the line intensities of multiply charged ions has been studied on other machines also [8, 9, 47–52]. It has been established in all cases that most

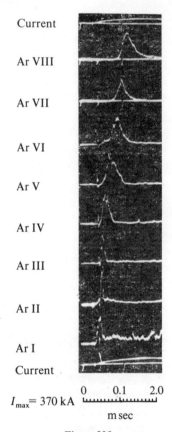

Current

Ar VIII

Ar VII

Ar VI

Ar V

Ar IV

Ar III

Ar II

Ar I

Current

$I_{max}$ = 370 kA

0    0.1    2.0

m sec

Figure 235

Time sweep of the intensity of argon lines A I through A VIII.
The intensities·of $L$ and ionized oxygen lines as a function of time.

spectral lines are at a minimum intensity when the current is at its maximum. A similar trend is observed for the time sweep of the integrated emission of the discharge between 2200 and 6000 Å. The intensity is minimum when the current is maximum. [48].

As the current increases, the electron temperature rises and the line intensities of the multiply charged ions correspondingly become higher. On the BETA machine, the dip in the $B = f(t)$ oscillograms is less for the O VI line than for the O V line, and there is apparently no dip for the O VII line.* On the Scylla machine [8], the dip in the O VI line corresponds to the peak intensity of the O VII line.

The higher the ionic charge, the shorter the wavelengths of the corresponding spectral lines. It is therefore worthwhile to isolate with a filter a narrow interval of wavelengths in the X-ray spectrum and to take a time sweep of the radiation inside that interval. In this case, there will apparently be no emission minimum at the time of maximum current. Time sweeps of spectral lines of multiply charged ions can also be obtained photographically [9].

The intensity time sweeps of spectral lines can be converted to time curves of ion concentrations [27]. To this end, the absolute apparent intensities of individual spectral lines are measured and the theoretical line intensity $J_{ki}$ is determined. The calculations use the equation

$$ J_{ki} = N_e N_i \frac{1}{\lambda_{ki}} \int_{v_{ik}}^{\infty} Q_{ik}(v) f(v) dv . \tag{66} $$

All these calculations are highly approximate.

This method was applied to study the variation of the oxygen ion concentration during a single pulse on the Stellarator [27] (Figure 237). The total concentration of oxygen increases over a few microseconds from the ignition time to about 4%.

The impurity radiation has a considerable effect on the energy budget of the machine [27, 53–56]. Almost the entire energy injected into the discharge may be lost in this way. This conclusion is based on theoretical calculations and has been confirmed experimentally, although the reliability of these experiments is questionable [57–60]. For example, in [59, 60] these experiments were carried out ignoring the spectrograph transmission. Other experiments are semiqualitative at their best.

On the Perhapsatron, a bolometer measured an energy loss amounting to 80% of the total energy injected from the current source [57]. The energy distribution in the spectrum was measured with filters. These experiments have established that 98% of the total emission are concentrated between 100 and 1000 Å. Tokamak experiments with a suitable filter [58] have established that 50% of the total emission is radiated at wavelengths shorter than 2000 Å.

---

* The O VII line was not registered on the BETA machine [48].

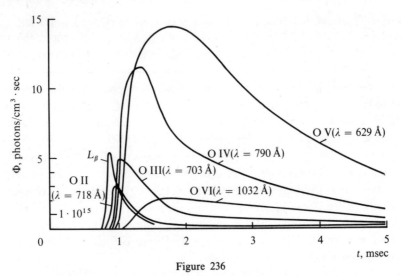

Figure 236

The intensities of $L_\beta$ and ionized oxygen lines as a function of time.

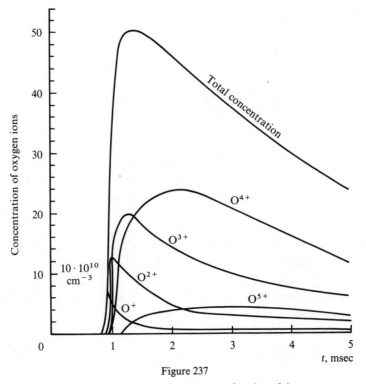

Figure 237

The concentration of oxygen ions as a function of time.

# 47. PLASMA PROBING WITH SHORT-WAVE ULTRAVIOLET RADIATION

The absorption of radiation in plasma in the visible and the near ultraviolet has been studied in a number of experimental works. Ladenburg [61] studied the absorption spectrum of the positive column, Garton and Rajaratnam [62, 63] studied the arc absorption spectrum. This method gives the concentration of the excited atoms in the discharge if the oscillator strengths of the spectral lines are known.

The transparency of an impulsive discharge plasma to visible radiation from a pulsed source has been studied by Rozhdestvenskii's method of anomalous dispersion (the hook method), and the concentration of the excited atoms has been determined in this way [64]. Recordings of absorption spectra taken with excellent time resolution make it possible to investigate the discharge mechanism.

Transmission studies of this kind were also carried out in the vacuum ultraviolet. The degree of ionization of xenon in a shock tube was determined in this way [65, 66]. The method is based on the following relation, which applies to a mixture of several absorbing components:

$$\ln \frac{\Phi_{0\lambda}}{\Phi_\lambda} = \sum n_i \sigma_{\lambda_i} l, \tag{67}$$

where $n_i$ is the concentration of the $i$-th component in the plasma, $\Phi_{0\lambda}$ and $\Phi_\lambda$ are the incident light flux and the transmitted light flux, respectively, $\sigma_{\lambda_i}$ is the photoionization cross section of the $i$-th component at wavelength $\lambda_i$, $l$ is the length of the absorbing column.

Let the number of normal xenon atoms before the ignition of the discharge be $n_0$. Suppose the plasma is made up of two components: normal xenon atoms ($n_1$) and singly charged xenon ions ($n^+$). We can then choose two wavelengths $\lambda_1$ and $\lambda_2$ so that the radiation of wavelength $\lambda_1$ is not absorbed by the singly charged xenon atoms and the radiation of wavelength $\lambda_2$ is absorbed by both species. Then we have

$$\left.\begin{array}{ll} \ln\left(\dfrac{\Phi_{01}}{\Phi_1}\right) = \sigma_1 n_0 l, & \ln\left(\dfrac{\Phi_{02}}{\Phi_2}\right) = \sigma_2 n_0 l, \\[4mm] \ln\left(\dfrac{\Phi'_{01}}{\Phi'_1}\right) = \sigma_1 n_1 l, & \ln\left(\dfrac{\Phi'_{02}}{\Phi'_2}\right) = \sigma_2 n_1 l + \sigma_2^+ n^+ l, \end{array}\right\} \tag{68}$$

where $\Phi_{01}$ and $\Phi_1$ are the incident light flux and the light flux transmitted through the absorbing gas at wavelength $\lambda_1$ in the absence of discharge, $\Phi'_{01}$ and $\Phi'_1$ are the incident and the transmitted fluxes after the ignition of the discharge; the same notation is used for wavelength $\lambda_2$.

Equations (67) and (68) can be solved for $n^+\sigma_2^+/n_0\sigma_2$. To find $n^+$, we have to measure $n_0$ and $\sigma_2$, whereas $\sigma_2^+$ is assumed known from theoretical calculations [66].

A different approach is also possible: $n^+$ is found independently, and then absorption measurements give $\sigma_2^+$. Once $\sigma_2^+$ has been determined, $n^+$ can be measured under any experimental conditions. This method [65, 66] has been put to work on an experimental setup shown in Figure 238.

Transmission measurements were made with the light from a discharge in a ceramic capillary [67]; the voltage was 8 kV, source pressure 0.2 T, $C = 1\ \mu F$, the discharge was ignited in a mixture of air and argon. The absorption was measured at two wavelengths, $\lambda_1 = 760\ \text{Å}$, $\lambda_2 = 555\ \text{Å}$. Radiation of wavelength $\lambda_1$ is absorbed by atomic xenon only, whereas radiation of wavelength $\lambda_2$ is absorbed by both neutral atoms and singly charged ions (the ionization limit of xenon is at 575 Å).

A U-shaped shock tube was used in these experiments, and the time sweeps of the absorption spectrum of the gas in the shock tube were recorded. The data plotted in Figure 239 were obtained for a shock wave velocity $v = 0.27\ \text{cm}/\mu\text{sec}$ and a pressure of 0.27 T. The observations were begun 18 $\mu$sec before the shock. We see from Figure 239 that $n_1$ has a maximum at the shock, whereas the maximum ionization is attained only a few microseconds later. After 2 $\mu$sec, the degree of ionization is found to be 15%.

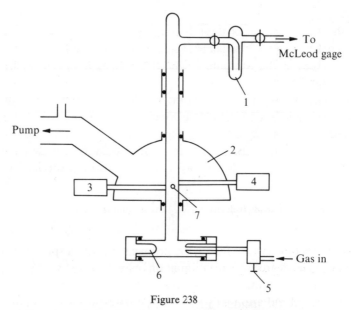

Figure 238

Experimental setup for taking the absorption spectrum of a plasma:

1) liquid nitrogen trap,   2) differential pumpout chamber,   3,4) photomultipliers,   5) needle valve, 6) electrode,   7) 1 mm aperture accommodating the optical axis (perpendicular to the plane of the drawing).

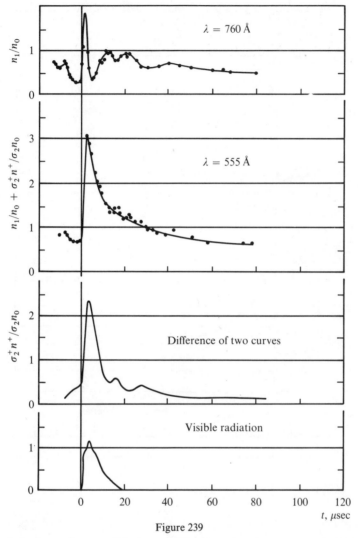

Figure 239

A shock wave in xenon (velocity $v = 0.27$ cm/$\mu$sec, initial pressure $p = 0.27$ T).

Figure 240 shows time sweeps for a wave propagating with a speed of 0.47 cm/$\mu$sec at 0.1 T pressure. The degree of ionization in this case is substantially higher.

The above examples show that transmission measurements of a plasma using short-wave ultraviolet radiation may give the concentration of ions in the discharge. The ion concentration probably also can be determined from linear absorption measurements. Linear absorption is additionally applied to investigate the degree of dissociation of molecules in the discharge.

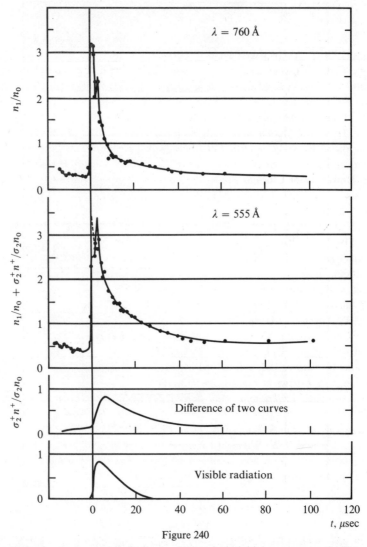

Figure 240

A shock wave in xenon (velocity $v = 0.47$ cm/$\mu$sec, initial pressure $p = 0.1$ T).

The absorption of radiation in plasmas has been used in studies of reaction kinetics in high-temperature air heated by a shock wave [68]. Variation of the absorption coefficient of the plasma at 1470 Å gave the rate of dissociation of oxygen as a function of temperature.

# BIBLIOGRAPHY

1. ELWERT, G. *Z. Naturforsch.,* **9a**, 637 (1954).
2. ALLEN, C.W. *Astrophysical Quantities.* Univ. of London, Athlone Press. 1955.
3. KOGAN, V.I. and A.B. MIGDAL, In: *Fizika plazmy i problema upravlyaemykh termoya-dernykh reaktsii,* **1**, 172. Izdatel'stvo AN SSSR. 1958.
4. ALLER, L.H. *Astrophysics,* **1**. London, George Ronald. 1953.
5. GRIEM, H.R., A.C. KOLB, and W.R. FAUST. *Phys. Rev. Lett.,* **2**, 281 (1959).
6. STRATTON, T.F. *Spectrometric Determination of Electron Temperatures above* **100** *ev, in Optical Spectrometric Measurements of High Temperatures,* P.J. Dickerman, Editor, p. 99 University of Chicago Press, 1961.
7. SAWYER, G.A., F.C. JAHODA, F.L. RIBE, and T.F. STRATTON. *J. Quant Spectr. Rad. Trans.,* **2**, 467 (1962).
8. JAHODA, F.C., E.M. LITTLE, W.E. QUINN, G.A. SAWYER, and T.F. STRATTON. *Phys. Rev.,* **119**, 843 (1960).
9. GABRIEL, A.H., G.B.F. NIBLETT, and N.J. PEACOCK. *J. Quant. Spectr. Rad. Trans.,* **2**, 491 (1962).
10. GRIEM, H.R. *Plasma Spectroscopy.* New York, 1964.
11. McWHIRTER, R.W.P. *Bull. Amer. Phys. Soc.,* **8**, 164 (1963).
12. PAGE, T. *Astrophys. J.,* **96**, 78 (1942).
13. SEATON, M.J. *Monthly Notices Roy. Astron. Soc.,* **115**, 279 (1955).
14. HEROUX, L. *Proc. Phys. Soc.,* **83**, 121 (1964).
15. HEROUX, L. *Nature,* **198**, 1291 (1963).
16. SCHWOB, J.L. *J. phys. et radium,* **25**, 713 (1964).
17. SHKLOVSKII, I.S. *Fizika solnechnoi korony (Physics of the Solar Corona).* Fizmatgiz. 1962.
18. WILLIAMS, R.W. and S. KAUFMAN. *Proc. Phys. Soc.,* **75**, 329 (1960).
19. KAUFMAN, S. and R.W. WILLIAMS. *Nature,* **182**, 557 (1958).
20. THONEMANN, P.C. *The Measurement of Ultra-High Temperatures,* P.J. Dickerman, Editor, p. 56. University of Chicago Press, 1961.
21. ZAIDEL', A.N., G.M. MALYSHEV, and E. YA. SHREIDER. *ZhTF,* **31**, 129 (1961).
22. ZAIDEL, A.N., G.M. MALYSHEV, and E.A. PTITSYNA. *ZhTF,* **33**, 200 (1963).
23. MANDEL'SHTAM, S.L. *Izvestiya AN SSSR,* phys. ser., **26**, 848 (1962).
24. PIS'MENNYI, V.D., I.M. PODGORNYI, and SH. SUKEVER. *ZhETF,* **43**, 2008 (1962).
25. FRISH, S.E. *Opticheskie spektry atomov (Optical Spectra of Atoms).* Fizmatgiz. 1963.
26. SEATON, M.J. In: *Atomic and Molecular Processes,* D.R. Bates, Editor. N.Y., London, Academic Press. 1962.
27. HINNOV, E. *Phys. Fluids,* **7**, 130 (1964).
28. McNALLY, J.R. *J. Opt. Soc. America,* **49**, 328 (1959).
29. SOBEL'MAN, I.I. *Uspekhi Fizicheskikh Nauk,* **54**, 551 (1954).
30. BARANGER, M. In: *Atomic and Molecular Processes,* D.R. Bates, Editor. N.Y., London, Academic Press. 1962.
31. UNSÖLD, A. *Physik der Sternatmosphären, mit besonderer Berücksichtigung der Sonne.* [Russian translation of 1st edition, 1951] [2nd edition, Berlin, Springer. 1955.]

32. FRISH, S.E. and YU.M. KAGAN. *Vestnik LGU,* No. 1, 12 (1948).
33. KHARDING, G.N. *Radiotekhnika i Elektronika,* **4**, 1326 (1959).
34. ZAIDEL', A.N., G.M. MALYSHEV, E.YA. SHREIDER, V.A. BELYAEVA, A.B. BEREZIN, V.I. GLADUSHAK, V.V. SKIDAN, and L.V. SOKOLOVA. *ZhTF,* **30**, 1422 (1960).
35. GRIEM, H.R., A.C. KOLB, and K.Y. SHEN. *Phys. Rev.,* **116**, 4 (1959).
36. ELTON, R.C. and H.R. GRIEM. *Phys. Rev.,* **135**, 1550 (1964).
37. HOLTSMARK, J. *Ann. Phys.,* **58**, 577 (1919).
38. HILL, R.A. *J. Quant. Spectr. Rad. Trans.,* **4**, 857 (1964).
39. HANSEN, C.F. *J. Opt. Soc. America,* **54**, 1198 (1964).
40. GRIEM, H.R. *Astrophys. J.,* **136**, 422 (1962).
41. BOLDT, G. and W.S. COOPER. *Z. Naturforsch.,* **19a**, 968 (1964).
42. BOLDT, G. *Proc. V. Int. Conf. Ionizat. Phenom. Gases,* 1961, I, 925.
43. UNSÖLD, A. *Physik der Sternatmosphären.* Berlin, Springer. 1955.
44. MOZER, B. and M. BARANGER. *Phys. Rev.,* **118**, 626 (1960).
45. BURTON, W.M. and R. WILSON. *Proc. Phys. Soc.,* **78**, 1416 (1961).
46. WILSON, R. *J. Quant. Spectr. Rad. Trans.,* **2**, 477 (1962).
47. FAWCETT, B.C., B.B. JONES, and R. WILSON. *Proc. Phys. Soc.,* **78**, 1223 (1961).
48. AVERIN, V.G., M.A. MAZING, and A.I. PISANKO. *ZhETF,* **41**, 42 (1961).
49. AVERIN, N.G., M.A. MAZING, and A.I. PISANKO. *ZhTF,* **34**, 767 (1964).
50. ZAIDEL', A.N., G.M. MALYSHEV, A.B. BEREZIN, and G.T. RAZDOBARIN. *ZhTF,* **30**, 1437 (1960).
51. BRETON, C. and L. HERMAN. *Proc. IV. Int. Conf. Ioniz. Phenom. Gases,* 1959, p. 17.
52. SCHWOB, J.L., N. DAMANY-ASTOIN, and C. BRETON. *J. phys. et radium,* **23**, 586 (1962).
53. KOLB, A.C. and R.W.P. MCWHIRTER. *Phys. Fluids,* **7**, 519 (1964).
54. KNORR, G. *Z. Naturforsch.,* **13a**, 941 (1958).
55. KOGAN, V.I. *Doklady AN SSSR,* **128**, 702 (1959).
56. MCWHIRTER, R.W.P. *J. Phys. Soc.,* **75**, 520 (1960).
57. KARR, H.I., E.A. KNAPP, and J.E. OSHER. *Univ. of Calif., Los Alamos, New Mexico (Report).* 1960.
58. DOLGOV-SAVEL'EV. G.G., V.S. MUKHORATOR, V.S. STRELKOV, M.N. SHEPELEV, and N.A. YAVLINSKII. *ZhETF,* **38**, 394 (1960).
59. KIRILLOV, V.D. *ZhTF,* **30**, 320 (1960).
60. KIRILLOV, V.D. *ZhETF,* **37**, 1142 (1959).
61. LADENBURG, R. *Uspekhi Fizicheskih Nauk,* **14**, 721 (1934).
62. GARTON, W.R.S. In: *Na poroge v kosmos,* p. 218. IL. 1960.
63. GARTON, W.R.S. and A. RAJARATNAM. *Proc. Phys. Soc.,* **A70**, 815 (1957).
64. EGOROV, V.S., YU.G. and A.M. SHUKHTIN. *Optika i Spektroskopiya,* **17**, 154 (1964).
65. WEISSLER, G.L. *J. Quant. Spectr. Rad. Trans.,* **2**, 383 (1962).
66. BLACKWELL, H.E., G.S. BAJWA, G.S. SHIPP, and G.L. WEISSLER. *J. Quant. Spectr. Rad. Trans.,* **4**, 249 (1964).
67. WAINFAN, N., W.C. WALKER and G.L. WEISSLER. *J. Appl. Phys.,* **24**, 1318 (1953).
68. KIVEL, B. *J. Quant. Spectr. Rad. Trans.,* **2**, 509 (1962).

CHAPTER X

# The Short-Wave Radiation of the Sun

## 48. THE SOLAR SPECTRUM

The Sun is the only celestial object whose energy flux at the Earth is sufficient for detailed spectroscopic studies of the short-wave radiation using the currently limited instrumental means provided by rockets and satellites.

Nevertheless, the short-wave radiation of such extended celestial objects as the night sky, nebulae, and planets can also be measured. The few studies in this direction deal mainly with the twilight sky, and are thus essentially studies of the solar spectrum scattered in the upper atmosphere and of atmospheric luminescence excited by the solar radiation. There is also a small number of spectroscopic studies of radiation from stars, some using ionization chambers to record the radiation in narrow spectral intervals [1–4]. An interesting result of these studies is the discovery that only early-type stars (mainly B-type stars) emit short-wave radiation between 1300 and 1500 Å. No agreement was observed between the theoretically predicted stellar luminosities and the experimental results.

Stellar spectra at wavelengths shorter than 3000 Å were first observed by Stecher and Milligan [5, 6]. The observations were carried out with a high-speed instrument and a quartz-window photomultiplier. The energy distribution in the continuous spectrum was recorded between 4000 and 1600 Å. The luminous fluxes reached considerable values for seven stars only. For all the early-type stars the fluxes at wavelengths shorter than 2400 Å were less than the theoretical predictions. This

351

result is of considerable interest for unraveling the mysteries of stellar radiation processes.

Without full-scale observatories on the Moon, we cannot hope to obtain in the near future any detailed information on the short-wave radiation of stars, as this requires high-precision instrument guiding, long exposures, and large condenser mirrors. Spectroscopic work in the vacuum ultraviolet is therefore still confined mainly to the Sun.

The Earth's atmosphere absorbs most of the radiation at wavelengths shorter than 2900 Å. At wavelengths between 2900 and 2000 Å, the solar radiation is absorbed by the atmospheric ozone, whose concentration maximum is observed at 25 km, although substantial quantities of this gas are detected at altitudes up to 100 km. Radiation with wavelengths shorter than 2000 Å is absorbed by oxygen, nitrogen, and other atmospheric gases.* Therefore, the first photographs of the solar spectrum in the short ultraviolet region ($\lambda < 2900$ Å) were obtained with rocket-borne spectrographs. The first spectrogram was taken from a rocket on 10 October 1946 [8]. It recorded the visible and the ultraviolet spectrum to $\lambda = 2100$ Å. The spectrogram was obtained at an altitude of 55 km. The aim of later work was to advance deeper into the short-wave region. Deficient instrumentation, however, permitted recording only the strongest spectral lines, such as $L_\alpha$ [9, 10].

Solar spectrograms were obtained using a two-axis tracking system which pointed the spectrograph toward the source of light regardless of the orientation of the rocket [11]. The American photographs were mostly taken from Aerobee rockets, which reached altitudes not exceeding 230 km; the duration of each recording was 4–5 min. At 230 km altitude, the atmospheric absorption is still considerable. Thus, the $L_y$ line (972.5 Å) is markedly absorbed, since its wavelength nearly coincides with the wavelength of the edge of the nitrogen band (972.1 Å).

The first clear photograph of the solar spectrum in the vacuum ultraviolet was taken on 21 February 1955 [12]. The optical system is shown in Figure 138. The scattered light was suppressed with the aid of a diaphragm and a filter which covered the image of the zero-order spectrum. To avoid defocusing, the spectrograph was thermostated. On the ground, the spectrograph was filled with helium, and during the flight of the rocket the helium leaked through the spectrograph at pressures above atmospheric.

The solar spectrum was photographed at an altitude of 115 km with a maximum exposure of 30 sec, using Eastman IVO-UV and SWR film. The photographs show a continuum extending up to 1500 Å. A total of 40 lines were identified, including the lines of H, He II, C I, C II, C III, C IV, N V, O I, O VI, Al II, Si II, Si III, Si IV, S II, Fe II, P II. The strongest line was $L_\alpha$.

The spectrum photographed during the rocket launch of 6 August 1957 is described

---

* On the absorption in the upper atmosphere see [7] and §39 of this book.

in [13] and [14]. The spectrograph used an aluminum replica with a radius of curvature of 39 cm and 600 lines/mm. The incidence angle was 49.5°, slit width 6 microns, SWR film. The spectrum was photographed at altitudes of 95, 110, 130, 140, and 150 km using various exposures from 1.5 to 90 sec. The photographs recorded the spectral region from 1000 to 1900 Å. The spectrograms show a continuous spectrum extending to 1650 Å. The continuum intensity was estimated very crudely for two wavelengths, 1720 and 1800 Å. The observed intensity at 1720 Å was 15% of the blackbody brightness at 5800 °K. At 1800 Å the radiation intensity was 75% of the blackbody brightness at this temperature. The number of observed lines was the same as in [12]. The half-widths of the strongest lines were measured, but the results are highly tentative, as the line shapes were markedly distorted by instrumental broadening. The half-width of the $L_\alpha$ line was found to be 0.80 Å, and that of the He II line (1640 Å) 0.30 Å. Rough line intensity comparison showed that $L_\alpha$ was the brightest line, followed by the Si II lines at 1808.0 Å and 1816.9 Å.

Photographs of the solar spectrum taken on 4 June 1958 and 30 March 1959 from rockets at altitudes greater than 200 km are described in [15]. The region from 80 to 1216 Å was photographed. A grazing-incidence spectrograph was used ($\alpha = 85°$), with a toroidal mirror in front of the slit; the grating was ruled with 600 lines/mm and had a radius of curvature of 49.8 cm. A total of 147 lines were recorded, of which 73 were identified. Most of the recorded lines correspond to highly ionized atoms, and the very appearance of the spectrum is close to the spectrum of a discharge observed in a hot-plasma machine in the laboratory.

It has been noted [16, 17] that some of the lines recorded in [15] were given an erroneous identification, since they apparently belong to spectra of higher orders. It is further noted that because of defective film, other errors could have crept into the wavelength determinations. For example, the spectrograms obtained in [15] did not show the high terms of the Lyman series, although other authors observed these terms under identical conditions [16].

Neither the wavelength measurements of [15] nor the detailed identification of the spectrum published in [18] have been confirmed by other authorities, and their reliability is thus highly questionable.

Clear spectra between 584 and 2110 Å were obtained on 13 March 1959 at an altitude of 198 km [16, 19]. The same spectrograph with a toroidal quartz mirror as in [12] was used. The grating was coated with a layer of germanium, topped by a layer of $Al_2O_3$ of such thickness that the reflection coefficient at 4000 Å was virtually zero. Nine lines of the Lyman series were identified in the spectrum and the lines of He I, He II, C II, C III, C IV, N I, N II, N III, N IV, N V, O I, O II, O III, O IV, O V, O VI, Ne VIII, Mg X, Al II, Si II, Si III, Si IV, P I, P II, P III, P IV, P V, S II, S VI, Fe II.

A good photograph of the solar spectrum was obtained on 19 April 1960 at an altitude of 220 km [19, 20]. This was the first photograph not distorted by the scattered light fog. Tousey remarked that "for the first time everything that we see here is real" [21]. The photograph covered the wavelengths from 500 to 1550 Å; a two-grating spectrograph was used (§18, Figure 131). Figure 241 shows photographs of these spectra. The continuum extends to 1000 Å, but it is relatively weak. The photographs also show some 200 lines which belong to H I, He II, Li I, Be I, C I, C II, C III, C IV, N I, N II, N III, N IV, N V, O I, O II, O III, O IV, O V, O VI, Ne VIII, Na I, Mg I, Mg II, Mg X, Al II, Al III, Si I, Si II, Si III, Si IV, Si XII, S I, S II, S III, S IV, S V, S VI.

A spectrograph with crossed gratings was launched on a rocket on 22 August 1962. Gratings with 1200 and 2400 lines/mm were used, giving resolutions of 0.1 Å between 2000 and 800 Å, where the continuous spectrum was also recorded [22].

Wavelengths shorter than 700 Å were recorded with a grazing-incidence spectrograph (α = 85°) launched on rockets on 22 June 1961, 22 August 1962, and 11 May 1963 [22, 23]. This spectrograph used a platinum-coated aluminum replica with a radius of curvature of 40 cm, ruled with 600 lines/mm. An aluminum film absorbing all radiation with wavelengths above 800 Å was mounted in front of the spectrograph slit. All interference from scattered long-wave radiation was thus avoided.

The lines were recorded in the spectral region from 45 to 700 Å; the region from 45 to 170 Å was substantially attenuated by the absorption of the aluminum film in this region. The resolution reached 0.3 Å. The identified lines include those of He II, O VI, Fe XV, C VI, and others.

The unique advantage of the photoelectric spectrum recording techniques in the vacuum ultraviolet is that the photocathodes are insensitive to long-wave radiation and all interference from long-wave scattered radiation is thus effectively eliminated

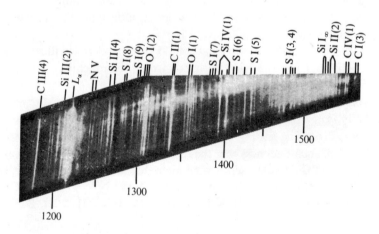

Figure 241a

The solar spectrum photographed on 19 April 1960, wavelengths 1200–1500 Å.

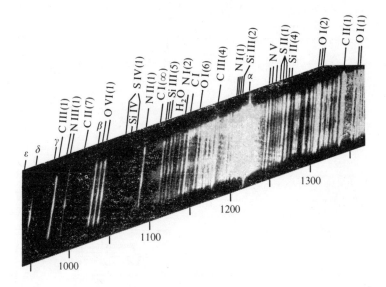

Figure 241*b*

The solar spectrum photographed on 19 April 1960, wavelengths 900–1400 Å.

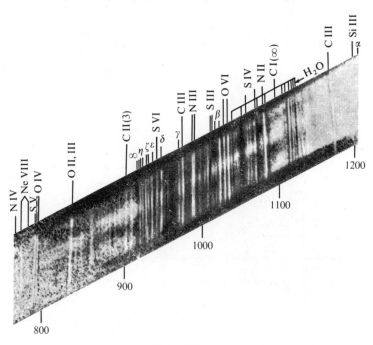

Figure 241*c*

The solar spectrum photographed on 19 April 1960, wavelengths 800–1200 Å.

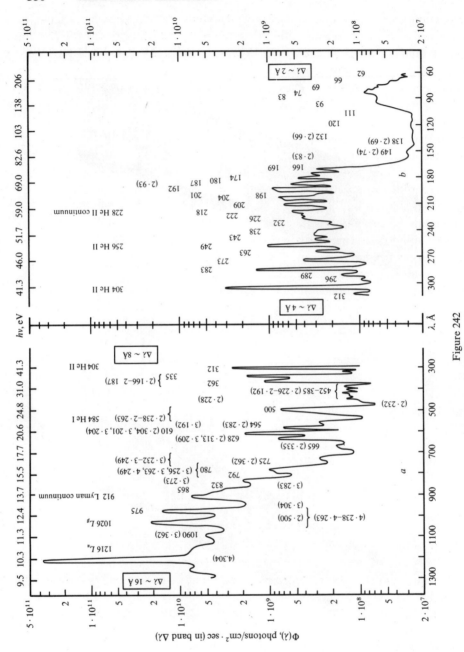

Figure 242

Fluxes of the extreme ultraviolet emission of the Sun in the upper atmosphere:

*a* data obtained on 19 January 1960 at an altitude of 210 km, *b* data obtained on 29 January 1960 at an altitude of 225 km. Figures in parentheses correspond to lines recorded in 2nd and 3rd orders.

(see §23). Hinteregger devised a photoelectric spectrometer with telemetry for the short-wave region of the spectrum [24–30]. The spectrometer was launched in a rocket on 12 March 1959, 19 January 1960, 29 January 1960, 23 July 1960, 23 August 1961, and 2 May 1963 to altitudes of 120–235 km.

A gold-coated grating with a 4° blaze angle was used in [27]. This ensured high efficiency at short wavelengths: 27% at 300 Å, 31% at 250 Å, and 7% at 100 Å. A magnetic focusing photomultiplier served as a radiation detector (see §23). The photocathode was lithium fluoride on a glass base. This photocathode is virtually insensitive to radiation with wavelengths greater than 1100 Å: its quantum yield is 0.3% at $L_\alpha$ and 45% at 584 Å [31]. The energy distribution in the solar spectrum was measured with this spectrometer. A detailed description of the calibration of the entire setup is given in [29]. A tungsten cathode of known quantum yield and an additional monochromator were used for calibration (see §34).

The telemetering monochromator recorded the solar spectrum between 60 and 1300 Å. Numerous lines were recorded in this region, and the solar flux in the continuous spectrum was measured.

The photoelectric intensity measurements are much more reliable than the photographic techniques. Photoelectric spectrum tracings are given in Figure 242. The tracings show the lines of C IV, N V, O VI, Ne VIII, Mg X, Si XII, Fe XVI, and others. These spectra are in good agreement with the photographic results.

The measurements were carried out at various altitudes, and it was thus possible to investigate the absorption of individual spectral lines in the upper atmosphere. Once the absorption coefficients for various lines have been determined, the line intensities beyond the atmosphere were obtained by extrapolation.

An attempt was made to estimate the electron temperature from the measured line intensities of the lithium isoelectronic series, but the accuracy of measurement was insufficient for this purpose [27].

A detailed analysis of the solar spectrum is given in [17, 28]. A complete list of lines from 57 to 310 Å can be found in [17]. Of the various identified lines, 5 belong to He II, 1 to C V, 1 to C IV, 5 to O VI, 1 to O V, 7 to Mg VIII, 6 to Mg IX, 3 to Mg X, 1 to Ne VII, 4 to Ne VIII, 2 to Si VI, 2 to Si VII, 12 to Si VIII, 8 to Si IX, 5 to Si X, 2 to Fe IX, 5 to Fe X, 7 to Fe XI, 2 to Fe XII, 5 to Fe XIII, 6 to Fe XIV, 3 to Fe XV, 2 to Fe XVI.

The solar spectrum was also recorded photoelectrically from the rocket launched on 13 March 1962 [32]. The grazing-incidence spectrometer ($\alpha = 88°$) with a glass grating of 1 m radius and 600 lines/mm recorded the spectrum from 10 to 400 Å [33]. The lines identified between 170 and 380 Å belong to Fe X–Fe XVI, Ni XV, Ni XVII, He II, Cu XIX, S X, Ar XI, Ar XIV, Ca XV, S IX, Cl IX.

Prokof'ev and Bruns [34] used a previously described spectrometer (§18, p. 128), to measure the He II flux (303.8 Å) at the top of the Earth's atmosphere. The value of this flux was estimated at 0.5 erg/cm$^2$ · sec apart from a numerical factor of 2–3.

The lines of the solar spectrum between 170 and 200 Å were compared with the lines of the discharge spectrum obtained on ZETA and Scylla machines and with the lines of a theta-pinch spectrum [35–40].

The Scylla was used to compare spectra recorded without any impurities and with $Fe(CO)_5$ added. The discharge spectrum with iron impurity showed the same lines as the solar spectrum. The solar spectrum lines between 150 and 220 Å were thus identified with iron. The classification of these lines is inconclusive, but they apparently belong to Fe VIII, Fe IX, and Fe X [40].

Some iron lines, e.g., Fe XV (284 Å) and Fe XVI (335 Å), show considerable brightness fluctuations between different flights [41].

These variations for the 284 Å line are shown in Table 44. The fluctuations are far beyond those permissible by the experimental errors, and they are apparently associated with significant variations in solar luminosity.

Numerous lines in the solar spectrum were predicted and identified in [42, 43]. Between 50 and 1100 Å, 180 out of the 225 lines observed in the solar spectrum were identified. The sum total of research work published on the solar spectrum provides a fairly conclusive description of the spectrum [22].

The solar spectrum below 2000 Å is made up mainly of emission lines. These lines are excited in various layers of the chromosphere and the corona, where different temperatures prevail [43a]. The absence of $Ne^+$, $Mg^+$, and $Si^+$ lines with ionization potentials of 100–300 eV in the solar spectrum reveals a sharp temperature discontinuity between the chromosphere and the corona. Fraunhofer absorption lines disappear almost entirely below 1700 Å. This is so because only the chromospheric and the coronal emission is received in this region, while the radiation from the photosphere is absorbed in the intervening solar atmosphere. Fraunhofer absorption lines originate in the photosphere. These are primarily lines of neutral atoms and singly charged ions.

The chromospheric and coronal spectra, very difficult to observe in the visible and the near ultraviolet (where the photospheric emission is much stronger), are

Table 44

| Rocket launching | Intensity ratio Fe XV (284 Å) to He II (304 Å) |
|---|---|
| 23 August 1960 | 0.25 |
| 23 August 1961 | 0.17 |
| 5 June 1962 | 0.07 |
| 25 October 1962 | 0.08 |
| 2 May 1963 | 0.06 |
| 12 December 1963 | 0.03 |
| 30 March 1964 | 0.04 |

readily observed in the vacuum ultraviolet, where the photospheric emission is effectively absorbed. All the lines discovered in the solar spectrum belong to light atoms, from hydrogen to iron. A total of several hundreds of lines were discovered. The wavelengths of these lines are best measured photoelectrically, but photographs give a more accurate estimate of their intensity.

We will briefly list the wavelengths of the lines of the various elements observed in the solar spectrum (for $\lambda > 300$ Å.)

### Hydrogen

Eleven members of the Lyman series recorded. The third and the tenth member highly attenuated by nitrogen absorption. For the intensity of $L_\alpha$, see §49. $L_\alpha$ is stronger than $L_\beta$ by a factor of approximately 85 [44].

### Helium

Two resonance lines discovered, 584.33 Å and 537.02 Å. The flux from the 584.33 Å line is 0.05 erg/cm² · sec; it is 9 times the flux from the 537.02 Å line. A continuum begins at the limit of the series ($\lambda = 504$ Å) and extends over 25 Å in the short-wave direction. Five members of the Lyman series were recorded in the He II spectrum. The emission of the strongest line (303.78 Å) gives a flux of 0.2–0.8 erg/cm² · sec at the top of the atmosphere. A continuum is observed near the series limit at 228 Å. Another He II line is recorded at 1640 Å.

### Carbon

Numerous C I lines from 1993.6 to 1100 Å, several C II multiplets at 1335 Å, 1037 Å, 903 Å, and 1010 Å, several C III multiplets at 977.03 Å, 1176 Å, 386.2 Å, and 310.2 Å. Among the C IV lines, only the 1548 Å doublet was observed.

### Nitrogen

The intensities of the nitrogen lines are fairly low. The N I multiplets observed include 1200 Å, 1134 Å, and 1164 Å. N II multiplets at 1085 Å, 916 Å, and 775.96 Å; a N III multiplet at 991 Å; a N IV multiplet at 765.14 Å; N V doublet at 1238.80 Å and 1242.80 Å.

### Oxygen

O I multiplets at 1357 Å, 1304 Å, 1040 Å, 1027 Å, 990 Å, 1152.13 Å, O II multiplet at 834 Å, O III multiplets at 835 Å, 702 Å, 508 Å, 526 Å. The spectrum also shows O IV multiplets at 790 Å and 554 Å, O V multiplets at 629.73 Å and 760 Å, and O VI doublet at 1031.91 and 1037.61 Å.

## Neon

Ne VIII lines at 770.4 Å and 780.3 Å; Ne VII line at 465.2 Å.

## Magnesium

Mg I and Mg II represented by their Fraunhofer lines. Other magnesium lines include the Mg IX line at 368.1 Å and the Mg X lines at 609.7 Å and 624.9 Å.

## Aluminum

Al I lines at 1931.9 Å and 1936.4 Å, Al III resonance doublet at 1854.72 Å and 1862.78 Å.

## Silicon

Silicon is widely represented in the solar spectrum. The numerous Si II lines include those at 1816.94 Å, 1808.01 Å, 1817.42 Å, and others. The Si III lines include 1892.03 Å and 1206.52 Å, and the Si IV lines 1393.73 Å and 1402.73 Å (the last two very strong). Other Si IV lines include those at 458 Å, 1128.3 Å, and 1122.5 Å. Si XII lines at 499.1 Å and 520.4 Å were also recorded.

## Sulfur

The solar spectrum shows numerous sulfur lines, starting with S I and ending with S VI. The S I emission lines include two multiplets at 1480 Å and the multiplets at 1430 Å, 1407 Å, 1389 Å, and 1322 Å. The S II spectrum is represented by the multiplet at 1250 Å. There are also S III lines at 1200 Å and 1020 Å, S IV lines at 1073 Å and 1063 Å, S V line at 786.48 Å, and S VI lines at 933.38 Å and 944.52 Å.

In addition to the lines of these elements, the solar spectrum also shows lines of ionized chlorine, argon, potassium, calcium, chromium, manganese, iron, cobalt, and nickel.

## The continuous spectrum of the Sun

It seems that the continuous spectrum of the Sun in the visible and the near ultraviolet is entirely determined by the emission of the photosphere. This continuous spectrum extends approximately to 1700 Å. For wavelengths below 1700 Å, the photospheric emission is of low intensity [45]. The peculiar distribution of radiation over the wavelengths makes it impossible to assign a certain temperature to the continuum. As the wavelength decreases, the temperature corresponding to the continuum emission falls.

In the visible spectrum, the continuum temperature is 6000°K, and at 2085 Å the temperature is as low as 5000°K. At 1400 Å the continuum is substantially weaker, with $T \approx 4750°K$; at still shorter wavelengths the continuum intensity is seen to increase. This enhancement is particularly noticeable near $L_\alpha$. The continuum intensity corresponds to 5300 °K at 1100 Å, nearly 6000 °K at 970 Å, and about 6500 °K at 912 Å. The continuum associated with the emission of atomic hydrogen originates in the chromosphere.

## 49. HYDROGEN LINES IN THE SOLAR SPECTRUM AND PHOTOGRAPHS OF THE SUN IN $L_\alpha$ LIGHT

$L_\alpha$ is the strongest line in the solar spectrum. It can be recorded by various dispersion-free methods, using photon counters and ionization chambers responsive to wavelengths from 1100 to 1350 Å and a $CaSO_4$–Mn thermophosphor responding at 1050–1240 Å [46–49].

The results obtained for the $L_\alpha$ intensity in various experiments differ by as much as one order of magnitude [3]. Some of these differences are accounted for by the variation of solar emission intensity with the phase of solar activity. However, fundamentally these differences are traceable to measurement errors, since the measurement of absolute intensities under these conditions is a very laborious undertaking. We will briefly describe the results of the most reliable and consistent measurements.

The $L_\alpha$ flux amounts to 6.0 erg/cm$^2 \cdot$ sec [50]. Ionization chamber measurements [48, 49] give an average figure close to 6 erg/cm$^2 \cdot$ sec. Measurements carried out on board the second Soviet spaceship-satellite on 19 August 1960 gave an $L_\alpha$ radiation flux of 5–6 erg/cm$^2 \cdot$ sec [51]. No enhancement was observed during the active phase of the Sun. The measurements made in July–August 1960 [52] could not give accurate absolute values, as one of the counters did not function, but it is nevertheless clear that the radiation flux changed insignificantly and remained unaffected by solar flares.

The intensities of other hydrogen Lyman lines were also measured. Unlike the results for $L_\alpha$, these findings are widely divergent [3].

The $L_\alpha$ line shape was studied by various authors [14, 53–57]. The line shape was observed using a spectrograph with two identical crossed gratings (see §18, p. 135). Figure 243 shows a photograph and a microphotometric tracing of the $L_\alpha$ line obtained at an altitude of 134–163 km with 30 sec exposure. The half-width of $L_\alpha$ is of the order of 1 Å. The $L_\alpha$ line shows considerable self-reversal: the distance

*a*

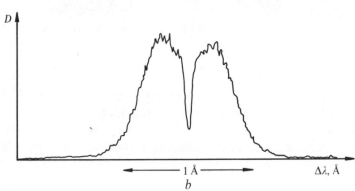

*b*

Figure 243

Photograph (*a*) and microphotometric tracing (*b*) of the $L_\alpha$ line.

between its two peaks is 0.4 Å. The fairly wide absorption gap in the middle is produced by solar hydrogen, and the deep narrow nucleus at the center is contributed by
the absorption in interplanetary hydrogen between the Sun and the Earth. The width
of the central nucleus, corrected for instrumental broadening, is 0.025–0.03 Å, which
corresponds to Doppler broadening in hydrogen at temperatures between 800
and 2100°K. The energy absorbed in this nucleus is about 0.1 erg/cm² · sec. If we
assume that all the absorbed energy is re-emitted, the emission intensity of the sky
in $L_\alpha$ light should amount to $10^{-2}$ erg/cm² · sec · sterad. This estimate fits the results
of night glow observations [58].

The $L_\alpha$ line shape is variable for different parts of the solar disk recorded on the
spectrogram. Figure 244 shows the $L_\alpha$ profiles for a facula and for an area of low facular

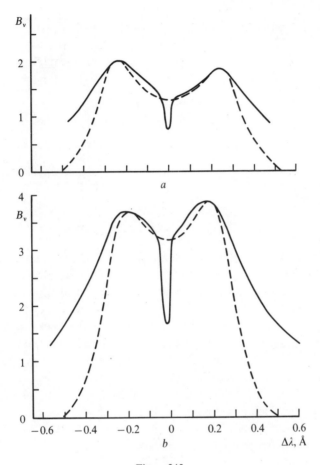

Figure 245

$L_\alpha$ profiles:

a   for a region of low facular activity,   b   for a facula (dashed curve—theoretical).

activity. The $L_\alpha$ profile also changes on passing from the center of the solar disk to its limb (Figure 245).

The $L_\alpha$ line shape was calculated, and the theory predicted the existence of two maxima whose separation is a function of temperature [55]. Comparison of theory with experiment (see Figure 244) makes it possible to determine the temperature of the solar plasma where the observed emission originates. For regions of low facular activity, the temperatures reach 70,000–115,000°K, and in faculae 55,000–90,000°K. This shows that the temperature difference for the active and nonactive regions of the Sun is as high as 20,000°K. The $L_\alpha$ and $L_\beta$ profiles were also studied in [59].

The high emission intensity of the Sun in $L_\alpha$ permits photographing the Sun in

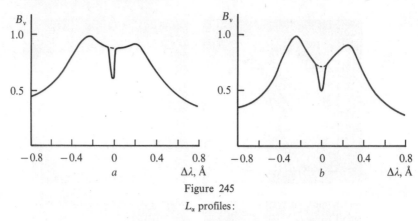

Figure 245

$L_\alpha$ profiles:

*a*   near the center of the solar disk,   *b*   near the limb.

the filtered light of this line. First photographs of this kind were taken in [60]. These very low-quality photographs, and much better results were obtained on 13 March 1959 [61]. Figure 139 (see §18) is a diagram of the spectroheliograph used on that occasion.

Figure 246 gives some photographs (exposure time 0.02 sec) which clearly show that the image in $L_\alpha$ light is very much like the image in Ca II light. However, in spectro-heliograms taken in $L_\alpha$ light the contrast between background and faculae is more pronounced than in Ca II spectroheliograms. When facular areas occupy more than half the solar disk, the $L_\alpha$ line is enhanced in these areas. Some photographs taken in $L_\alpha$ light show clear solar prominences. The Sun also can be photographed in the light of other strong lines lying in the vacuum ultraviolet (303.78 Å He II, 284.2 Å Fe XV, 335.4 Å Fe XVI, 977.03 Å C III, 1025.72 Å $L_\beta$, 1031.91 Å O VI, 1037.61 Å O VI) [61a].

## 50. IDENTIFICATION OF CORONAL LINES

The coronal spectrum is very difficult to observe in the visible region because of the intense radiation from the photosphere. In the vacuum ultraviolet, on the other hand, the photospheric emission is virtually nil, and the observed solar spectrum is determined by the coronal glow.

The identification of the coronal spectrum presented an unsolvable problem over a long period. This accounts for the advent of the "coronium" hypothesis, which assigned the coronal emission to a new chemical element, and other abortive attempts which associated the coronal spectrum with doubly excited helium, etc. [62]. It was 1939 before Grotrian [63] outlined a valid solution of this problem, which was further developed and substantiated by Edlén in 1942 [64].

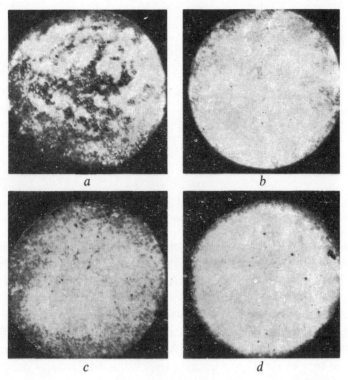

Figure 246

Photographs of the Sun:

*a*  in $L_\alpha$ light;  *b*  in Ca II light;  *c*  in $H_\alpha$ light;  *d*  in white light.

In his identification of the coronal lines, Grotrian [63] established that the wavenumber of the 6374 Å coronal line is equal to the difference in the wavenumbers of the Fe X terms, and the wavenumber of the 7892 Å coronal line is equal to the difference in the wavenumbers of the terms of Fe XI. The scheme of terms of these ions was borrowed from Edlén [65], who based it on his study of the spectrum of the vacuum spark. Subsequently, Edlén established that the wavenumbers of the coronal lines in the visible spectrum show a good fit with the differences in the wavenumbers of the short-wave lines of multiply charged ions that he had measured (Figure 247). This led to a fairly certain identification of the coronal lines with the corresponding ions.

The results of Edlén's measurements and calculations, undertaken for the identification of the coronal lines, are listed in Table 45.

To identify other lines in the coronal spectrum, Edlen had to study the isoelectronic series containing iron ions from Fe X to Fe XIV and nickel ions from Ni XII to Ni XVI. These series start with Cl I . . . , S I . . . , Si I . . . , and Al I . . . .

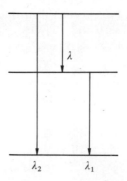

Figure 247

Level diagram illustrating the method used in the determination of wavelengths of the coronal lines. $\lambda$ is the coronal line in the visible, $\lambda_1$ and $\lambda_2$ are the lines measured in the vacuum ultraviolet.

Extrapolation from the known doublet splitting for the first members of the series gave the other splittings. If the ground term is a doublet, this method is very simple and highly reliable. It was therefore successfully applied to the identification of the lines of Fe XIV, Ni XVI, Ni XII. These lines correspond to the $^2P_{1/2}-^2P_{3/2}$ transitions. Of the 24 coronal lines known in 1942, Edlén was able to identify 19. Of the other 5 lines, 3 were identified on a later occasion. A complete list of identified coronal lines is given in [66]. It also includes the identified lines of Ar XV [67].

Table 45

| Series | $\lambda$, Å (vacuum spark) | $\nu$, cm$^{-1}$ | Term difference, cm$^{-1}$ | $\nu$ of coronal lines ($\lambda$, Å) |
|---|---|---|---|---|
| Fe X $(3s^23p^5-3s^23p^44s)$ | | | | |
| $^2P_{3/2}-^2P_{1/2}$ | 95.338 | 1,048,900 | 15,714 | 15,683 |
| $^2P_{1/2}-^2P_{1/2}$ | 96.788 | 1,033,186 | | |
| $^2P_{3/2}-^2P_{3/2}$ | 96.122 | 1,040,345 | 15,660 | (6,374) |
| $^2P_{1/2}-^2P_{3/2}$ | 97.591 | 1,024,685 | | |
| Fe XI $(3s^23p^4-3s^23p^34s)$ | | | | |
| $^3P_2-^3D_2$ | 87.025 | 1,149,095 | 12,667 | 12,668 |
| $^3P_1-^3D_2$ | 87.995 | 1,136,428 | | |
| $^3P_2-^3S_1$ | 89.185 | 1,121,265 | 12,679 | (7,892) |
| $^3P_1-^3S_1$ | 90.205 | 1,108,686 | | |
| Ca XII $(2s^22p^5-2s2p^6)$ | | | | |
| $^2P_{3/2}-^2S_{1/2}$ | 141.036 | 709,039 | 30,028 | 30,039 |
| $^2P_{1/2}-^2S_{1/2}$ | 147.273 | 679.011 | | (3,328) |
| Ca XIII $(2s^22p^4-2s2p^5)$ | | | | |
| $^3P_1-^3P_2$ | 161.748 | 618,246 | 24,464 | 24,465 |
| $^3P_1-^3P_2$ | 168.412 | 593,782 | | (4,086) |

So far, 96 coronal lines have been recorded in the spectral region from 3010 to 10,798 Å; of these, 39 lines, i.e., some 40%, have been identified. These lines belong to Ar X, Ar XI, Ar XV, Ar XIX, K XI, K XIV, Ca XII, Ca XIII, Ca XV, V X, Cr IX, Cr XI, Mn X, Mn XII, Mn XIII, Fe X, Fe XI, Fe XII, Fe XIII, Fe XIV, Fe XV, Co XI, Co XII, Co XV, Co XVI, Ni XII, Ni XIII, Ni XV, Ni XVI, Ni XVII.

The coronal lines are difficult to observe in laboratory, because these are forbidden lines. They are generally associated with magnetic dipole transitions and electric quadrupole transitions, whose probabilities are exceedingly low, and the lifetimes of the excited states are correspondingly long. In laboratory work, where the characteristic pressures are relatively high and the reaction volumes are small, the excited ions invariably return to the ground state by nonradiative transitions, which are triggered by atomic collisions and interaction with the walls.

Eldén's remarkable work on the identification of coronal spectra has established the existence of multiply charged ions in the corona. The electron temperature of the corona is thus extremely high (a few million degrees) [67].

Various aspects relating to the identification of coronal lines still cause a lively dispute in scientific circles [62, 66]. Much still remains unsolved, but the work of Elwert [67], Shklovskii [62], and others has shed some light on the physical processes in the corona. This progress was greatly assisted by the correct identification of the spectral lines, which emerged from the advances of vacuum UV spectroscopy.

## BIBLIOGRAPHY

1. Chubb, T.A. and E.T. Byram. *Astrophys. J.*, **138**, 617 (1963).
2. Byram, E.T., T.A. Chubb, and H. Friedman. In: *Ul'trafioletovoe izluchenie Solntsa, i mezhplanetnaya sreda*, G.M. Nikol'skii, Editor, p. 199. IL. 1962.
3. Gurzadyan, G.A. In: *Teoriya zvezdnykh spektrov*, V.V. Sobolev et al., Editors, p. 203. Izdatel'stvo "Nauka." 1966.
4. Byram, E.T., T.A. Chubb, H. Friedman and J.E. Kupperian. *Astron. J.*, **62**, 9 (1957).
5. Stecher, T.P. and J.E. Milligan. *Astrophys. J.*, **136**, 1 (1962).
6. Stecher, T.P. and D.E. Milligan. In: *Korotkovolnovoe izluchenie nebesnykh tel*, I.S. Shklovskii, Editor, p. 9. IL. 1963.
7. Watanabe, K. *Advances Geophys.*, **5**, 153 (1958).
8. Baum, W.A., F.S. Johnson, J.J. Oberly, C.C. Rockwood, C.V. Strain, and R. Tousey. *Phys. Rev.*, **70**, 781 (1946).
9. Rense, W.A. *Phys. Rev.*, **91**, 299 (1953).
10. Johnson, F.S., J.D. Purcell, and R. Tousey. *Phys. Rev.*, **95**, 621 (1954).
11. Stacey, D.S., G.A. Stith, R.A. Nidey, and W.B. Pietenpol. *Electronics*, **27**, 149 (1954).
12. Johnson, F.S., H.H. Malitson, J.D. Purcell, and R. Tousey. *Astrophys. J.*, **127**, 80 (1958).
13. Aboud, A., W.E. Behring, and W.A. Rense. *Astrophys. J.*, **130**, 381 (1959).
14. Behring, W.E., H. McAllister, and W.A. Rense. *Astrophys. J.*, **127**, 676 (1958).
15. Violett, T. and W.A. Rense. *Astrophys. J.*, **130**, 954 (1959).
16. Purcell, J.D., D.M. Packer, and R. Tousey. *Proc. 1st COSPAR Intern. Space Sci. Symp., Nice*, 1960, **I**, 581. Amsterdam, North-Holland Publ. Co. 1960.

17. ZIRIN, H. *Astrophys. J.,* **140**, 1332 (1964).
18. PECKER, C. and F. ROHRLICH. *Astrophys. J., Suppl.,* ser. 8, No. 79, 227 (1963).
19. TOUSEY, R. In: *Space Astrophysics*, W. Liller, Editor, p. 11. N.Y., McGraw-Hill. 1961.
20. DETWILER, C.R., J.D. PURCELL, and R. TOUSEY. *The Profile of the Solar Lyman-α-line of Hydrogen*, In: *Proc. Intern. Space Sci. Symp., Liège.*
21. TOUSEY, R. *J. Opt. Soc. America,* **51**, 384 (1961).
22. TOUSEY, R. *Space Sci. Rev.,* **2**, 3 (1963).
23. TOUSEY, R., W.E. AUSTIN, J.D. PURCELL, and K.G. WIDING. *Space Research*, W. Priester, Editor, **III**, 772. Amsterdam, 1963.
24. HALL, L.A., K.R. DAMON, and H.E. HINTEREGGER. *Space Research*, W. Priester, Editor, **III**, 745. Amsterdam, 1963.
25. HINTEREGGER, H.E. *Astrophys. J.,* **132**, 801 (1960).
26. HINTEREGGER, H.E. *Proc. 2nd COSPAR Intern. Space Sci. Symp., Florence,* 1961, **II**, 1036. Amsterdam, North-Holland Publ. Co.
27. HINTEREGGER, H.E., L.A. HALL, and W. SCHWEIZER. *Astrophys. J.,* **140**, 319 (1964).
28. ZIRIN, H., L.A. HALL, and H.E. HINTEREGGER. *Space Research*, W. Priester, Editor, **III**, 760. Amsterdam, 1963.
29. HINTEREGGER, H.E. In: *Space Astrophysics*, W. Liller, Editor, p. 45. N.Y., McGraw-Hill.
30. HINTEREGGER, H.E. *J. Geophys. Res.,* **66**, 2367 (1961).
31. BYRAM, E.T., T.A. CHUBB and H. FRIEDMAN. *J. Geophys. Res.,* **66**, 2095 (1961).
32. BEHRING, W.E., W.M. NEUPERT, and J.C. LINDSAY. *Space Research*, W. Priester, Editor, **III**, 814. Amsterdam, 1963.
33. NEUPERT, W.M. and W.E. BEHRING. *J. Quant. Spectr. Rad. Trans.,* **2**, 527 (1962).
34. BRUNS, A.V. and V.K. PROKOF'EV. *Iskusstvennye Sputniki Zemli,* No. 11, 15, 23 (1961).
35. House, L.L. *Ann. astrophys.,* **27**, 763 (1964).
36. HOUSE, L.L., W.A. DEUTSCHMAN, and G.A. SAWYER. *Astrophys. J.,* **140**, 814 (1964).
37. FAWCETT, B.C., A.H. GABRIEL, W.G. GRIFFIN, B.B. JONES, and R. WILSON. *Nature,* **200**, 1303 (1963).
38. MANDEL'SHTAM, S.L., S.P. FEDOSEEV, E.YA. KONONOV, and S.V. LEBEDEV. *Optika i Spektroskopiya,* **18**, 923 (1965).
39. ELTON, R.C., A.C. KOLB, W.E. AUSTIN, R. TOUSEY, and K.G. WIDING. *Astrophys. J.,* **140**, 390 (1964).
40. COWAN, R.D. and N.J. PEACOCK. *Astrophys. J.,* **142**, 390 (1965).
41. HALL, L.A., W. SCHWEIZER, L. HEROUX, and H.E. HINTEREGGER. *Astrophys. J.,* **142**, 13 (1965).
42. IVANOV–KHOLODNYI, G.S. and G.M. NIKOL'SKII. *Astronomicheskii Zhurnal,* **38**, 828 (1961).
43. IVANOV–KHOLODNY, G.S. and G.M. NICOL'SKII. *Space Research,* W. Priester, Editor, **III**, 787. Amsterdam, 1963.
43a. ZIRIN, H., L.A. HALL, and H.E. HINTEREGGER. In: *Korotkovolnovoe izluchenie nebesnykh tel,* I.S. Shklovskii, Editor, p. 126. IL. 1963.
44. DETWILER, C.R., D.L. GARRET, J.D. PURCELL, and R. TOUSEY. *Ann. Geophys.,* **17**, 263 (1961).
45. GOLDBERG, L. *J. Quant. Spectr. Rad. Trans.,* **3**, 519 (1963).
46. FRIEDMAN, H., S.W. LICHTMAN, and E.T. BYRAM. *Phys. Rev.,* **91**, 1278 (1953).

47. TOUSEY, R., K. WATANABE, and J.D. PURCELL. *Phys. Rev.,* **83**, 792 (1951).
48. BYRAM, E.T., T.A. CHUBB, H. FRIEDMAN, and J.E. KUPPERIAN. *Astrophys. J.,* **124**, 480 (1956).
49. CHUBB, T.A., H. FRIEDMAN, R.W. KREPLIN, and J.E. KUPPERIAN. *J. Geophys. Res.,* **62**, 389 (1957).
50. HINTEREGGER, H.E. In: *Spektry zvezd v dalekom ul'trafiolete,* p. 78. IL. 1964.
51. EFREMOV, A.I., A.L. PODMOSHENSKII, O.N. EFIMOV, and A.A. LEBEDEV. *Iskusstvennye Sputniki Zemli,* No. 10, 3 (1961).
52. KREPLIN, R.W., T.A. CHUBB, and H. FRIEDMAN. *J. Geophys. Res.,* **67**, 2231 (1962).
53. RENSE, W.A. In: *Space Astrophysics,* p. 26. W. Liller, Editor. N.Y., McGraw-Hill. 1961.
54. PURCELL, J.D. and R. TOUSEY. *J. Geophys. Res.,* **65**, 370 (1960).
55. PURCELL, J.D. and R. TOUSEY. *The Profile of Solar Lyman-α-line of Hydrogen. Proc. Intern. Space Sci. Symp., Liège.* 1960.
56. MORTON, D. and D. WIDING. *Astrophys. J.,* **133**, 596 (1961).
57. MENZEL, D.H. and L.R. DOHERTY. In: *Spektry zvezd v dalekom ul'trafiolete,* p. 144, IL. 1964.
58. KUPPERIAN, J.E., E.T. BYRAM, T.A. CHUBB, and H. FRIEDMAN, *Planet. Space Sci.,* **1**, 3 (1959).
59. TOUSEY, R., J.D. PURCELL, W.E. AUSTIN, D.L. GARRETT, and K.G. WIDING. *Space Research,* **IV**, 703. 1964.
60. MERCURE, R., S.C. MILLER, W.A. RENSE, and F.J. STUART. *J. Geophys. Res.,* **61**, 571 (1956).
61. PURCELL, J.D., D. PACKER, and R. TOUSEY. *Nature,* **184**, 8 (1959).
61a. FRIEDMAN, H. *Astron. J.,* **68**, 679 (1963).
62. SHKLOVSKII, I.S. *Fizika solnechnoi korony (Physics of the Solar Corona).* Fitzmatgiz. 1962.
63. GROTRIAN, W. *Naturwissenschaften,* **27**, 214 (1939).
64. EDLÉN, B. *Z. Astrophys.,* **22**, 30 (1942).
65. EDLÉN, B. *Z. Phys.,* **104**, 188, 407 (1937).
66. PRYCE, M.H.L. *Astrophys. J.,* **140**, 1192 (1964).
67. ELWERT, G. *Z. Naturforsch.,* **7a**, 432 (1952).

# CHAPTER XI

# Spectroscopic Analysis
# in the Vacuum Ultraviolet

## 51. SPECIFIC FEATURES OF SPECTROSCOPIC ANALYSIS IN THE VACUUM ULTRAVIOLET

The resonance lines of numerous elements (some 20%) fall in the vacuum ultraviolet. These include the resonance lines of the inert gases, halogens and others. The sensitivity of determination of these elements by vacuum UV spectroscopy is higher than by spectroscopic analysis in the near ultraviolet or in the visible spectrum.

Table 46 lists the resonance lines of elements which lie below 2000 Å.

Table 46

| Element | $\lambda$, Å | Element | $\lambda$, Å | Element | $\lambda$, Å |
|---------|----------|---------|----------|---------|----------|
| H  | 1216; 1026 | P  | 1783; 1775 | Br | 1576; 1489 |
| He | 584;  537  | S  | 1900; 1807 | Kr | 1236; 1165 |
| C  | 1657; 1561 | Cl | 1380; 1347 | I  | 1830       |
| N  | 1200; 1135 | Ar | 1067; 1048 | Xe | 1470; 1296 |
| O  | 1356; 1302 | As | 1938; 1890 | Hg | 1849       |
| F  | 955;  952  | Se | 1961       | Rn | 1786; 1452 |
| Ne | 744;  736  |    |            |    |            |

In general the analytical sensitivity is higher for elements with relatively simple spectra (i.e., for systems with a single optical electron) [1–4]. Hence it follows that carbon, say, can be determined with higher sensitivity using the C IV lines than the C I lines, and the sensitivity of arsenic determination using the As V lines is higher than that for As I lines [3]. This conclusion is naturally valid if the concentration of the corresponding ions in the discharge is comparable with the concentration of normal atoms; this condition can be met by using a sufficiently hot source for spectrum excitation. The lines ensuring maximum sensitivity are thus mostly the lines of ions with a single optical electron, and not the lines of the neutral atoms. We generally know from theoretical considerations what the last lines of each element are, and so we can always choose a suitable excitation source and an appropriate wavelength range for analysis. With sources capable of exciting the lines of multiply charged ions, the analytical sensitivity is independent of the ratio of the ionization potentials of the mixture components. And yet, normally, a considerable difference in the ionization potentials of the components in a gas cloud lowers the sensitivity of determination of the component which is less readily excited; the emission predominantly originates in the low ionization potential component, whose presence lowers the source temperature [1, 5–7].

This entire approach to vacuum UV spectroscopy, however, requires development of fairly simple experimental systems for the excitation of the resonance lines of multiply charged ions.

So far, only methods for the analysis of gases and nonmetals in ores, metals, and alloys have been developed. No methods are currently available for the analysis of gas mixtures in the vacuum ultraviolet, although it is clear beyond all doubt that this analysis is much more sensitive than any conventional analytical technique at longer wavelengths. For example, in tubes filled with a mixture of helium with a small impurity of krypton and xenon, the Kr and Xe resonance lines are sufficiently strong, whereas the lines of these elements in the visible spectrum are too weak to be recorded. This is so because in inert gases the concentration of atoms in the excited states $np^5(n+1)s$ is several orders of magnitude higher than the concentration of atoms in the $np^5(n+1)p$ states. For example, in a high-frequency argon discharge at 0.6–1.5 T, the concentration of atoms in the $3p^54s$ states is about three orders of magnitude higher than in the $3p^54p$ states [8].

Such gases as hydrogen, oxygen, nitrogen, chlorine, argon, krypton, and xenon can be determined in sealed tubes with fluorite or lithium fluoride windows. Therefore, these gases can be determined with very high absolute, as well as relative, sensitivity.

Helium and neon can be analyzed only in open discharge tubes, since their resonance lines fall at wavelengths shorter than 1050 Å (the transmission threshold of lithium fluoride). A current of gas should therefore be passed through the tube, and because of the substantial gas flow rate only the relative sensitivity can be high.

The lines of the inert gases are extremely numerous in the vacuum ultraviolet, and they are so widely spaced that sometimes gas mixtures can actually be analyzed without using a spectrometer. For example, when neon is determined in a mixture of heavy inert gases, the neon lines can be recorded using a thin aluminum film as a filter transmitting only radiation of wavelengths below 800 Å (see § 10) [9]. The xenon resonance line at 1295 Å in the spectrum of a helium + xenon mixture can be recorded without a spectrometer using a NO ionization chamber with a LiF window.

Finally, gases and nonmetals can be analyzed in the vacuum ultraviolet by absorption spectroscopy, so that the method of linear absorption is applicable [10]. This method has considerable advantages for the determination of minor components whose ionization potentials are higher than the ionization potential of the main component in the mixture. The analytical sensitivity of the method of linear absorption is known to be independent of the ratio of the excitation potentials of the mixture component and it is not affected by the presence of a third component either. The application of absorption methods to the analysis of gas mixtures therefore seems to be highly promising.

## 52. EMISSION ANALYSIS

Emission analysis in the vacuum ultraviolet was first attempted in 1936 by Harrison [1], who determined sulfur using the lines 1807 Å, 1820 Å, and 1826 Å, and selenium from its lines at 1961 Å, 2040 Å, and 2063 Å. Other authors at that time tried to avoid this spectral region because of experimental difficulties, shortage of stable sources, and lack of simple and convenient spectrometers for the vacuum ultraviolet.

McNally, Harrison, and Rowe [11] made a determination of fluorine from lines in the short-wave region of the spectrum, but the vacuum arc was exceedingly unstable and the analytical procedure took too much time, so that eventually the authors had to develop a technique for fluorine determination using the visible spectrum of this element excited in a hollow cathode.

The instability of the vacuum spark confined the spectroscopic analysts to the use of a conventional spark burning in an inert gas atmosphere or in nitrogen. Bills [12] used a closed chamber with a fluorite window in his determination of sulfur and phosphorus in steels from the 1807 Å S I line and the 1775 Å P I line. The sensitivity of this analytical procedure was 0.002% for sulfur and 0.005% for phosphorus. Its application, however, is limited by the transparency of the fluorite window, which moreover readily accumulates opaque deposits.

The resonance lines of atoms are also used in quantometers, e.g., the 1657 Å C I line, 1775 Å and 1783 Å P I lines, 1807 Å and 1820 Å S I lines [13, 14].

Multichannel photoelectric instruments covering a wide range of wavelengths, including the vacuum ultraviolet and the near ultraviolet, are capable of determining various elements, which would normally require a variety of different spectrometers. The DFS-31 quantometer has 10 channels, but only 2 in the vacuum ultraviolet. Analysis of steels with this instrument gave the results listed in Table 47.

A number of similar instruments are used in analytical practice. The *Spectrovide* will record the spectrum from 1600 to 3500 Å. It is equipped with thirty-two photomultipliers, five of which cover the vacuum ultraviolet. According to the manufacturer's specifications, this instrument will analyze on the average 15–20 samples per hour, each sample with about 10 elements; the total number of determinations may reach 3000 daily.

Carbon, sulfur, and phosphorus are generally determined with an accuracy of about 10%, which is substantially lower than the accuracy attainable in the analysis of most other elements. However, this relatively low accuracy is apparently associated with the uneven vaporization of the elements in the arc, and has nothing to do with the fact that the analytical lines fall in the vacuum ultraviolet. Table 48 lists some

Table 47

| Element | Analytical line, Å | Concentration range | Variance, % |
|---------|--------------------|---------------------|-------------|
| C I | 1657 | $10^{-2}$–1.5 | 10–1 |
| P I | 1783 | $5 \cdot 10^{-3}$–$5 \cdot 10^{-2}$ | 20–8 |
| S I | 1820 | $5 \cdot 10^{-3}$–$5 \cdot 10^{-2}$ | 20–6 |

Table 48

| Element | $\lambda$, Å | Concentration of element, % | | | |
|---------|--------------|------------------|-------------------|---------------|-----------|
| | | in low-alloy steel | in high-alloy steel | in cast iron | in iron |
| P | 1782.83 | 0.005–0.1 | 0.005–0.1 | 0.01–0.1 | 0.01–1.0 |
| S | 1807.31 | | | 1.5–2.5 | |
| | or | | | | |
| | 1820.37 | 0.005–0.2 | 0.005–0.2 | 0.01–0.35 | 0.01–0.2 |
| Sn | 1899.89 | 0.005–0.1 | 0.005–0.4 | — | — |
| C | 1930.93 | 0.1–1.5 | 0.01–1.5 | 2.5–4.5 | 1–4.5 |
| As | 1972.62 | 0.005–0.1 | 0.005–0.1 | — | — |
| W | 2029.98 | 0.01–0.2 | 0.01–22 | — | — |
| | or | | | | |
| | 2079.11 | | | | |
| B | 2088.93 | 0.0005–0.02 | 0.0005–0.02 | — | — |

basic data on the determination of various elements with the *Spectrovide*, taken from the manufacturer's literature (Philips).

Analyses of gases and nonmetals in the vacuum ultraviolet are treated in detail by Vodar and co-workers [3, 15–19], who worked with a creeping spark (see §7). The usual parameters of the spark circuit were $U \approx 18$ kV, $C \approx 2\,\mu$F. The spectra were recorded both photographically and photoelectrically. Photoelectric recording used an averaging circuit which accumulated 10–1,000 discharges each time. In the analyses and in the construction of calibration curves, the capacitor voltage was measured and the average of five measurement series was taken. In some cases, a comparison line was recorded simultaneously with the analytical lines. The reproducibility of the photographic technique was 20%, and that of the photoelectric technique about 10% at impurity concentrations of the order of a few hundredths of a percent. The results of Vodar and co-workers are summarized in Table 49.

Numerous calibration curves are given in [15–19]. As an example, consider the analytical plot for the determination of sulfur in steels (Figure 248). The ordinate gives the voltmeter readings. The plot covers the range of sulfur concentrations from 0.01 to 0.08%.

Gases in metals were determined using a low-voltage spark [20] (see §7). The discharge was ignited between two rods made of the metal being analyzed. In some cases, the sample served as the anode, and a carbon electrode was used as the cathode (in determinations of oxygen in copper and steel). In the determination of oxygen in metals and alloys, the first pulses after the insertion of each new sample were ignored, as the surface is always contaminated with air oxygen. All tests used photographic recording. The analytical results obtained with a low-voltage spark are listed in Table 50. Figure 249 gives curves for the determination of oxygen in metals.

The low-voltage spark readily excites the lines of the following ions: O III, O IV, O V, N III, N IV, P IV, P V, S IV, S V, S VI, As IV, and As V.

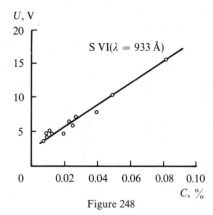

Figure 248

Analytical plot for the determination of sulfur in steels.

Table 49

| Element | Sample | Analytical line, Å | Concentration range, % | Minimum concentration, % | Reproducibility, % | Recording method |
|---|---|---|---|---|---|---|
| C | Steel | C III 977.0 | 0.04–0.45 | $10^{-2}$ | 20 | Photographic |
| S | Steel | S VI 944.5 ⎫<br>S VI 933.4 ⎭ | 0.012–0.11 | $5 \cdot 10^{-3}$ | 20 | Photographic |
| P | Steel | P V 1118.0 ⎫<br>P IV 950.7 ⎭ | 0.009–0.063 | $5 \cdot 10^{-3}$ | 20 | Photographic |
| S | Steel | S VI 933.4 | 0.006–0.08 | — | 10 | Photographic |
| P | Copper | P V 1118.0 | 0.011–0.033 | $10^{-2}$ | 15 | Photographic |
| P | Al alloys | P V 1118.0 | 0.008–0.0125 | $3 \cdot 10^{-4}$ | 20 | Photographic |
| Ge | Titanium oxide | Ge IV 1189.0 ⎫ | | $56 \cdot 10^{-4}$ | — | Photographic |
| | | Ge IV 1229.8 ⎬ | 0.01–1 | — | — | Photographic |
| | | Ge III 1088.5 ⎭ | | — | — | Photographic |
| As | Titanium oxide | As V 987.7 ⎫<br>As V 1029.5 ⎭ | 0.01–1 | $56 \cdot 10^{-4}$<br>— | —<br>— | Photographic<br>Photographic |
| As | Titanium oxide | As IV 892.7 | 0.01–1 | — | 20 | Photographic |
| Se | Titanium oxide | Se VI 844.2 ⎫<br>Se VI 886.8 ⎭ | 0.01–1 | $100 \cdot 10^{-4}$<br>— | —<br>— | Photographic<br>Photographic |
| Br | Titanium oxide | Br VI 661.1 ⎫<br>Br VII 736.1 ⎭ | 0.033–1 | $330 \cdot 10^{-4}$<br>— | —<br>18 | Photographic<br>Photographic |
| Br | Titanium oxide | Sb V 1104.3 ⎫<br>Sb V 1226.0 ⎭ | 0.01–1 | $100 \cdot 10^{-4}$<br>— | 7.5<br>7.5 | Photographic<br>Photographic |
| Br | Titanium oxide | Sn IV 1042.2 | 0.056–1 | — | — | Photographic |
| Sn | Titanium oxide | Sn IV 1314.5 | 0.01–1 | $100 \cdot 10^{-4}$ | — | Photographic |
| Sn | Titanium oxide | Sn IV 1437.6 | 0.01–1 | — | — | Photoelectric |
| Sn | Titanium oxide | Sn III 1251.4 | 0.033–1 | — | — | Photoelectric |
| Te | Titanium oxide | Te VI 951.0 ⎫ | | $100 \cdot 10^{-4}$ | — | Photoelectric |
| Te | Titanium oxide | Te VI 1071.4 ⎬ | 0.01–1 | — | — | Photoelectric |
| Te | Titanium oxide | Te V 895.2 ⎭ | | — | — | Photoelectric |
| F | Titanium oxide | F VII 883 ⎫ | | <0.01 | — | Photoelectric |
| Cl | Titanium oxide | Cl VII 813.0 ⎪ | 0.01–1 | <0.01 | — | Photoelectric |
| Cl | Titanium oxide | Cl VI 730.3 ⎪ | | <0.01 | — | Photoelectric |
| Br | Titanium oxide | Br VII 736.1 ⎭ | | <0.01 | — | Photoelectric |
| O | Titanium | O III 835.3 ⎫ | | <0.01 | >25 | Photoelectric |
| O | Titanium | O IV 790.2 ⎪ | | <0.01 | 25 | Photoelectric |
| O | Titanium | O V 760.2 ⎬ | 0.02–1 | <0.01 | 25 | Photoelectric |
| O | Titanium | O VI 1031.9 ⎪ | | <0.01 | — | Photoelectric |
| O | Titanium | O V 1371.3 ⎭ | | — | — | Photoelectric |
| N | Titanium | N IV 765.1 ⎫<br>N V 1238.8 ⎭ | 0.003–0.04 | $3 \cdot 10^{-3}$<br>$3 \cdot 10^{-3}$ | —<br>— | Photographic<br>Photographic |

When comparing the low-voltage vacuum spark and the creeping spark as sources for spectroscopic analysis, it should be remembered that both sources give spectra of similar composition, but the low-voltage arc is much easier to manufacture

Table 50

| Element | Sample | Analytical line, Å | Concentration range, Å | Minimum concentration, % | Capacitance, μF | Reproducibility |
|---------|--------|--------------------|------------------------|--------------------------|------------------|-----------------|
| O | Copper | O III 703.8 | 0.0026–0.12 | — | — | 16 |
| O | Titanium | O IV 787.7 | 0.02–1.5 | 0.001 | 8000 | 10 |
| O | Zirconium | O III 703.8 | 0.02–0.2 | 0.001 | 8000 | — |
| O | Steel | O III 703.8 | 0.0067–0.1 | — | — | — |
| S | Steel | S V 786.5 | 0.021–0.2 | — | 4000 | — |
| P | Steel | P IV 905.6 | 0.003–0.35 | — | 4000 | — |

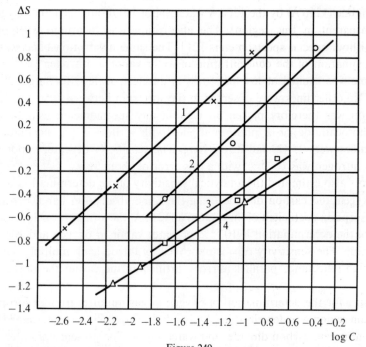

Figure 249

Analytical plot for the determination of oxygen in metals:

1) copper, O III 703.8 Å–Cu III 802.8 Å;   2) titanium, O IV 787.7 Å–Ti IV 729.4 Å;   3) zirconium, O III 703.8 Å–Zr III 718.3 Å;   4) steel, O III 703.8 Å–Fe III 728.8 Å.

technically. The analytical sensitivity attainable with both sources was of the same order of magnitude.

Spectroscopy in the vacuum ultraviolet markedly increases the sensitivity of the determination; this is apparently the most promising method of attaining substantially higher sensitivities in spectroscopic analysis, especially in the determination of elements with high excitation potentials.


## 53. ABSORPTION ANALYSIS

The application of absorption spectroscopy in the vacuum ultraviolet is greatly restricted by the shortage of durable materials which are transparent at wavelengths shorter than 1050 Å. Absorption analysis is therefore applicable only to elements with resonance lines at wavelengths longer than 1050 Å. Very little analytical work has been published, using absorption spectra in the vacuum ultraviolet.

The concentration of water vapor in air was determined from absorption of the $L_\alpha$ hydrogen line (1216 Å) by the 1220 Å water vapor band (nitrogen and oxygen are almost transparent in this region). The absorption was measured with photon counters, without special spectrometers [21]. The same absorption band was used in the determination of the concentration of water vapor in nitrogen [22]. The $L_\alpha$ hydrogen line was excited at low pressures in an electrodeless discharge (20 MHz frequency). No other lines were observed in the spectrum between 1050 and 1500 Å. The radiation was therefore picked up without any spectrometer, using a simple tungsten photocathode or a photomultiplier with a Be–Cu photocathode. The absorbing tubes were 1, 42, and 82 cm long. The sensitivity of water vapor determination in nitrogen was $10^{-4}\%$, with a rms error of about $15\%$.

The authors also estimated the analytical sensitivity of the determination of water vapor in oxygen and carbon dioxide using the same absorption band. Proceeding from the absorption coefficient of these gases at 1216 Å, the authors conclude that the sensitivity of the determination is $10^{-3}\%$ of water vapor in oxygen and $10^{-2}\%$ in carbon dioxide. The sensitivity can be improved by introducing multiple reflection from two high-reflectance parallel mirrors, artificially increasing the optical path length.

A procedure for the determination of oxygen in gas mixtures from absorption in the Schumann region was described in [23, 24]. In [23] oxygen was determined in the presence of nitrogen, carbon dioxide, and water vapor. The presence of water vapor greatly interferes with the analysis, since it absorbs at the same wavelengths as the oxygen (see §39). However, between 1350 and 1600 Å, the absorption in oxygen is much stronger than the absorption by water vapor; as the partial pressure of water vapor in all the test mixtures was lower than the oxygen pressure, the resulting error in determination was insignificant. The percentage content of oxygen varied in various mixtures from 11 to 20%.

The xenon lamp used as the radiation source had only one emission line between 1300 and 2000 Å (the line at 1470 Å). The hydrogen lamp emitted a strong line spectrum at 1553 Å and 1608 Å (see §2). The spectra were recorded without a spectrometer, using simple photocathodes responding to the vacuum ultraviolet. The best results were obtained with a tungsten photocathode. Continuous analysis was performed, with an accuracy of about 1%.

A similar procedure was used in determining the degree of dissociation of oxygen in a glow discharge [24].

Absorption spectroscopy in the vacuum ultraviolet apparently can also use the absorption spectra of atomic oxygen, atomic hydrogen, and atomic nitrogen in the discharge (and not only the molecular spectra of these elements). Application of the method of linear absorption to measurements in very narrow cuvettes makes it possible to determine very small absolute quantities of inert gases. For example, as little as $10^{-12}$ g of krypton, xenon, and argon can be determined.

If we know the emission and the absorption line profiles and the oscillator strengths of the resonance lines, the analysis can be carried out without any reference standards. The method of linear absorption gives the concentration of hydrogen and mercury atoms in closed tubes. The analytical sensitivity of the 1849 Å mercury line is one order of magnitude higher than that of the 2537 Å line, which is an intercombination line with an oscillator strength equal to 1/50 of the 1849 Å oscillator strength.

The method of linear absorption is also applicable to the analysis of isotope mixtures [4, 10], e.g., mixtures of hydrogen and deuterium can be analyzed using the $L_\alpha$ line. The mixture is pumped into an emission or an absorption tube, and another tube is filled with the light hydrogen isotope. The light in the emission tube is modulated, and a special amplifier picks up the radiation from this tube only. A discharge is ignited in the absorption tube, to dissociate the molecular hydrogen. The absorption is clearly a function of the isotope composition of the mixture.

A similar method was applied to analyze mixtures of hydrogen isotopes in an excited gas (using the 6563 Å $H_\alpha$ line) [4]. This analytical technique apparently can be applied to determine the isotope composition of all monatomic gases with a sufficiently wide isotopic structure. These gases include, e.g., mercury vapor, helium, and neon.

# BIBLIOGRAPHY

1. HARRISON, G.R. *Metals and Alloys,* **7**, 290 (1936).
2. MEGGERS, W.F. *J. Opt. Soc. America,* **31**, 39 (1941).
3. BALLOFFET, G. *Ann. phys.,* **5**, 1243 (1960).
4. ZAIDEL', A.N., N.I. KALITEEVSKII, L.V. LIPIS, and M.P. CHAIKA. *Emissionnyi spektral'nyi analiz atomnykh materialov (Atomic Emission Spectroscopy).* Fitzmatgiz. 1960.
5. MANDEL'SHTAM, S.L. *Vvedenie v spektral'nyi analiz (Introduction to Spectral Analysis).* Gostekhizdat. 1946.
6. DORGELO, H.B., H. ALTING, and C.J. BOERS. *Physica,* **2**, 959 (1935).
7. ZAITSEV, A.A. *Vestnik MGU,* No. 10, 69 (1947).
8. RAZUMOVSKAYA, L.P. *Optika i Spektroskopiya,* **14**, 189 (1963).
9. SOROKIN, O.M. *Optika i Spektroskopiya,* **16**, 139 (1964).
10. WALSH, A. *Spectrochim. acta,* **7**, 108 (1955).
11. MCNALLY, J.R., G.R. HARRISON, and E. ROWE. *J. Opt. Soc. America,* **37**, 93 (1947).
12. BILLS, K.M. *Österr. Chem.-Ztg.,* **55**, 73, 1954.
13. *The Encyclopedia of Spectroscopy,* G. Clark, Editor, p. 627. London, 1960.
14. ZAIDEL', A.N. *Osnovy spektral'nogo analiza (Principles of Spectral Analysis).* Izdatel'stvo "Nauka." 1965.
15. ROMAND, J. and G. BALLOFFET. *J. phys. et radium,* **18**, 641 (1957).
16. ROMAND, J., G. BALLOFFET, and B. VODAR. *Spectrochim. acta,* No. 6, 454 (1959).
17. ROMAND, J., G. BALLOFFET, and B. VODAR. *Rev. universelle mines,* **15**, 353 (1959).
18. BALLOFFET, G., J. ROMAND, and B. VODAR. *J. phys. et radium,* **20**, 509 (1959).
19. VODAR, B. *Proc. X. Colloq. Spectroscop. Intern., Washington,* 1963, p. 217.
20. KAPORSKII, L.N., I.S. LINDSTREM, and Z.I. SHLEPKOVA. In: *Problemy povysheniya tochnosti, pravil'nosti i chuvstvitel'nosti emissionogo spektral'nogo analiza,* p. 26. 1964.
21. CHUBB, T.A. and H. FRIEDMAN. *Spectrochim. acta,* **8**, 121 (1956).
22. GARTON, W.R.S., M.S.W. WEBB, and P.C. WILDY. *J. Scient. Instrum.,* **34**, 496 (1957).
23. PRUGGER, H. and W. ULMER. *Z. agnew. Phys.,* **11**, 467 (1959).
24. JACOBS, T.A., B.H. CARSON, and K.R. GIEDT. *Appl. Optics,* **4**, 754 (1965).

**EXPLANATORY LIST OF ABBREVIATIONS OF U.S.S.R. INSTITUTIONS AND JOURNALS APPEARING IN THIS TEXT**

| Abbreviation | Full name (transliteration) | Translation |
|---|---|---|
| AN SSSR | Akademiya Nauk SSSR | Academy of Sciences of the U.S.S.R. |
| GOI | Gosudarstvennyi Opticheskii Institut | State Optical Institute |
| LGU | Leningradskii Gosudarstvennyi Universitet | Leningrad State University |
| *Zav. Lab.* | Zavodskaya Laboratoriya | Industrial Laboratory |
| *Zh. Prikl. Spektr.* | Zhurnal Prikladnoi Spektroskopii | Journal of Applied Spectroscopy |
| *ZhETF* | Zhurnal Eksperimental'noi i Teoreticheskoi Fiziki | Journal of Experimental and Theoretical Physics |
| *ZhTF* | Zhurnal Tekhnicheskoi Fiziki | Journal of Technical Physics |

# SUBJECT INDEX

**381**

Printed in Israel
Manufactured at the Israel Program for Scientific Translations, Jerusalem